Elephants and their habitats

Elephants and their habitats

THE ECOLOGY OF ELEPHANTS IN NORTH BUNYORO, UGANDA

R. M. LAWS
NATURAL ENVIRONMENT RESEARCH COUNCIL, LONDON

I. S. C. PARKER
DIRECTOR, WILDLIFE SERVICES LTD., NAIROBI

R. C. B. JOHNSTONE
DISTRICT FOREST OFFICER, FORESTRY COMMISSION, MIDLOTHIAN, SCOTLAND

CLARENDON PRESS · OXFORD

1975

Oxford University Press, Ely House, London W. 1

GLASGOW NEW YORK TORONTO MELBOURNE WELLINGTON
CAPE TOWN IBADAN NAIROBI DAR ES SALAAM LUSAKA ADDIS ABABA
DELHI BOMBAY CALCUTTA MADRAS KARACHI LAHORE DACCA
KUALA LUMPUR SINGAPORE HONG KONG TOKYO

ISBN 0 19 854387 5

© OXFORD UNIVERSITY PRESS 1975

Printed in Great Britain
by Fletcher & Son Ltd., Norwich

Acknowledgements

We are indebted to many organizations and individuals for help and encouragement in the elephant programme. The scientific work originally (1965–6)
formed part of the programme of the Nuffield Unit of Tropical Animal
Ecology, when it was financed by the Nuffield Foundation and later partly by
Wildlife Services Ltd. and the Ford Foundation. The photography of the vegetation transects was carried out using an aircraft on loan to the Tsavo Research
Project by the East African Wildlife Society, being considered as part of a wider
study of elephant habitats that has since been interrupted (Laws 1969b).

Our particular thanks are due to the Trustees of the Uganda National Parks
and to the Director, the late F. X. Katete, for permitting the work to be carried
out in the National Park. We are also grateful to the Chief Conservator of Forests,
Uganda, M. Rakuba, for encouraging the work in Budongo Forest and for allowing the use of the data. He commissioned Wildlife Services Ltd. to study and
report on the elephant problem in Budongo. The collaboration of the Uganda
Game Department is much appreciated, particularly in the collection of data
from elephants shot in the vicinity of the Budongo Forest. This collection was
initiated for us by P. Martin, who was then a Canadian External Aid advisor
attached to the Game Department. After Martin's departure from Uganda,
J. A. Bindernagel helped by storing some of this material.

We should also like to acknowledge the assistance of K. G. McCullagh, who
carried out important studies on material provided by the programme. The East
African Agriculture and Forestry Research Organization kindly provided facilities for the storage of frozen material. We have also to thank the other directors
of Game Management (Uganda) Ltd., A. Graham, J. M. Rowbotham, and
A. D. M. Seth-Smith, for permitting so much time to be devoted to the collection of
scientific data and material, and for collaborating in the field work.

The field work, particularly the collection of material resulting from the
elephant cropping operations, would have been impossible without the willing
help of many volunteer assistants. We would like to single out the following for
particular mention of our appreciation: T. Allen, Mrs. A. L. Archer, R. Backus,
C. R. Field, J. H. Fletcher, A. Graham, L. Hartley, Mrs. M. I. W. Laws,
K. G. McCullagh, Mrs. A. C. Parker, Mr. and Mrs. R. H. Perdue, A. Root,
B. Wakeman, R. M. Watson, P. Hemingway, F. Poppleton, Boru Bachora,
Abakuna Gumundi, Karisa Kathuo, Lino Aboma, A. Omal, Principal Forester
Kavuma, Forest Rangers Awiet, Kandolem Munyonyi, Ndyababwe, Game
Assistant Omasa, and all other members of the Forest Department staff who
assisted in collecting the field data for this study. We are also indebted to
R. J. Wheater and his staff in the Murchison Falls National Park.

The hospitality and many kindnesses shown us by R. J. Wheater and
D. Bardana in the Murchison Falls Park are particularly appreciated.

We are grateful to the Smuts Memorial Fund, Cambridge University, and the
Leverhulme Trust for grants to one of us (R.M.L.) to finance the analysis of the
material. Also to the Royal Society and the Medical Research Council who
finanaced the work of our colleague K. G. McCullagh on material provided by
the programme, and to Professor R. A. McCance, F.R.S. and Dr. E. M. Widdowson
who supervised his work.

In the assessment of the material and its preparation for publication we have
benefited from discussions with and information from a number of colleagues,
in particular A. S. Watt, R. J. Wheater, A. Stuart-Smith, M. Trussler, M. Philipp,
P. Martin, J. M. Boyd, R. V. Short, R. H. V. Bell, R. M. Watson, and G. Caughley.

We are indebted to the late Professor C. F. A. Pantin, F.R.S., and Professor
A. S. Parkes, F.R.S., for encouragement and for providing accommodation in
their departments; also to Professor T. Weiss-Fogh for laboratory facilities in
Cambridge.

Finally we would like to express our thanks to our wives for their continuing
help and encouragement. More specifically, Mrs. M. I. W. Laws assisted in the
examination of the elephant material and by typing several drafts of this report,
and Mrs. A. C. Parker supervised the domestic arrangements in field camps, and
assisted in the recording of data and labelling of specimens.

NOTES

Throughout this book we refer to the Murchison Falls National Park and the
Queen Elizabeth National Park, because they were so named when the study was
carried out. They have now been re-named the Kabalega National Park and the
Rwenzori National Park, respectively. Lake Albert has been re-named Lake
Mobutu.

The present address of R. M. Laws is: British Antarctic Survey, 2 All Saints
Passage, Cambridge; and of R. C. B. Johnstone is: Forestry Commission, Bush
House, Penicuik, Midlothian, Scotland.

Contents

List of plates

(Photographs taken by R.M.L. except where stated otherwise)

Introduction

During the past century an expanding human population has displaced elephant from most of their former range in Bunyoro District, Uganda. Today only two significant elephant communities remain in the district, the larger occuping the northern quarter, and the other inhabiting the south-west corner around the Bugoma Forest. The former of these is the subject of this book.

The North Bunyoro elephant population is now confined to an area of approximately 3200 square kilometres (1200 square miles), comprising the Murchison Falls National Park south of the Victoria Nile, the Budongo Central Forest Reserve, and the Bugungu and Karuma Controlled Hunting Areas, and peripheral unoccupied land around them (see Chapter 1, Fig. 1.2). The process of confinement to this area has been the result of a deliberate policy of the Uganda Game Department since 1925. The increase in elephant densities brought about by the restriction in range has resulted in progressive changes in the habitats, the most obvious of which has been the elimination or marked reduction in density of trees and bushes over most of the area. The over-all effects on the ecology of the region are very far-reaching and it is generally accepted that the results of elephant overcrowding are deleterious to all of the current forms of land-use practised in the area. Conservation and tourism (the National Park) suffer from a loss of diversity of flora and fauna; forestry is influenced by damage to commercial timbers; and agriculture subjected to loss of crops.

Early recognition of the harmful effect of elephant on forest in North Bunyoro is given by Eggeling (1947b), but it was not until the late 1950s that the magnitude of the changes affecting other habitats in the area was recognized. A straightforward approach to this large-scale problem was impeded by the division of the area used by elephants into National Park, Forest Reserve, and Game Controlled Areas, each administered by separate Departments under different Ministries. Instead of a unified, integrated approach to a common problem, each organization has considered the problem from a Departmental point of view and evolved individual policies towards its solution. Thus, although it is primarily a biological problem, human politics have contributed to the development of the present situation. A number of earlier workers (Buechner and Dawkins 1961; Buss 1961; Brooks and Buss 1962; Buechner, Buss, Longhurst, and Brooks 1963; Buss and Smith 1966; Buss and Savidge 1966; Laws and Parker 1968) have examined various aspects of the problem but most have been influenced to some degree by the political division of the area. There has been a tendency to concentrate the work on the elephant population, rather than on habitat changes, which are everywhere clearly apparent. As a result no comprehensive study of the North Bunyoro elephant population, or of its effects on the habitats, has previously been undertaken.

In 1965 the Uganda National Parks reported that from counts done two years back it had been estimated that the elephant population should be reduced by approximately 2000. A decision had been taken earlier by the Trustees that in order to save the habitats, something should be done to reduce the elephant population. This decision was upheld by the Scientific and Technical Committee of the East African Wildlife Society. At their meeting held at Paraa in the Murchison Falls National Park in October 1964, the Committee (after considering the data available on both the Murchison Falls and Tsavo elephant problems, including a brief visit to one of the worst areas of damage in the Murchison Falls Park), noted that:

(1) there was already sufficient evidence in both Parks to establish beyond doubt that elephant populations in them have reached excessive numbers;

(2) the damage to the habitat caused by the elephants had reached the stage when disaster was imminent both for the elephants themselves and for many other species which depend on the same areas.

The Committee therefore recommended that the authorities responsible for the running of these National Parks proceed to reduce the elephant population of these Parks, and carry out investigations in such other allied factors as fires and the carrying capacities of areas affected.[†]

Initially the Uganda National Park authorities gave Game Management (Uganda) Ltd. (a subsidiary of Wildlife Services Ltd.) a contract to crop 200 elephants in the Murchison Falls Park, North. Cropping began in April–May 1965 when some 17 elephants were taken in order to develop techniques of killing, examining, and marketing. In August–September 1965, large scale cropping by complete herds was undertaken for the first time anywhere. In a seven week period 178 elephants were taken in the Chobe area of the Park. The same firm was given a second contract for 200 animals to be taken in Murchison Falls Park, South and 185 elephants were taken in the Rabongo area in November 1965. The contracts specifically provided that the Company should cooperate in research to be carried out on the carcasses of the cropped elephants by the Nuffield Unit of Tropical Animal Ecology (N.U.T.A.E.).

The basic methods of sampling and examination were developed in these early operations. Subsequently, the National Parks Trustees, having satisfied themselves of the efficient and humane nature of the operations, the absence of disturbance, and the absence of any effect on tourism, extended the contract and further cropping began in February 1966. A total of 800 elephants were taken in Murchison Falls Park, South and 1200 in Murchison Falls Park, North. (The reasons for taking the majority in the northern sector were that it was here that there was most chance of stopping or reversing the unfavourable habitat trends, since the destruction of woodland had not proceeded so far as on the South bank. On the South bank it was felt that the habitat change had progressed so far that only a very large reduction could be expected to have a significant effect. The operations in the southern section of the Park were viewed as a preliminary reduction pos-

† *Uganda National Parks Annual Report 1964–5*, p. 16.

sibly to be followed by further cropping if the scientific investigations indicated that it was desirable.) Recommendations for further reduction cropping are made in Chapter 12 of this book.

The cropping operations were completed on 25 May 1967, when some 2000 elephants had been cropped and examined. From the start and throughout the operations there was close cooperation between the National Parks (R. J. Wheater, Chief Warden), Game Management (Uganda) Ltd. (I.S.C.P.), and the Nuffield Unit of Tropical Animal Ecology (R.M.L.). Preliminary results of work on the animals cropped in 1965 were presented at a Symposium of the Zoological Society of London in October 1966, but the proceedings were not published until 1968 (Laws and Parker 1968).

In 1966, while these operations were in progress, the Uganda Forest Department engaged Wildlife Services Ltd. (the parent company of Game Management (Uganda) Ltd.) to undertake investigations and propose a solution to the problem of elephant damage in the Budongo Forest. At the same time the Forest Department and the Game Department made available to us data and material from some three hundred elephants shot in attempts to prevent them using the forest.

These samples of elephants are the most important new source of data considered in this book, but a number of related investigations have been made which are essential for an understanding of the over-all problem. These include a survey of the history of the area in the light of our new knowledge of elephant behaviour and population dynamics; studies of the habitats, including aerial surveys and quantitative analysis and aerial photographic transects; information on the effect of elephant usage on the forest habitat; and aerial and ground surveys of elephant numbers, distribution, and density in the area; as well as observations on elephant behaviour, physiology, nutrition, growth, and reproduction. The value of the present study stems largely from the unique and fruitful collaboration between biologists, commercial enterprise, and Government Departments.

Earlier papers (Laws and Parker 1968; Laws 1969a) were based on partial and preliminary analyses of the data. By mutual agreement between the individuals, departments, and companies involved, all the relevant information available has now been pooled to form the basis of this book. It is thus possible to attempt an over-all description of the North Bunyoro elephant population in relation to its habitat. For reasons beyond our control, much of this work has had to be opportunist and part-time; funds for research have been very limited despite the revenue from the cropping operations, which has not been used to support research. For this reason there are gaps in the pattern that emerges and the quality of the information is variable. The investigation has been essentially cross-sectional in nature and inferences have had to be made about the dynamic situation, from the results of short-term studies. This is amply justified by the urgency and seriousness of the problem but clearly a continuous monitoring of the system is desirable and we hope that others may be able to extend the study in time, building on our findings. However, we do not believe that the general conclusions will be altered by further work, although there is clearly much detail, particularly as regards the response of vegetation to changing elephant use, to be filled in.

Although this account is basically ecological, we have accepted responsibility to formulate preliminary plans for the solution of the present problem, and the future management of the North Bunyoro elephant population. These are included as an integral part of the work and were submitted to the responsible authorities in 1969. In 1972 the Uganda National Parks decided to implement the first phase of our recommendations made in Chapter 12.

1. Historical survey

It is likely that both man and elephant have occupied what is today the North Bunyoro elephant range (see Plate 1.1) for a considerable span of time. At Chobe, on the north bank of the Victoria Nile, Fagan and Lofgren (1966) recorded abundant middle and late Stone Age, and Iron Age artifacts (40 000 B.C. to 1000 A.D.). On the same site in 1965 Graham (personal communication) found the semi-fossilized skeleton of an immature elephant exposed by erosion. It seems reasonable to assume that both man and elephant occurred on the south bank of the Nile at the same time. During the course of elephant and hippopotamus cropping in 1965—7 numerous pottery shards were found over much of the Murchison Falls National Park, indicating widespread human settlement of this section of the Nile valley in the past.

Bantu peoples are believed to have colonized Bunyoro about the fourth century A.D. and in turn believed to have been subjugated by the Bahima pastoralists in the thirteenth century A.D. (Philip 1965). Intermarriage between the two races

PLATE 1.1. Murchison Falls; North Bunyoro is on the right.

produced the present Banyoro people who, though owning some cattle have for
the past hundred years at least been primarily agriculturalists.

1.1. The former habitats

The earliest written records of the area were made by Sir Samuel Baker
(1866, 1874). From his description it is possible to compare vegetation and
human distribution in the 1860s and 1870s in North Bunyoro with those of the
present day, and some of his descriptions are worth quoting in full. Of the
country within 16 kilometres (10 miles) of Karuma (Fig. 1.1) he says '. . . thickly
populated and much cultivated with sesame, sweet potatoes, beans, tallaboon,
dura, indian corn and plantains.' Proceeding inland, between 10 miles and 20 miles
(16–32 km) from Karuma he describes the country as '. . . forest interspersed
with villages.' Within sound of and immediately south of the Murchison Falls he
says '. . . we were in precisely the same parklike land that characterises Chobe
and Bunyoro, the grass was above seven feet high; and from the constant rain,
and the extreme fertility of the soil, the country was choked with vegetation.'
He records human settlement along the east shores of Lake Albert and a fishing
camp below the Murchison Falls at what is today Fajao.

Less than 10 miles upstream from the falls, Baker describes an island called
Patooan that was inhabited; Garstin (1904) places it 48 kilometres downstream

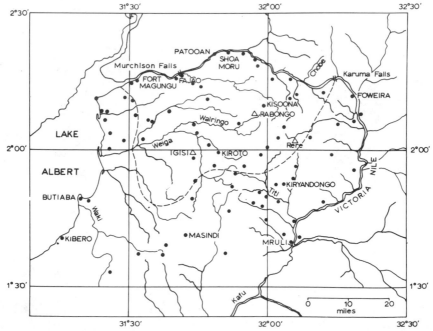

Fig. 1.1. Map to illustrate historical account. Black circles—approximate position of larger
villages shown by Owen (1905) and Vandeleur (1897). Broken line indicates present limit of
the elephant range (*ca* 1970).

from Karuma, which is about 16 kilometres upstream from the Falls. On the
south bank some 3 miles from Patooan was a village called Shoa Moru (Fig. 1.1).
Between the latter and a village called Kisoona near the present Rabongo Hill
(position given by Dunbar (1959)), he states '. . . the country was the same as
usual, being a vast park overgrown with immense grass.' Between Shoa Moru and
Kisoona the country was 'excessively wild and uncultivated.'

   Kisoona itself was comprised of some 3000 huts and gives some idea of the
number of Banyoro in the area; in its neighbourhood 'was a mass of extensive
plantain groves.' About the natural vegetation in the vicinity of Kisoona, Baker
says '. . . it was a mere forest of trees and tangled herbage 10 or 12 feet high . . .'.
Between Kisoona and Foweira (Fig. 1.1) 'we rode at once into the low forest . . .
the march had been through forest and grass about 4 feet in height which was
now growing vigorously after the recent showers.' A similar description is given
of the vegetation between Kisoona and Masindi. He makes reference to park-like
trees and grass 2·7 metres (9 feet) tall near Masindi.

   From Baker's account it is apparent that much land that is vacant today, in
the east of what is now the Murchison Falls National Park and Karuma Controlled
Hunting Area, was then heavily populated. The distribution of Mvule trees
(*Chlorophora excelsa*) which in Bunyoro are associated with cultivation (Brasnet
1944)—either because cultivation creates conditions for their development and/or
as a relic of forest left by the cultivators (Thomas 1942)—corresponds to the pattern of human distribution suggested by Baker's remarks (Chapter 2, Fig. 2.1).
South of the Nile, Baker made no reference to the open grassland so characteristic
of it today. However, north of the river he described as 'well watered, undulating
prairie . . . clear of trees', where there is still open grassland in the Kilak Elephant
Sanctuary.

   This is very similar in appearance to the country today found south of the
Nile, and (although negative records are perhaps of dubious value) had it been so
in Baker's day he would surely have applied a similar description to both areas. It
is also clear that what Baker refers to as 'low forest' and 'park land' is the
Terminalia-Combretum, Hyparrhenia, or *Pennisetum* woodland characteristic of
much of latter-day central and western Uganda. Garstin (1904) remarks that
'downstream of Patooan the gorges become wilder and more rugged, and the
country on either side is covered with much forest'.

   Buechner and Dawkins (1961, p. 753) give additional evidence, quoted from
Schweinfurth, Ratzel, Felkin, and Hartlaub (1888) indicating that the country
between Fort Magungu, near the mouth of the Victoria Nile, and Kiroto, 10
kilometres east of Igisi Hill, was tall grassland with scattered trees, banana
plantations and huts. 'In all directions well-worn paths cross the country, a
testimony to the intercourse of natives among themselves.' Garstin (1904)
remarks that 25 kilometres downstream from Fajao the left bank was thickly
wooded and there were many huts.

   A map prepared in 1895 (Vandeleur 1897, p. 472) shows an area halfway between Igisi Hill and the Victoria Nile (in the position of the present Wairingo Ranger Post), and the position of Rabongo Forest, as 'wooded'. Immediately south of the Murchison Falls and in two locations between Igisi Hill and Masindi 'grass' is indicated. About twenty villages are shown scattered along the Victoria Nile and the route from Murchison Falls to Masindi.

A sketch map of Owen (1905) showed 'forest' north-west of the confluence of the Weiga and Wairingo Rivers and 'scrub' eastward from it; but nothing in the vicinity of Rabongo Hill. The area south-east of the Park along the Titi River is shown as cultivated. This map (if reliable) shows that woodland extended much further west than at present.

In this connection Churchill (1908, p. 157) gives a description of the view looking northwards from Igisi Hill, now the southern boundary of the Murchison Falls National Park. On the march from Masindi

the forest was a little thinner on the second day, although the jungle was of the same dense and tangled fertility. We started an hour before sunrise, and by eight o'clock had climbed to the saddle of the high rocky wall which contains the valley of the Victoria Nile. From this elevation of, perhaps, six hundred feet above the general level of the plain a comprehensive view of the landscape was for the first time possible. In every direction spread a wide sea of foliage, thinning here into bush, darkening there into forest, rising and falling with the waves of the land, and broken only by occasional peaks of rock.

Garstin (1904) mentions that the Waki River (just south of Butiaba) runs through a thick belt of forest which is a 'favourite haunt of wild elephants'. The escarpment is steep and 'behind the first ascent stretches an extent of steep rounded hills covered with forest, which rise in a series of steps until the full height of the plateau is attained some 500 metres above the lake. North of Butiaba the same scenery continued and the eastern flats widen out as the hills recede from the lake'. Garstin also writes that 'the entire surface of these flats is covered with very high and dense bush. Nearer the hills occasional large trees are met with'. The Butiaba flats are now much more open country.

1.2. Past elephant numbers, distribution and movements

Clearly elephant were formerly exceptionally abundant in Bunyoro. Thus Burton (1860), writing of the country of Unyoro remarks: 'the country is rich and fertile, and magnificent tales are told concerning the collections of ivory, which in some parts are planted in the ground to pen cattle'. This accumulation of ivory was largely due to the previous ruler, Suma, who would not permit Arab traders to penetrate the area.

The only elephant Baker recorded in Bunyoro were along the eastern shores of Lake Albert. Had he seen them or their signs elsewhere he would almost certainly have made some comment, as he was an ardent sportsman and such evidence is unlikely to have escaped his notice. Despite the fact that Baker himself did not see many elephant in Bunyoro he nonetheless makes note of the vast quantities of ivory in the possession of Kamrasi, the King of Bunyoro.

Ivory was almost the only currency with which the Banyoro could conduct trade with the outside world and limited as contact with the world was, the value of ivory was such that the king monopolized the commodity for himself. With reference to an Arab slaver who was in league with Kamrasi the King, Baker comments 'the country was so rich in ivory that it was a perfect bank upon which he [the slave trader] could draw without limit, provided that he remained an ally of the King.' The caravan which Baker accompanied on leaving Bunyoro is described thus: '. . . the quantity of ivory in camp was so large that we required 700 porters to carry both tusks and provisions . . .'. It is certain that Bunyoro contained a very substantial elephant population at that time.

Dunbar (1959) quotes Gordon as follows: 'I am in rags from the thorn bushes . . . the elephant uproot the trees and leave them in the path . . .'. This experience occurred as Gordon was travelling between Mruli and Foweira (Fig. 1.1) in 1876. From this account it is evident that there were some elephant in north-east Bunyoro at the time. However, from Baker's descriptions of the dense human population and his lack of any record of elephant in the area, it is unlikely that there were many elephant in that part. The large elephant populations of Bunyoro, indicated by the ivory produced, must have been elsewhere than in the north and north-east, their present day range. An indication of the whereabouts of these elephant is presented by Casati (1891), as he wrote 'elephants are to be found in great numbers in the woods of Kafu' (Fig. 1.1); and about the eastern shores of Lake Albert 'elephants and buffaloes come out at sunset from the recesses of the forest in crowds to drink the waters of the lake.'

All in all, this varied evidence suggests that elephants existed in large numbers, in south-central and western Bunyoro, at the turn of the century.

In 1890 the British East Africa Company assumed control of Buganda, and in the following years their influence spread to other districts. In 1894 the British Government took over from the company and formally established the Protectorate of Uganda. In 1894 Uganda's only export was ivory, valued at £5481 (Thomas and Scott 1935) and, until 1904 at least, it was the country's major export, exceeding the combined value of all other commodities. It is therefore not surprising that first the British East Africa Company, and then the British Government took an interest in the exploitation of elephant. Evidence of this is given by Lugard (1893), with regard to Toro District, (the kingdom south of Bunyoro) as follows: 'I made a treaty with him [King Kasangama of Toro] . . . elephant were not to be shot without permission, and were the monopoly of the Company [British East Africa Company]. This was an important provision, as these animals swarmed in enormous herds throughout this country.' Although this passage pertains to Toro, it was the Company's attitude (and latterly that of the Protectorate Government) toward elephant everywhere in the country including Bunyoro. It is thus seen that from the outset the control and exploitation of elephant was of fundamental interest to the British Administration of Uganda.

As in other parts of Africa, the tsetse fly (*Glossina palpalis*) has played an important part in the ecology of North Buñyoro. Winston Churchill (1908, p. 160) noted that 'Fajao as a native town was no more. At hardly any point in Uganda has the sleeping sickness made such frightful ravages. At least six thousand persons had perished in the last two years. Almost the whole population had been swept away'. Fajao was a village, now gone, immediately downriver of the Murchison Falls on the Bunyoro bank of the Nile (Fig. 1.1).

The outbreak of human sleeping sickness (Trypanosomiasis) in widespread lacustrine and riverine areas resulted in 1912 in a Government-enforced migration away from the affected areas—riparian habitats occupied by the tsetse fly. This was of major ecological consequence in Bunyoro. Large numbers of people took up residence in central and southern Bunyoro, and at the same time the formerly heavily populated Lake Albert shores and Victoria Nile regions became vacant. After the withdrawal of the human population, most of the land designated today as the Murchison Falls National Park, and the Karuma and Bugungu Controlled Hunting Areas was declared a Game Reserve. The expanded human communities in central and southern Bunyoro immediately entered into conflict with the local elephant and commenced the trend of displacing the elephants from their nine-teenth century range to their present confinement in northern Bunyoro.

An early official estimate of the number of elephant in Uganda was made by Swynnerton (1924). Although the actual numbers he gives are open to question, it is to be expected that his estimates of relative abundance from one district to another would be of some value, and from his figures it is apparent that more than half the elephant in Uganda were resident in Bunyoro or adjacent districts. It is worth noting that in 1924 the Bunyoro elephants, according to official thinking, were divided into two groups: the 'Budongo herd' and the 'Bugoma herd'. It is stated that these terms did not imply that the elephant were confined to the two forests bearing these names, but frequented their vicinity and comprised many actual herds (Anon 1928, p. 10).

By 1924, conflict between elephant and human interests, due to the shift and expansion of human populations, had reached such proportions that the Protectorate Government decided to create a special department for elephant control. This was formed in 1925, by Captain C.R.S. Pitman, and by the time its first annual report was printed it had assumed the title of Game Department. The following statement of policy is extracted from the Department's first annual report (Anon 1925, p. 13).

The aim therefore more or less, is to divide the Protectorate into elephant and 'non-elephant' areas: in the former the elephants are free from the unwelcome activities of rangers and native guards and others: in the latter they are shot sufficiently severely when they put in an appearance to associate those areas in their minds with danger to themselves.

In other words a system of defensive fronts has been instituted to ward off encroachment of elephants on the more thickly inhabited areas. In instances where the native population has encroached or has settled on traditional elephant grazing grounds, little protection can be afforded.

These fronts vary greatly according to the locality; in one district there may be a straight front for 150 miles, such as in Bunyoro. Here is an endeavour to prevent the huge herds from emerging from the Bugoma and Budongo Forests and the Game Reserve.

This policy of confinement has been the aim of the Game Department from 1925 until the present day, but it has never been able to enforce its intention of refusing protection to cultivation on 'traditional elephant grazing grounds'. The bulk of 'control' work has always taken place at the point of greatest human-elephant conflict; that is on the outer edges of expanding human communities. The growth of the human population is discussed in Chapter 3.

This human expansion has radiated outwards from central Bunyoro, particularly along roads as they were constructed, and resulting in relentless encroachment on 'traditional elephant grazing grounds'. Game Department activity throughout has contributed to this process.

In 1952 the Murchison Falls National Park was established, totalling some 4033 square kilometres (1557 square miles), lying astride the Victoria Nile (Fig. 1.2). Approximately 2098 square kilometres (810 square miles) is south of the river in Bunyoro, about 17 per cent of the total area of Bunyoro. In 1955 the Bugungu Elephant and Hippopotamus Sanctuary was created between the western boundary of the National Park and Lake Albert. It was partly designed 'to protect the normal seasonal migration of elephant to the lake shore areas from the National Park' (Anon 1955). It is now the Bukumi Bugungu Controlled Hunting Area, but so heavily settled that elephant no longer use it to any important degree. Controlled Hunting Areas are areas where hunting is restricted and the shooting of certain species limited under the provisions of the Game Ordinance. Human settlement is allowed and in 1967 continued up to and beyond the National Park boundary in places; this has now been rectified. The same applies to the Karuma Falls Controlled Area. It is interesting to note that when the Park was first opened, the then Warden considered that there were about 800 elephants in the Park! (Warden's Monthly Reports, MS.). There were probably some ten times as many. This illustrates the unreliability of early numerical estimates which is confirmed by data from other areas, for example the Tsavo National Park (Simon 1962; Laws 1969b).

The annual reports of the Uganda Game Department from 1925 until the advent of the American Fulbright Scholars in the 1950s (Buechner, Buss, Longhurst, and Quick) provide the only continuous record of the interaction between man and elephant, and the distribution of the elephant populations over this period. However, these reports, as is so often the case, are notable for their lack of factual data and their generally subjective and anecdotal nature. From a study of the reports it is not possible to establish past population sizes, movements or distribution, with accuracy or detail.

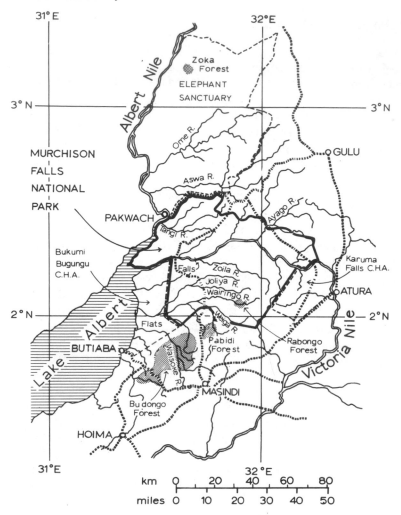

Fig. 1.2. Administrative areas. North Bunyoro is bounded by the Victoria Nile and Lake Albert. Thick black line—National Park boundary; thick broken lines—roads; thin broken lines—boundaries of Controlled Hunting Areas and Elephant Sanctuary. (After Laws *et al.* (1970.) Reproduced by permission of the East African Wildlife Society.

Pitman (Anon 1925) estimated the elephant population of Bunyoro to total 7000 and divided it into two groups, the Budongo community of 5000 and the Bugoma group of 2000. By 1950 Pitman estimated that the total elephant population of Bunyoro had declined to 1200 of which 200 were from the Bugoma herd (Anon 1950). No information is presented to indicate how these totals were obtained, and they were clearly grossly inaccurate, the 1950 estimate probably by a factor of at least ten. This not too surprising; in Kenya estimates of the number of elephant in the Tsavo National Park and vicinity in 1965 based on simultaneous aerial counts from several aircraft, were probably about 50 per cent low (Laws 1969b). It is certain that the sizes of elephant populations are almost invariably underestimated, even today.

No well-documented counts were made until 1957 when a series of twelve aerial counts was made in North Bunyoro between 1957 and 1959 (Buechner, Buss, Longhurst, and Brooks 1963). During this series the highest count (30 May–1 June 1958) revealed 12 389 elephant, an increase of 5389 (77 per cent over Pitman's 1925 estimate, and 11 189 (932 per cent) over his 1950 figure for the Budongo and Bugoma herds! It should be borne in mind that the 1958 count covered but a small proportion of Bunyoro and that there were certainly elephants elsewhere in the district when the count was made (including the present 'Bugoma herd') thus suggesting an even greater difference from Pitman's figures (see also Appendix A).

Brooks and Buss (1962) summarized information on elephant movement and distribution in Uganda since 1925. On the basis of verbal accounts from Game Rangers (the officials responsible for implementing Game Department policy in the field), and from observations published in the Game Department Annual Reports, they formed the conclusion that in the past elephant communities in Uganda undertook regular and extensive seasonal migrations. Obviously we do not have access to their verbal reports, but we have examined the Game Department's Annual Reports from 1925 to 1965. As the former must have been the primary source of the published reports, these reports should reflect the basic material analysed by Brooks and Buss. With one exception we were unable to find convincing evidence of any regular seasonal movement, greater than about 15 km (10 miles). The exception concerns elephant moving from the eastern border of the then Bunyoro Game Reserve, in a southerly direction toward the Kafu River (Fig. 1.3), some 25 km (15 miles). This move apparently took place during the second, and beginning of the third, quarter each year; the elephants returning to the Game Reserve by the same route in November (Anon 1925–30, 1932, 1934–9, 1947, 1950, 1954, 1955).

Our conviction that this move did take place is due to the persistency of reports, rather than to detailed and accurate description. It is clear that this move involved only part of the population inhabiting the Game Reserve and Budongo Forest environs, as, at the time the 'migrants' were said to be close to the Kafu River (June to November), other elephant were variously recorded from Budongo, the Game Reserve, and the flats below the Rift Valley escarpment (Anon 1927, 1928, 1935). The report for 1955–6 comments 'this does not mean that the whole of the vast number which collects north-west of Katulikire, crosses the road in the wet weather, but numbers in the order of 600–1000 move south, leaving the remainder around the area of Katulikire and the National Park boundary . . .'. These numbers correspond in size to one of the large peripheral herds (described in Chapter 5), which was seen to move a similar distance during one of our aerial counts (Fig. 5.4).

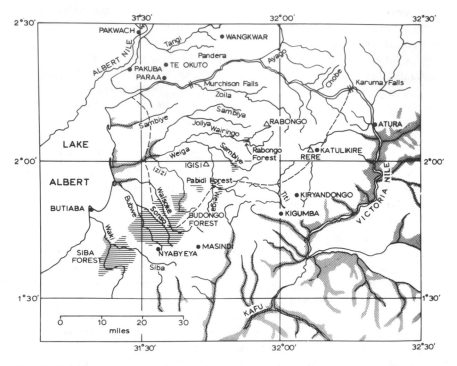

Fig. 1.3. General map of the area. Forests—horizontal shading; areas of impeded drainage—stippled. Broken line indicates present limit of the elephant range.

A new view of this movement was put forward in the Report for 1954–5, which remarked: 'there has been much discussion as to the reason for the annual break-out of elephant from the Murchison Falls National Park, southwards across the Masindi-Atura road. From recent observations it appears that the reverse may be the case. The majority of elephant, particularly the breeding herds, seem to prefer the country outside the National Park and only go back in to it when forced by circumstances.' The move into the Park was attributed to seasonal burning and lack of water in the area the elephant prefer.

Pitman (1931) (and Anon (1925, 1928)) states that major seasonal fordings of the Victoria Nile were effected by elephant from Bunyoro. He presents no eye-witness descriptions of any such migrational crossings, which is odd, in view of the detail accorded for occasional crossings of the Albert Nile by a few elephant (Anon 1930, 1936, 1937). Occasional reports of elephant crossing the Victoria Nile below the Murchison Falls have been made since the establishment of the National Park in 1952; any major crossings since this time would have been noticed, but none are recorded.

Sanctuary has existed for elephant on both sides of the Nile since the sleeping sickness evacuation of humans, and human activity has placed no barrier to elephant crossing the Victoria Nile between Karuma Falls and Lake Albert. Although both banks are populated by elephant communities in states of decline due to overpopulation, that on the south (Bunyoro) bank is under considerably more stress, having begun to decline in the 1940s, than that on the north bank, which probably began to decline in numbers as late as 1957 (Laws and Parker 1968). This being the case, there has existed for many years a strong inducement for migration from south to north across the Nile. That this has not happened is demonstrated by the differences existing between the two populations, which confirm their lack of close contact (Laws and Parker 1968). We are therefore led to believe that there was previously no seasonal migration of Bunyoro elephant back and forth across the Victoria Nile and that records to that effect were erroneous.

In the Uganda Game Department Annual Reports (Anon 1925, 1928, 1929, 1934, and 1935) Pitman alludes to elephant crossing the Kafu-Nkussi rivers between Bunyoro and Buganda. In the 1925 report he makes no reference to any specific observation but merely states that elephant 'undoubtedly cross' the rivers between the two districts. Again in 1928 he gives no particular instance or observer when claiming that 'migratory herds from Budongo are known to cross that river [the Kafu] . . . after which there is possibly a drift much further south . . .'. In 1929 he asserts that the Butengesa herd (in Buganda) was visited by elephants from Bunyoro, but no detail is presented. In 1934 he records that the local natives claim that many elephant crossed from Bunyoro into Buganda, and in 1935 he states that a reverse movement took place. These movements are specifically attributed by him to Game Department Control measures.

The elephant inhabiting south-west Bunyoro referred to as the 'Bugoma herd', receive only erratic mention throughout the period 1925—60. In 1925 Pitman claims that the 'Bugoma herd . . . has now to confine its activities to the north of the Kafu River.' In 1928 he felt that movement of Bugoma elephant influenced the elephant situation in Mubende (Buganda) and possibly in Toro District, but no evidence is presented. It was also stated that Buyaga (Buganda) elephant were not unduly disturbed by the control operations that year and as a result their movement into Bugoma (Bunyoro) was reduced; in the 1947 Report Mubende and Bugoma elephant are treated as one community. None of the foregoing can in any way be considered as evidence of regular seasonal movement between Bunyoro and Buganda.

In a later section of this book, it is shown that within the present North Bunyoro elephant populations there are well-defined sub-populations. These would not exist had there been the constant intermingling of herds that extensive migrations would have induced. Observations have been made of ten elephant 'unit populations' in Tsavo National Park and vicinity, in Kenya and Tanzania (Laws 1969b); of a number of individuals in the North Bunyoro community during the present study; in the Queen Elizabeth National Park (Laws, unpublished); and in Lake Manyara National Park (Douglas-Hamilton 1972), and these indicate that elephant are normally localized in distribution to a degree hitherto unsuspected. Together with the complete absence of acceptable historical data this suggests that widespread seasonal migrations never did take place in Uganda, and in particular Bunyoro.

Apart from one observation, we do not know of any convincing evidence of large scale migrations elsewhere in Africa (other than local displacements of the order of 15–50 kilometres (10–30 miles)). However, one of us (I.S.C.P.) has a definite record from Kenya of a 'population' of about 2000 elephants, moving from the Tiva River north west of Dakadima to Dera, between Wachu and the coast in 1961–2 (November to May). This distance is at least 60 miles, but we regard the move as an extension of the usual erratic displacement movements rather than a true migration.

Buechner *et al.* (1963) recorded large fluctuations in elephant numbers in Murchison Falls National Park, but it is felt that these were due in part to the counting technique adopted (Appendix A) and that local movements of less than 15 kilometres could well have led to concealment of elephants in fairly dense *Terminalia* woodland and forest. The evidence available indicates that in the past elephant were far more widespread than today (Brooks and Buss 1962, Fig. 2), but that movements were small and communities localized. The longest regular seasonal 'migrations' for which there is any real evidence took place in eastern Bunyoro about an axis less than 30 kilometres (20 miles) long.

1.3. Control shooting

Between 1925 and 1965, when the present investigation commenced, a minimum of 11 558 elephant were killed in Bunyoro by the Game Department and 2858 were shot on licence, making a total of at least 14 416 for the 40-year period, averaging at least 360 a year. These can only be considered as approximate figures, because there are no records for the war years 1940–5, and the figures extracted from the Game Department Annual Reports for the period 1947–65 do not agree with the summary given in the Annual Report for 1965. This discrepancy is not too important, because the totals for elephant shot on control are derived from actual tusks obtained and sold by the Game Department, and represent minimal values. The real totals must be very much higher as the methods used by the Game Department were such that a great number of animals escaped wounded during control operations, and some of these later died.

In the 1925 Annual Report, it is stated 'elephants are occasionally shot which are found to have had their tails cut off by someone else'; that is to say they have been previously stunned by a bullet. In 1934 Game Ranger Salmon is quoted:

killing elephants at this rate necessitates the taking of every opportunity which presents itself and inevitably leads to considerable wounding and temporary loss of animals which should be recovered subsequently. The numbers wounded were naturally added to quite considerably by both myself and the qualified Guards having recruits and trainees with us all the time, and I shall not be surprised if the total wastage accounted for exceeds 500 head.

This, in an operation in which he killed between 400 and 500 animals. For every animal killed another was wounded!

Again in the 1934 Report is the following quote from Salmon: '. . . the custom of allowing the Bunyoro Guards to shoot from trees has undoubtedly resulted in many Bunyoro elephants' sterns being bullet battered to such an extent that they have permanently removed themselves . . .'. In the 1950 Report Pitman writes 'a very high percentage of large bull elephant that have been examined by Game Department staff have carried old or recent bullet wounds.' Further evidence of the high incidence of wounding is given in the 1925 report where it is stated that most elephant found dead are believed to be so as the result of wounds inflicted by the Department's staff when carrying out elephant control. (See also our comments in Chapter 10 on deaths of elephant along the Weiga River since 1957.)

In addition to elephant poaching and control operations, licence holders were responsible for a great deal of wounding and Pitman (Anon 1950) makes the following comment: 'many of these licence holders are also so inexperienced or so frightened of elephants that they wound several before they kill one.'

Although it was the Department's policy to divide the country into elephant and non-elephant areas, this policy was not closely followed. Even when they were in areas in which there was no cultivation or human settlement, elephant were wantonly and wastefully slaughtered by the Department's staff, as illustrated by the Annual Reports. In the 1926 Report is a description of the Kafu area, '. . . the majority [of elephant] . . . avoid the cultivation and move into the uninhabited country . . . along the rivers Nile and Kafu, leading a harmless existence', which highlights the following extract from the 1928 report:

In November, as an experiment, the guards were permitted to molest the enormous herd which normally stands by the Kafu River from May to November. Backwards and forwards went the frightened animals, smashing great highways through the tall grass and scrubby bush, and it was particularly interesting to note how the elephants associated roads with danger to themselves causing a herd—hundreds strong—to bunch before crossing, thus leaving a trail as if dozens of steamrollers travelling abreast had completely flattened the countryside. These elephants resent undue interference; some disappeared north-west into the triangle, the stronghold of no. 3, but the majority fled to the Kafu swamps in the vicinity of and south of Masindi Port and there with their 'backs to the wall' prepared to resist in no uncertain fashion the intrusion of the hunter. At such times these elephant are best left alone *until they have recovered from their punishment* [our italics].

That elephant were shot wantonly is again illustrated in the 1937 Report, when commenting on the redeployment of staff, '. . . to afford a measure of relief to the elephants in certain uninhabited regions from which control can be con-

veniently withdrawn'. It can only be concluded that they had earlier been shot
in these uninhabited regions.

In 1948 protection of young trees necessitated elephant shooting in the Budongo
Forest, hitherto a sanctuary, and from the mid-1950s this developed into a programme of attempted complete exclusion.

The foregoing intensely disturbing extracts have been quoted at length to
illustrate the great harassment elephant were subjected to in the past everywhere
except in the then Bunyoro Game Reserve. This represents a prime factor, together
with human occupation of land, in changing elephant distribution in Bunyoro
and compressing them into their present limited range (Fig. 1.4).

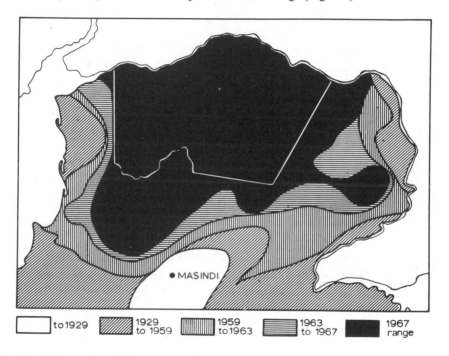

| | to 1929 | | 1929 to 1959 | | 1959 to 1963 | | 1963 to 1967 | | 1967 range |

Fig. 1.4. Contraction of the North Bunyoro elephant range since 1929.

1.4. Vegetation trends

Concurrent, though poorly documented, changes were affecting the habitats
in the shrinking areas occupied by the elephants. The impression gained from the
accounts of early explorers is of largely open grassland, with patches of woodland
and forest. Nevertheless ten years ago, and even as recently as 1967, the relics of
dead trees (particularly stumps and fallen trees which are not conspicuous) were
very widely distributed. Thus, Buechner and Dawkins (1961, p. 755) concluded,
'relict trees may be encountered nearly everywhere in the Park today, attesting to

the far greater abundance of trees in the recent past. If extensive treeless grassland existed, it probably occurred between the Zoila and Victoria Nile Rivers where Baker made his observation'. But even in this area extensive patches of dead *Terminalia* are present today, and we have given reasons for believing that Baker saw little open grassland such as now characterizes the area, and that the present elephant range was a mosaic of high forest, gallery forest, closed canopy *Terminalia* woodland, wooded grassland, and grassland with scattered trees.

Pitman (1931) described the effect of elephant overbrowsing along the Victoria Nile's south bank between Murchison Falls and Lake Albert in these terms: 'the most striking feature in the landscape is the havoc wrought by elephants amongst the trees and bushes; this is carried to such an extent that not a single one is free from damage.' Though this inevitable result of compressing elephant into North Bunyoro was predicted in various Annual Reports of the Game Department (Anon 1927–9, 1935–9), the fact that it was taking place was totally ignored until 1949, when the Game Ranger of the area made the following comment '. . . the elephant population is too big for the potential food supply available, as practically every small tree and bush of the species which the elephants eat is broken off and stunted.' (Anon 1949).

This trend in the woodlands was described in detail by Buechner and Dawkins (1961) and mentioned by other workers since then (Buss 1961; Laws and Parker 1968; Laws 1970b; Laws, Parker, and Johnstone 1970). However, until the present study no action has been attempted to halt or reverse the trend.

Because of its economic potential the ecological changes in the Budongo Forest have been better documented than the area to the north and it has been the subject of four working plans, 1935–44, 1945–54, 1955–64, and 1964–74 (Philip 1965). The early history of the forest is summarized by Philip.

Records of Kenya lake levels, those of tribal movement within East Africa and Egyptian records of the flow of the Nile, led Dale [1954] to deduce wetter conditions from about the years 1400–1600 A.D., resulting in a considerable spread of high forest, followed by a halt, and later possibly by a retrogression in the dry years of the first half of the nineteenth century. If one accepts the findings of Eggeling [1947b] and others that *Cynometra* forest has superseded mixed mahogany forest, then one may say with some confidence that the older areas of *Cynometra* represent the extent of the forest before the spread of 1400 A.D. and that the oldest mahogany areas correspond with the extent of the spread during the ensuing years.

. . . there is good proof of the spread of forest and woodland in Budongo and in western Uganda as a whole. All the *Maesopsis* forest and much of the younger mixed mahogany woodland are ascribable to this period.

Before the advent of Europeans the Bunyoro forests were apparently shunned by natives and until the present century they remained practically unvisited by travellers.

In 1905 M. T. Dawe, the first Superintendent of Forests in Uganda, visited Budongo during the course of a botanical survey of western and northern Uganda.

European settlers had by then been tapping wild rubber (*Funtumia elastica*) in it for at least a year, but this is the first record of a biologist visiting the area. This exploitation continued until 1910 when the price of rubber fell. In 1910 Dawe spent about two months in Budongo; he sketch-mapped the whole of the forest, identified many of the timber species, and made a 0·26 per cent enumeration of all exploitable *Funtumia* and all timber species of 2 ft (0·6 m) diameter at breast height and over.

Troup visited Budongo in 1921 and stressed the need for the examination and demarcation of the forest and the preparation of management plans. No action was taken on the reports of Dawe and Troup until, in 1932, Budongo was gazetted as a Forest Reserve. Budongo had been declared a game reserve in 1906, but this was repealed in 1913. The present Masindi-Butiaba road was completed in 1915, making the forest more accessible, and the forest was aerially photographed in 1931.

The Rabongo Forest has never been classed as a Reserve, probably due to its inacessibility, its relatively small size, and the fact that it is now included within the National Park.

1.5. Summary

Much of the present elephant range was densely populated by man until the sleeping sickness clearance in the early years of this century. The vegetation was formerly a varied mosaic of woodland, high forest, gallery forest, and grasslands. This was a favourable habitat for elephants, but owing to the dense human settlement, elephants were evidently not numerous over their present range at that time, although there is good evidence for the former existence of large populations of elephant elsewhere in Bunyoro.

The outbreak of human sleeping sickness at the turn of the century led to Government-enforced evacuation of the riverine and lacustrine areas of north Bunyoro, which had major ecological consequences. Large numbers of people were displaced to central and south Bunyoro and the formerly densely populated Lake Albert shore and Victoria Nile regions became vacant. The northern area was declared a Game Reserve. Expanded human communities in central and southern Bunyoro then entered into conflict with local elephants and commenced the process of displacing them from their nineteenth century range to their present confinement in northern Bunyoro. The conflict between human and elephant interests reached such proportions that a special department for elephant control was created in 1925. This became the Game Department and pursued a policy of harassment and confinement, which continues today. Between 1925 and 1965 at least 15 000 elephants were shot in Bunyoro in implementing this policy.

Concurrently the human population explosion has led to the expansion of human settlement and activity, outwards from central Bunyoro, resulting in a progressive decrease in the area available to elephant. The Murchison Falls

. National Park was created in 1952 and its southern sector now comprises two-thirds of the elephant range in north Bunyoro.

Significant but poorly documented changes were affecting the habitats in the shrinking areas occupied by elephants. From 1930 onwards observers recorded serious elephant damage to woody vegetation, but it was not until 1949 that the implications were realized and not until 1965 that any significant action was taken.

2. The environment

2.1. Climate

Climate is of considerable ecological importance, both in relation to the growing seasons of the vegetation, as an ultimate and proximate factor in relation to the elephant seasonal cycles, and as a factor in elephant diurnal behaviour. The climate of the elephant range is influenced by its equatorial situation, elevation, and the major air currents; by Lake Albert and the Victoria Nile and by the distribution of forest. Day length is close to 12 hours throughout the year. Unfortunately there are no full meteorological stations in the present elephant range, largely because there is little human settlement. Some rainfall data are available from Paraa and Wairingo, but for humidity and temperature it is necessary to extrapolate from stations outside the range.

2.1.1. *Rainfall*

The rainfall pattern is of most interest, largely through its effect on the length of the growing season, which determines the relative development of the different levels in the catena. Records from a number of stations in the vicinity of the elephant range are summarized in Table 2.1. The annual averages of these stations range from 766 millimetres (30 inches) at Butiaba on the Rift Valley floor (elevation 621 metres), to 1546 millimetres (61 inches) at Nyabyeya on the southern fringe of Budongo (see Chapter 1, Fig. 1.2). Wairingo and Paraa (elevation 1189 metres), within and immediately outside the elephant range, have average annual rainfalls of 1270 millimetres (50 inches) and 1227 millimetres (48 inches) respectively. At Kigumba and the Uganda Sisal Estate just south-east of the elephant range, the rainfall averages 1188 millimetres (47 inches) and 1021 millimetres (40 inches).

The seasonal distribution of rain is more important than the total annual precipitation and in Bunyoro the pattern is bimodal, with a well-marked dry season from mid-December to mid-February (see Chapter 9, Fig. 9.8). Even Nyabyeya averages less than 30 millimetres (1·2 inches) in January and Butiaba has only 14 millimetres (0·6 inches) in this month. April and May, and August to October (or November) are the wettest months, the earlier peak being much shorter. June and July show only about half to two-thirds the monthly rainfall of the peak months. These two peaks in rainfall coincide with the passage of the intertropical convergence system. The pattern of any one year shows considerable variation; the second peak is in general more reliable than the April peak, but the main fall may come in either the first or second half of the year.

The amounts of rainfall are extremely localized and as Eggeling (1947b) pointed out, there is much less variation in the numbers of days on which rain was recorded than in the total amount of rain that fell at any one station. The annual total of rain days per month varies from 86 at Butiaba to 145 at Nyabyeya; for

Table 2.1

Mean monthly rainfall (mm) for seven stations in or near the elephant range

	Jan.	Feb.	Mar.	Apr.	May	June	July	Aug.	Sept.	Oct.	Nov.	Dec.	Annual	Rainfall balance
Nyabyeya (22)	29·5	52·9	117·1	212·0	164·1	96·7	123·5	172·1	190·1	186·2	145·7	55·9	1545·8	+505
Masindi (55)	30·2	56·1	105·7	161·9	144·8	97·5	109·7	139·9	143·1	144·2	119·8	47·0	1299·9	− 218
Wairingo (12)	22·9	36·1	92·6	150·3	153·4	101·3	98·1	137·5	154·6	157·3	121·4	44·5	1270·0	− 76
Paraa (12)	27·0	48·4	109·8	171·6	97·0	73·3	74·5	121·5	150·5	170·4	128·9	54·0	1226·9	− 193
Kigumba (16)	37·7	51·0	98·8	141·2	130·9	75·7	88·2	124·1	139·1	138·0	106·5	56·6	1187·8	− 150
Uganda Sisal Estates (16)	28·5	36·7	84·3	137·6	110·8	67·0	83·6	121·3	118·4	98·3	89·3	45·6	1021·4	− 140
Butiaba (60)	14·1	32·1	57·6	101·9	95·1	53·5	66·3	82·8	75·2	84·4	72·9	30·2	766·1	− 719

Notes. Rainfall balance estimated by comparing annual rainfall with potential evapo-transpiration at the altitude of the station (Sansom 1954).
Figures from East African Meteorological Department, Annual Summary of rainfall, 1968.
Figures in parentheses refer to the number of years' records.

Wairingo and Paraa the figures are 117 and 107 respectively. Although rain may occur at any time of day it is most common in the afternoon and evening as thunderstorms build·up during the day. This means that much of the rain is poorly distributed; it falls in brief, violent thunderstorms so that the run-off can be spectacular. This pattern may contribute significantly to erosion, especially on slopes and where run-off is channelled along game trails, or roads.

Most storms seem to come from the north-east, over the higher ground. The rainfall in the centre of the Budongo Forest may often be as high as 1800 millimetres (70 inches); in 1961 the year's rainfall at Nyabyeya was 2204 millimetres (87 inches), but this was exceptional. Over most of the present elephant range the rainfall averages between 1150 millimetres and 1270 millimetres (45—50 inches), which is high for grassland areas in East Africa, and as we shall see the climatic climax vegetation is woodland rather than grassland. Sansom (1952) has examined the evidence for rainfall trends in East Africa, up to 1951. For Butiaba he concluded that there was a downward trend from 1920—49 of —3·8 millimetres (—0·15 inches) per year, equivalent to a proportional annual decrease of —0·52 per cent; for Masindi Port, south-south-east of the elephant range the downward trend was —9·4 millimetres (—0·37 inches) per year or —9·96 per cent. The downward trend appears to have continued at least until 1960, but 1961—4 were years of abnormally high rainfall throughout East Africa. By 1967 the rainfall amounts were again consistent with the downward trend, at least for three stations in the general area (Masindi, Butiaba, and Gulu).

The altitude and exposure to moisture-bearing winds affects the annual rainfall recorded, but from an ecological point of view the relationship between precipitation and evaporation is more important. Unfortunately there are no data for the study area from which to calculate evaporation by the method of Penman (1950). Instead we have obtained a rough appreciation of the annual evaporation from Sansom's graph of potential evapo-transpiration (Sansom 1954) which relates potential evapo-transpiration to altitude. The effectiveness of the rainfall can be assessed approximately by comparing evapo-transpiration, estimated in this way, with the mean annual rainfall, and the estimated deficit or excess of rain (shown in Table 2.1). This has considerable bearing upon plant growth, and for most of the elephant range it suggests that rainfall and evapo-transpiration are roughly in balance over the year, that in the Budongo forest there is a considerable excess of rainfall, and near the lake a considerable deficit. Consideration of the data on rainfall, relative humidity, and temperature indicates that November to March are the main deficit months and probably April and August to October the months of rainfall excess.

2.1.2. *Temperature*

Temperature is important because rates of photosynthesis, respiration, and other processes are related to it. Air temperatures throughout the study area are equable with small diurnal variations. At Butiaba the annual mean maximum temperature is 29·3 °C (monthly range 27·7—30·2 °C), and at Masindi the mean maximum is 28·8 °C (range 26·9—31·2 °C). Mean minimum temperatures are 21·9 °C (range 21·3—22·9 °C) and 16·8 °C (range 16·2—17·6 °C) for Butiaba and Masindi respectively. The averages for the elephant range should be intermediate between these two stations.

There are no data available on solar radiation but we may reasonably assume that it will be of the same order as the value obtained in the Queen Elizabeth Park, at a similar altitude but some two degrees further south, on the Equator. The mean daily solar radiation there was in the range 328—83 calories per square centimetre (Laws and Field 1965). A comparison with mean sunshine hours suggested that in the drier months smoke haze reduces the incoming solar radiation, and this would also be the case in North Bunyoro.

2.1.3.   *Humidity*

Humidity is not very high. Again the only figures come from the recording stations at Masindi and Butiaba. For Masindi the monthly mean relative humidity is 56 per cent (range 41—64 per cent) and for Butiaba the mean is 69 per cent (range 66—71 per cent). Seasonal fluctuations are much greater at Masindi, further from the influence of Lake Albert, and over most of the elephant range conditions are intermediate.

2.2.   Topography and soils

The most important topographical feature of the area is the Rift Valley, formed as a result of earth movements which began late in the Pliocene period and continued throughout the Pleistocene. The eastern wall of the Western Rift Valley forms a steep escarpment (Plate 2.1), running from the south-western corner of the North Bunyoro elephant range in a north-easterly direction for some 64 kilometres (40 miles) before it peters out. In the south the escarpment, which forms the eastern shore of Lake Albert, is 305 metres (1000 feet) high, but progressively decreases until it is less than 60 metres (200 feet) high at its northernmost extremity. From this point on the Rift wall becomes broken and indistinct. It is discernable here and there by low downwarped scarps less than 30 metres (100 feet) high, and follows a more northerly direction than the major escarpment, to cross the Victoria Nile River at about 31° 50′E. To the east of the escarpment are basement complex rocks of great age, mainly undifferentiated acid gneisses intruded by granites.

Land above 1097 metres (3600 feet) forms a broad and more or less continuous ridge running from near the north-east corner of the area in a south-westerly direction paralleling the escarpment. From this ridge protrude numerous small hills of basement complex rocks, the most northerly of which is Rabongo (1292 metres, 4239 feet), and the most southerly, Kitonya (1347 metres, 4420 feet) near Masindi town. In between there are several isolated hills, the main ones being Lukohe Hill (1160 metres, 3807 feet), Igisi Hill (1274 metres, 4178 feet),

PLATE 2.1. The escarpment from the west.

both in grasslands; Busingiro Hill (1201 metres, 3940 feet) and Nyabyeya Hill (1246 metres, 4090 feet) which are on the fringe of the Budongo Forest; and Kasenene Hill (1170 metres, 3841 feet) and Little Kasenene Hill (1173 metres, 3850 feet) which lie in the forest. In the extreme eastern part of the elephant range stands Rere Hill (1211 metres, 3973 feet), which provides an important landmark to which observations of elephant distribution and movements can be related (see Chapter 1, Fig. 1.3).

The land between the escarpment and the shores of Lake Albert contrasts with the rest of the area in being low-lying and very flat; covered with Pleistocene sediments (Plate 2.1). Thus, the greater part of the North Bunyoro elephant range is gently undulating country lying between 610 metres and 1160 metres (2000–3800 feet) above sea level (Plate 2.2).

The high central ridge creates three drainage systems (see Chapter 1, Fig. 1.3). The first is characterized by all those rivers flowing in a westerly direction into Lake Albert. From source to outlet the majority have a fall in excess of 490 metres (1600 feet) and are fairly fast flowing, particularly in their upper reaches. The majority of the streams which flow through the Budongo Forest, from south-east to north-west, act as tributaries to the six larger rivers which flow over the escarpment.

The Weiga is the largest river in the western drainage area. It is more than 64 kilometres (40 miles) long and, together with its tributaries, the Joliya, the Sambiya, the Wairingo, and the Izizi, drains a greater area than any other river in North Bunyoro. In its final 24 kilometres (15 miles), the Weiga becomes slow flowing and contains extensive papyrus swamps (*Cyperus papyrus*). The majority

PLATE 2.2. Elephants in grassland north-east of Rabongo.

of the other rivers in the western catchment area are less than half the length of the Weiga. There are many small streams, particularly in the forest area, but most of these are mere trickles which have no apparent flow in the dry season. The variation in depth of many of the large rivers throughout the year is considerable; from almost dry in a very dry season to over 3·7 metres (12 feet) during heavy rains.

The second drainage area contains the rivers flowing northwards into the Victoria Nile (Plate 2.2). For the most part these are relatively short un-named streams up to 24 kilometres long, that have small catchment areas and often cease to flow in dry weather. Their intermittent flow is perhaps causally related to the destruction of woodland and forest in the region of their headwaters and the fact that most originate at a relatively low altitude and in a relatively low rainfall zone. An exception to this rule is the Zoila (or Murchison) River, which is more typical of those in the western drainage area, being more than 40 kilometres (25 miles) long and fast flowing, taking its origin in higher ground near Rabongo Hill.

The third drainage area contains easterly and southerly flowing rivers which join the Victoria Nile or the Kafu River to the south and east of the elephant range. Although every bit as long as the westward flowing rivers, they have a fall of less than 150 metres (500 feet) and as a result are very slow-flowing and swampy.

As a result of this dense network of streams and rivers, water is not limiting to the larger animals even in the dry season, except perhaps in the eastern part of the range, near Kiryandongo.

Although the mapping of the area distinguishes six main types of soil, over broad areas, there is a smaller scale mosaic related to topography, especially the slope of the ground and its effects on drainage and erosion. The term catena (Milne 1935, 1936) indicates a sequence of soil types and related moisture levels from ridge to valley bottom that is repeated throughout areas of similar topography. Thus, over most of the grasslands the valley bottoms contain areas of impeded drainage with black cotton soils, clays, or clay loams, varying through intermediate types to sandy loams and loose sandy soils or rock outcrops on the ridges. The ecological significance of the catena lies in the relation of soil types and moisture to vegetation, and hence to herbivore distributions and densities.

Morrison, Hoyle, and Hope-Simpson (1948) have pointed out that there are four principal catena variants related to stages in the evolution of landscape by erosion. In North Bunyoro the earliest stage leaves steep-sided rocky hills or plateaux standing above the major drainage lines, often with short tributaries at right angles to the hillsides. This is characteristic of the topography of the central ridge above about 1000 metres (3400 feet), extending up to Rabongo (1292 metres, 4239 feet).

Next, between about 800 metres and 1000 metres (2600–3400 feet), is the watershed region where dissection has proceeded further. Here are the characteristic rounded ridges and gently sloped valleys of the central north-east and eastern part of the elephant range with a well-marked catena sequence including sumps of 'black cotton' soil. Proceeding westwards, the country below the escarpment between about 670 metres and 800 metres (2200–2600 feet) has widely spaced larger rivers, with flat or gently rounded watersheds between. The rivers are relatively slow flowing with large areas of black cotton soils in the valleys. This topography is also characteristic of the extreme eastern part of the range, near the Victoria Nile River.

The fourth variant, along the Lake Albert shore, is a very flat region (the Butiaba-Bungungu Flats) (Plate 2.1) about 10–11 kilometres (6–7 miles) broad, lying between 610 metres and 670 metres (2000–2200 feet). This zone is also characterized by low rainfall (for the most part less than 890 millimetres (35 inches) a year), with swamps along the lake shore and main rivers, and extensive areas of 'black cotton' in between.

Harrop (1962) has summarized the distribution of soil types in Uganda, which he has grouped according to the classification devised by D'Hoore (1961).

The productivity rating of the soil of the western two-thirds of the range is 'low', and to the east 'medium' (Lands and Surveys Department, Uganda (1959). Soil map USD 12, NA-36-6, 1-USD). Considerable deposits of carbon are said to occur in the top soil layers of Kitigo, presumably formed by the annual grass fires that sweep the area.

2.3. Vegetation

Langdale-Brown, Osmaston, and Wilson (1964) outline the ecological zones, range resources, and vegetation of North Bunyoro. Eggeling (1947b) describes

the Budongo Forest in some detail and gives a general description of the
vegetation outside the forest. Buechner and Dawkins (1961) give a picture of the
vegetation of the Murchison Falls National Park and discuss changes induced by
elephant and fire over the past hundred years. A full discussion of these habitat
changes is presented in Chapter 11. In the present chapter it is not therefore
necessary to describe the structure and composition of the vegetation in detail.
Following Langdale-Brown *et al.* (1964) it is classified under the following
general types:

(a) closed forest formations; and

(b) mixed forest-grassland formations and grassland formations.

Distribution of these types and their major subdivisions was recorded in 1967
during periodic flights over the area and plotted on 1 : 50 000 maps while
in flight. Where possible, verification of these observations was made on the ground
during other field work, but it was always subsidiary to other work. Later these
data were transcribed onto a 1 : 250 000 map to produce Fig. 2.1. In addition to
this vegetation survey, eight aerial transects covering 237 kilometres, and 130 square
kilometres were photographed and analysed for gross habitat features (see Chapter
11, Fig. 11.1). Only a summary analysis of these transects is presented in this book,
but the photographs form a permanent record of the vegetation along these
transects as it was in May 1967. From them more detailed information can be
extracted, if necessary, by future workers.

The bushed grassland and medium *Hyparrhenia* zone, is related to the low
rainfall and to a probable annual deficit of rainfall to evaporation, influenced by
the low elevation. Conversely the forest belt and the giant *Pennisetum* zone is
related to higher rainfall, or, where the rainfall is not significantly higher than
over most of the tall *Hyparrhenia* zone, to higher ground, which means that there
is a potential excess of rainfall over evaporation. The regular zonation is reinforced
or modified by edaphic factors.

2.3.1   Closed forest formations

There are three main blocks of forest in northern Bunyoro, namely Budongo,
Pabidi, and Rabongo (Plates 2.3 and 2.4). The forests have been described as a
medium-altitude, moist, semi-deciduous type (Langdale-Brown *et al.* 1964) and
extensions of the forest borders in general follow the lines of the rivers. The
Rabongo Forest lies approximately 30 kilometres (19 miles) north-east of the
Budongo Forest, while the small Pabidi forest is situated between the two and is
almost continuous with the Budongo forest (see Chapter 1, Fig. 1.3). A discontinuous chain of relict forest patches (several of which comprise Rabongo Forest)
extends north-eastwards from Pabidi Forest, almost to the Victoria Nile (Fig. 2.1,
Plate 2.5). All are associated with the central ridge of higher ground and the
majority are located on the uppermost reaches of the eastern drainage system.

The three main forests are of similar species composition, although the stand
structure is very different. All three show a canopy dominated by *Cynometra*

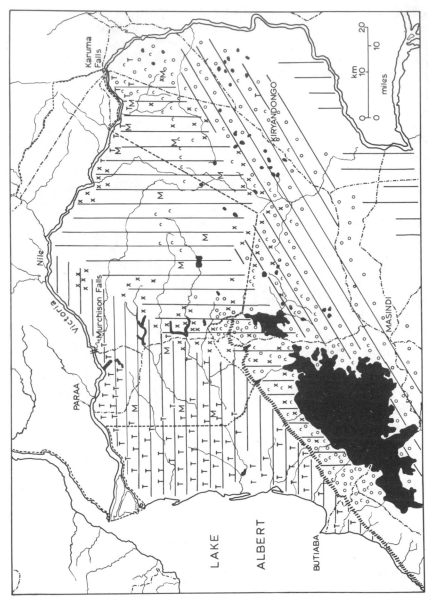

Fig. 2.1. Vegetation map. Key: T–thicket; M–mvule (*Chlorophora excelsa*); X–stands of dead *Terminalia*; O–living *Terminalia*; ∩–*Combretum* and *Lonchocarpus* type shrubs; black–forest or forest relic; horizontal lines–medium *Hyparrhenia* grassland; vertical lines –tall *Hyparrhenia* grassland; oblique lines–giant *Pennisetum* grassland; heavy shading–escarpment.

PLATE 2.3. Pabidi Forest patches, with *Terminalia* woodland in the distance

PLATE 2.4. Elephants at edge of Rabongo Forest. Note absence of normal ecotone

alexandri with *Rinorea ardisiiflora* dominating the understory. However, the Rabongo Forest has *Phyllanthus discoideus* and *Sapium ellipticum* as colonizers instead of *Maesopsis eminii* as at Budongo and *Khaya grandifoliola* in place of *Khaya anthotheca.*

This would indicate an affinity between the Rabongo Forest and the forests of West Acholi to the north. It is probable that all forest patches in the area are remnants of a single continuous forest that formerly extended from the Eastern Congo and Semliki to the Imatong Mountains in the Sudan (Buechner and Dawkins 1961), and including the Bugoma Forest in Bunyoro and the Zoka Forest in Acholi (see Chapter 1, Fig. 1.2).

In all, *Cynometra alexandri* are dominant. They are part of a gradation from true tropical rain forest to a moist deciduous high forest, all stages of which can still be found. If they had been left undisturbed (that is uninfluenced by high elephant densities) the Rabongo and Zoka Forests would probably represent the most advanced development of the Budongo type. Moreau (1933, 1966) considers that the great African equatorial forest became discontinuous at least 20 000 years ago, and Dale (1954) believed that weather conditions between 1400 A.D. and 1600 A.D. resulted in a spread of high forest, followed by a halt to the expansion and later probably a retrogression in the dry years of the nineteenth century.

Because of its size and economic importance, considerably more scientific work has been done on Budongo than on any other forest in East Africa, and there is more information available relating to Budongo than to the others. The Budongo Forest comprises about 474 square kilometres (183 square miles) and Pabidi about 26 square kilometres (10 square miles) of forest. As they are very close and separated by little more than a main road they are best treated as one.

Eggeling (1947b) recognizes three main types of forest; colonizing forest, mixed forest, and ironwood (*Cynometra*) forest. Colonizing forest normally consists of a narrow belt of *Acanthus arboreus* which has been colonized by *Maesopsis eminii* and forms the boundary between forest and grassland. Below the canopy of *Maesopsis*, saplings of the species characteristic of mixed forest grow. In general, the younger the forest the more numerous are the saplings of such species as *Cordia millenii*, *Khaya anthotheca*, and *Entandrophragma* spp.

Mixed forest is characterized by its several layers, its density of species, and the great height of its emergents; the presence of large buttresses and flutes; and the abundance of epiphytes and lianes. In this forest type there is a large number of species, and it is here that the majority of exploitable mahogany trees are found. The emergent layer is dominated by *Khaya anthotheca* and *Entandrophragma* spp., with *Alstonia boonei* and *Mildbraediodendron excelsum* commonly associated. In the upper continuous canopy are found *Celtis mildbraedii*, *Chrysophyllum albidum*, *Funtumia elastica*, *F. latifolia*, *Erythrophleum guineense*, *Cynometra alexandri*, *Celtis zenkeri*, and *Trichilia prieuriana*. The lower parts of the canopy are marked by the presence of numerous poles and saplings of the species that can produce tall forms. There are spreading shade-tolerant species such as *Trichelia rubescens* and erect understory trees such as *Lasiodiscus mildbraedi, Rinorea ardisiflora, Techlea nobilis,* and *Celtis brownii.* In all layers epiphytic and parasitic self-supporting figs are numerous.

In the older mixed forest the regeneration of emergent and upper canopy trees is restricted to shade-tolerant species such as *Chrysophyllum perpulchrum, C. albidum, Celtis mildbraedii,* and *Cynometra alexandri;* pole-sized or larger mahoganies are usually absent. Where gaps due to falling trees occur, then colonizing species such as *Maesopsis eminii* and *Cordia millenii* occur, as might be expected.

Ironwood (*Cynometra*) forest was described by Eggeling (1947b) as the climatic climax forest. A feature of this forest is the small number of species which occur and the apparent absence of the lower layers in the canopy; there is also an absence of climbers and lianes. This forest is dominated by *Cynometra alexandri* which forms 70–80 per cent of the growing stock. No regeneration of mixed forest species is found and the understory consists of *Cynometra alexandri* regeneration and *Lasiodiscus mildbraedii.*

According to Eggeling (1947b), the normal succession to be expected in Budongo is thus grassland, colonizing forest, mixed forest, and ironwood forest. This pattern is found to the south of Budongo and around Siba where man has not interfered, and where elephants are not abundant. In areas where the forest is expanding it is not uncommon to see individual trees of *Terminalia glaucescens,* typical of the former grassland, being enveloped by the forest to become covered with epiphytes and eventually to die. To the north-east of the River Sonso (see Chapter 1, Fig. 1.3) and round the north-east boundary of the forest this succession does not occur, and areas are found where the succession would now appear to be directly from grassland to ironwood forest. This is particularly true in Kaniyo block (see Chapter 5, Fig. 5.9) and in Pabidi Local Forest Reserve. These areas are characterized by the large *Cynometra alexandri* found on the edge of the forest, with sickly *Acanthus arboreus* round their bases (Plate 2.4). The canopy is not closed and patches of grass occur. We believe this situation is due to heavy elephant use of the forest in these sectors.

As a result of expansion in the south-west and retreat in the north-east the whole forest is slowly shifting, demonstrating a slow process which has presumably occurred in the past in this and other areas, to produce the present dynamic mosaic of forest and grassland characteristic of East Africa.

Rabongo Forest is located within the National Park and is now represented by eight patches of closed high forest totalling 2·6 square kilometres (1 square mile) in area. Ten years ago there were seven patches (Buechner and Dawkins 1961, p. 760) and their increased number represents the continuing process of fragmentation. Two large, almost contiguous stands form about 80 per cent of the complex. The forest lies near the head waters of the westward flowing Wairingo River, south-west of Rabongo Hill (Chapter 1, Fig. 1.3) and the remaining stands appear to be

the survivors of a much more extensive forest which formerly covered the upper
Wairingo Valley. It is now almost impossible to determine what the original
vegetation structure and species composition was in the forest. Game (especially
elephant and buffalo) and fire have made considerable inroads and the continuing
future existence of this forest relic is in considerable doubt.

The present canopy consists mainly of *Cynometra alexandri*, with
Chrysophyllum albidum, Cola gigantea, Holoptelea grandis, and *Mildbraediodendron*
commonly occurring. In 1958 Buechner and Dawkins (1961) estimated that the
Cynometra formed 73 per cent of the total area of the stand for all the canopy
trees, demonstrating its similarity to the Budongo climax forest. The understory
comprises *Diospyros abyssinica, Argomuellaria macrophylla, Rinorea* spp., and
Randix spp.

It would appear that Rabongo was formerly very similar to the ironwood
climax of parts of Budongo, but that it has deteriorated rapidly under the
influence of elephant and fire damage. Comparisons between the Rabongo
Forest and areas on the north-east margin of Budongo and Pabidi give a strikingly
similar picture and it is not difficult to accept that within a few decades of intensive elephant use, Budongo as a whole could come to resemble Rabongo as it is
today.

Decaying riparian (gallery) forest exists in the gorges through which streams
descend the Rift Valley escarpment, in the lower middle sections of the Sambiya,
Joliya, and Wairingo Rivers and on the banks of the Nile immediately below
Murchison Falls (Fig. 2.1). In all instances these gallery strips are associated with
slopes that are steep enough to prevent elephant browsing. This, together with
their constituent species (including *Khaya grandifoliola, Blighia welwitschii,
Chlorophora excelsa, Diospyros abyssinica, Trichilia prieuriana, Spathodea
campanulata, Phyllanthus discoideus, Markhamia platycalyx, Acanthus pubescens,*
and *Canthium* spp.) suggests that rather than being true gallery forest, these stands
are relics of the former over-all forest cover. Isolated mvule trees (*Chlorophora
excelsa*) occur irregularly along the Nile, on much of the high ground in the
Karuma Falls Controlled Area, the eastern National Park, and also in the extreme
west of the Park (Fig. 2.1). The straight and clean boles (Plate 2.5, and Chapter 11,
Plate 11.4) indicate that these fire-sensitive trees grew up in forest, and are relics
spared by the cultivators and elephants, although often seriously ring-barked.

2.3.2.   *Mixed wooded-grassland and grassland formations*

We follow the detailed classification proposed by Pratt, Greenway, and Gwynne
(1966). They define woodland as 'a stand of trees, up to 18 m in height, with
open or continuous, but not thickly interlaced, canopy, sometimes with shrubs
interspersed, and a canopy cover of more than 20% [Plates 2.3 and 2.6] . Grasses and
herbs dominate the ground cover; epiphytic ferns are rare. Often subject to
periodic burning . . . Sub types should be classified by reference to the genera of
the dominant trees . . .'. On these criteria North Bunyoro now contains very little

PLATE 2.5. Relict forest patches at periphery of elephant range.

'woodland'. However, according to ecological classification it should support extensive *Vitex-Phyllanthus-Sapium-Terminalia* woods (Langdale-Brown *et al.* 1964). That this was formerly the case is evidenced by the arboreal constituents of the present woodland, particularly in the south of the North Bunyoro elephant range. The present degenerate state is attributable to the action of man, elephant, and fire over a protracted period.

Bushland is defined as 'an assemblage of woody plants, mostly of shrubby habit, having a shrub canopy of less than 6 m in height, with occasional emergents, and a canopy cover of more than 20%'.

Wooded grassland is 'grassland with scattered or grouped trees, and trees always conspicuous, but having a canopy cover of less than 20%. Often subject to periodic burning.' Bushed grassland is defined as 'grassland with scattered or grouped shrubs, the shrubs always conspicuous but having a canopy cover of less than 20%. May be subject to periodic burning'. Grassland (Plates 2.1 and 2.2) is defined as 'land dominated by grasses and occasionally other herbs; sometimes with widely scattered or grouped trees and shrubs, the canopy cover of which does not exceed 2%. Usually subject to periodic burning'. Subtypes should be classified by reference to the following criteria: height, genera of dominant grasses, degree of swampiness, and dominance of annual grasses or other herbs.

These broad definitions cover all the vegetation in North Bunyoro, excepting forest and swamps. Throughout, the vegetation is in a transitional state between forest, dense or open woodland, and grassland. In the main the transition is from

PLATE 2.6. Woodland south of present elephant range.

the former to the latter, although there are at least two restricted areas in which the converse succession may be taking place (see Chapter 11).

The greater part of the Murchison Falls National Park, South and Karuma Falls Controlled Hunting Area is now grassland (Fig. 2.1). Widely scattered dead trees and tree stumps indicate that much is of recent origin. In these open grasslands, particularly on steep slopes and along the Masindi-Karuma road there is a high density and vigorous growth of the fire-resisting shrub *Lonchocarpus laxiflorus*. However, elephant browse it so heavily that few specimens exceed 30 centimetres (1 foot) in height and it does not form a physiognomic feature (Plate 2.7).

South and east of the Park and Controlled Hunting Area, tree and shrub density and variety increases, progressing through wooded grassland and open woodland, until on the southern fringes of the area it approaches closed woodland and forest (Fig. 2.1). This pattern is illustrated by the results of analyses of the aerial photographic transects (Chapter 11). The dominant tree throughout the wooded grassland and woodland is *Terminalia glaucescens,* with *Combretum binderanum* dominant in the understory. *Stereospermum kunthianum, Vitex*

PLATE 2.7. Bull herd in geophyte stand after burn.

cunneata, Lannea larteri, and *Piliostigma thoningii* are also common as shrubs rarely reaching more than 2—3 metres in height. *Lonchocarpus laxiflorus* occurs in fairly dense bushy patches of 2—2·5 metres in height. Occasional *Khaya grandifoliola* and *Chlorophora excelsa* are found near the forest edge, particularly in the Waisoke River area.

Between Lake Albert, the Rift escarpment, and the western border of the National Park, and along the banks of the Victoria Nile below the Murchison Falls, the vegetation is a mixture of bushed grassland and wooded grassland. The grass stratum is heavily dotted with clumps of undifferentiated deciduous thicket. It occurs on free-draining sandy soils and in general is associated with low rainfall and, along the Nile, with high hippopotamus densities. The deciduous trees and shrubs tend to form clumped thickets with open canopies 3—7 metres high, often around termitaria, forming a mosaic with clearings of open grassland. This is a species rich community and no one species achieves dominance. Characteristic species are: *Acacia senegal, Euphorbia candelabrum, Balanites aegyptiaca, Allophyllus africanus, Bridelia scleroneura, Grewia mollis, Harrisonia abyssinica,* and *Ziziphus abyssinica.* Tree density is greatest north of the Weiga

River, with *Acacia* spp. and *Balanites aegyptiaca* prominent. South of this river there are far fewer trees and *Euphorbia candelabrum* is most common.

Bushland occurs only on the periphery of the elephant range in the eastern part of the area. It contains *Albizia zygia, Combretum binderanum, C. molle, Markhamia platycalyx, Piliostigma thonningii, Stereospermum kunthianum, Vitex cuneata,* and *Terminalia glaucescens* among others, but is characterized by a paucity of species compared with the bushed grassland. For the most part it probably represents a degradation from *Vitex-Phyllanthus-Sapium-Terminalia* woodland.

The grass stratum of all the grassland and woodland areas is divisable into three main types (Fig. 2.1).

1. Medium height *Hyparrhenia* grassland which comprises the type below the Rift escarpment, between Lake Albert and the National Park, and the western part of the Park below 850 metres (2800 feet) above sea level. Grasses seldom exceed 105 centimetres (3·5 feet) in height.

2. Tall *Hyparrhenia* grassland (Plate 2.2) comprising the type occupying most land between 850 metres and 1100 metres (2800–3600 feet) above sea level, and covering the central and eastern sectors of the Murchison Falls National Park and the Karuma Controlled Hunting Area. Grasses frequently grow to 2·5 metres (8 feet) in height.

3. Giant *Pennisetum purpureum* grassland which covers much of the high ground above 1100 metres (3600 feet), but particularly the upper reaches of the eastern watershed and in the valleys of the Siba basin. These stands occur on soils that are 'considerably deeper and more fertile than is usual in Bunyoro' (Eggeling 1947b, p. 36) and it is in the *Pennisetum* belt or close to its northern edge that most relict forest patches occur. This supports the hypothesis that the occurrence of *Pennisetum purpureum* indicates degradation of the forest (Thomas 1940; Eggeling 1947b; Worthington 1958), rather than it being a successful competitor with forest (Eggeling 1947b).

Divisions between these three major categories are not clear-cut and one zone tends to merge with the next. The dominance of *Hyparrhenia* spp. and *Pennisetum purpureum* is associated with the intense annual burning for they are fire climax species, although until recently the *Pennisetum* stands were burned less frequently than the *Hyparrhenia* stands (Eggeling 1947b). The general luxuriance of grass growth in the tall *Hyparrhenia* and giant *Pennisetum* areas produces vast quantities of flammable material annually and is an ecological factor of major importance in the region.

Although *Hyparrhenia* spp. and *Pennisetum purpureum* are dominant, a large variety of other grasses occur. Of particular importance are *Setaria sphacelata* dominant and *Brachiaria brizantha, B. fulva,* and *Setaria longiseta* abundant. Other common species include *Hyparrhenia filipendula, Paspalum commersonii, Imperata cylindrica, Sporobolus pyramidalis,* and *Panicum maximum.* With the onset of the rains in April, after the dry-season burning, these species grow faster than the *Hyparrhenias* (probably because they are shallow rooted), and until the onset of the drier spell in July, form the bulk of the grass stratum. By June-July these shorter grasses are being overtaken in growth and smothered by dense stands of *Hyparrhenias* (with *H. cymbaria* dominant, and *H. rufa, H. diplandra, H. schimperi, H. dissoluta, Andropogon gayanus,* and *Loudetia arundinacea* intermixed). *Pennisetum purpureum* and *Panicum maximum* are found in the wetter areas. This pattern is particularly noticeable in the moist *Hyparrhenia* zone and is of considerable importance to all grazing animals in the area.

According to Dougall and Bogdan (1958), *Hyparrhenia filipendula* and *H. rufa* are of low or very low nutritive value; *H. dissoluta* is completely grazed in its early growth stages, but later only the leaves are eaten (Dougall and Bogdan 1960). The chemical composition of whole *H. rufa* included only 0·32 per cent digestible protein but the leaves separately contained 1·97 per cent digestible protein (Juko and Bredon 1961). *Pennisetum purpureum* has a high nutritive value for cattle but there is a marked decrease in digestible protein content with increasing height; in plants 0·9—1·2 metre (3—4 feet) tall, crude protein was 7·35 per cent, and digestible protein 13·2 per cent; at 2·1—2·4 metres (7—8 feet) the values were 13·15 per cent and 9·7 per cent respectively (Marshall and Bredon 1963). In mature elephant grass the protein content is low. Bredon and Horrell (1961) state that *Brachiaria decumbens* and *B. brizantha* are palatable and nutritious. Thus the nutritive value of the vegetation is probably greater in the first half of the rains, when grasses are relatively short. The effect of this on seasonal growth, reproduction, and movement of elephants is discussed in later chapters.

Panicum maximum is particularly associated with shade close to clumps of bush and relict forest patches (see Chapter 11, Plate 11.4). It is also able to persist in the open, particularly around termitaria. This association with shade, together with the ability to exist without it, results in stands of *Panicum maximum* demarcating the sites of former forest patches for some time after the forest has disappeared. On this evidence it appears that many forest patches in the *Pennisetum* area's northern fringe disappeared quite recently.

Throughout the grasslands, as a result of the soil catenas, grass height tends to be shorter on ridge tops than on slopes and valley bottoms. This is most pronounced in the western half of the tall *Hyparrhenia* zone, where the slopes are generally steeper than in other areas.

Heavy grazing by hippopotamus has resulted in extensive areas of grass less than 15 centimetres (6 inches) in height, along the Nile (Plate 2.8). This is most pronounced in the dry-*Hyparrhenia* zone east of the Murchison Falls where the induced short grass extends up to 5 kilometres (3 miles) from the river. This heavy grazing tends to inhibit fire and favours the growth of grasses preferred by grazing herbivores. As a result there are relatively large concentrations of Uganda kob (*Adenota kob*), waterbuck (*Kobus defassa*), hartebeeste (*Alcelaphus bucelaphus jacksoni*), and warthog (*Phacochoerus aethiopicus*) in these areas and although

PLATE 2.8. Deciduous thicket along the Bunyoro bank of River Nile. Note erosion due to hippopotamus grazing, in foreground.

this situation was originated by hippopotamus, the other species probably now play a contributory role in maintaining (and possibly extending) the short-grass zone.

2.3.3. Geophytes

A number of woody species are fire resistant and able to exist in the face of annual burning by developing large root stocks, the stand also expanding in some areas by extensive root coppicing. The aerial parts of the plant are removed by fire annually, but are rapidly replaced after the burn (Plate 2.7). In the presence of heavy browsing (and for some species possibly even in its absence) the plant is unable to grow out of the growth stage during which it is vulnerable to fire. In some areas one gets an impression of great abundance of plants when they are viewed shortly after the burn, but as the grasses grow, and the geophytes are browsed by elephants, they tend to become an understory dominated by the tall grasses. The species which characteristically develop geophytically in these conditions are *Lonchocarpus laxiflorus, Terminalia glaucescens, Combretum binderanum, C. guenzii, C. molle, Stereospermum kunthianum,* and *Strychnos innocua.* On their continued persistence depends the possibility of restoring stands of woodland in the elephant range. The significance of geophytes is discussed at greater length below and in Chapter 11.

2.3.4. *Areas of impeded drainage*

Virtually every valley and stream bed in the area contains some seasonal and/or permanently waterlogged sites, usually both. The gentle gradients of the eastern watershed result in larger and more permanent swamps than in the western drainage system, except in its lowest reaches. In the middle reaches of the western drainage system, seasonal swamps are the rule (Plate 2.9). In general they are too narrow to depict in Fig. 2.1, but they play a vital role in the ecology of all large herbivores in the region, and particularly elephant. They retain green uninflammable material, which is a most important food source for elephant when the grasslands are burnt each year. They also provide a partially effective fire-break system, which tends to hinder the progress of fires in all but very dry seasons (see below).

2.3.5. *Papyrus swamp*

Cyperus papyrus swamps occur along the Victoria Nile, above Karuma Falls, in the delta of the Nile where it flows into Lake Albert, and in the lower reaches of the Weiga and Waisoke rivers. Other common herbs in the association include *Cissampelos mucronata, Dissotis rotundifolia, Dryopteris striata, Leersia hexandra,* and *Polygonum salicifolium.* This community represents in terms of area a very

PLATE 2.9. Seasonal swamp in North Bunyoro.

small part of the range of the North Bunyoro elephants, but plays an important part in their ecology, particularly in the dry season.

2.4.   Fire

Seasonal grassland burning (Plate 2.10) has been practised for centuries by many African peoples, including the Banyoro. It was recorded in West Africa at the time of Hanno's voyage, before 480 B.C. (Richards 1964, p. 341). The reasons for burning are to clear the ground for cultivation; to provide a flush of green grass for cattle; to bait, drive, or encircle wild animals to facilitate hunting; formerly, in the long grass areas, to remove cover from which enemies might launch surprise attacks; and possibly burning for sheer pleasure in the spectacle. Another use of fire is road verge clearance by Ministry of Works personnel on the Masindi-Paraa and Masindi-Karuma roads. Eggeling (1947b) states that, in North Bunyoro, the giant *Pennisetum* grasslands are burned less frequently than the medium and tall *Hyparrhenia* grasslands. Seasonal burning occurs today on a scale greater than ever before.

Annually, with the onset of the dry season in December, the grasslands are burned, commencing in general in the vicinity of centres of human activity and progressively radiating from them. At first, while the grasses contain much green material and valley bottoms and seasonal swamps are still wet and lush, fires are seldom more than a few acres in extent. However, as the season proceeds, progressively more flammable material becomes available; valleys dry out, swamps

PLATE 2.10. Fire in M.F.P.N. (photograph C. A. Spinage).

retract and become less efficient as barriers, and fires become more intense, some exceeding 260 square kilometres (100 square miles) in extent. Fires also vary in intensity depending on the amount of fuel available. Thus, early in the dry season, when much grass is still green and uninflammable, their intensity is low and they are referred to as 'cool'. With the lengthening of the season, more and more fuel is made available as the grass matures and dries, resulting in increased intensity and progressively 'hotter' burns. In the distant past when fires were induced naturally (lightning, volcanic activity) they were probably much less frequent and therefore individually hotter and more catastrophic, because of the accumulation of fuel in the intervening period. 'Hot' burns result in the complete removal of the aerial parts of plants, except for woody growth large enough or resistant enough to withstand them.

This seasonal factor influencing the nature of burning has been widely recognized in conservation practice throughout Africa over the past sixty years. It is generally considered that the prevention of fire is impossible in extensive unoccupied grasslands. Although it is accepted that even a 'cool' early burn is degenerative (Darling 1960), it denies the possibility of a 'hot' and more damaging fire late in the dry season.

Conservationists wishing to inhibit or reduce the effect of fire on woody vegetation in grassland or bordering it, therefore deliberately induce 'cool' early burns at the onset of the dry season. Thus, the Forest Department policy is annually to burn the grasslands around the Budongo Forest as early in the dry season as possible, to minimize damage to the forest edge. Similarly the National Park authorities induce early burns in the Murchison Falls Park in an effort to reduce the effect of more intensive late season fires on woody vegetation. Game Department and sport hunting policy is the converse of this. To facilitate maximum visibility for driving motor vehicles across country, and sighting quarry, it suits them to achieve really intense burns so as to clear as much country as possible.

The primary and immediate effect of fire is to restrict the dry-season food supply of herbivores at a time when replacement is minimal. Owing to the relatively high rainfall and interrupted dry season in North Bunyoro, there is a short delay in replacement growth of grass, and fire is probably not as important as it is in the drier parts of East Africa. In the case of the very mobile elephant population, extensive fires can and do result in considerable concentration and pressure on the vegetation in unburnt areas for long periods depending on the rainfall. Thus an already serious trend in the vegetation is aggravated during the dry season.

Fire is also an important long-term factor in its effect on the composition and structure of the vegetation (Daubenmire 1968). Thus, a secondary long-term effect of regular annual burning (which has been well documented) is to restrict the spectrum of plants to those species which are tolerant of or dependent on fire, and thus severely to limit diversity.

Plants and communities vary in their tolerance to fire. The evergreen and semi-evergreen species, forests and thickets, succumb to fire; deciduous savanna trees and associated grasses show varying degrees of resistance while some grasses (e.g. *Themeda triandra*), geophytes, and densely caespitose herbs thrive on fire. The ecological effect is cumulative as, the denser the grass layer becomes, the more intense is the subsequent fire and so species with poor resistence are successfully eliminated.

(Langdale-Brown *et al.* 1964).

Lonchocarpus laxiflorus is a conspicuously fire-resistant species and ten years ago Buechner and Dawkins (1961, p. 762) noted that extensive patches of this species in Murchison Falls Park seemed destined to expand.

Probably it will increase both as a scattered component of open grassland and as nearly pure stands of small woodland. Large expanses of dense low coppice already present provide ample evidence of the trend towards the development of open *L. laxiflorus* woodlands. Currently, these trees seldom exceed 3 m in height, but strong resistance to fire and rapid growth are evident. It may be anticipated that growth will reach 15 m and that *L. laxiflorus* will become the most important tree species in the Park.

The survival of geophytic shrubs in annually burned grassland was recorded by Buechner and Dawkins (1961, Table III and p. 762). They list some thirty species of shrubs and trees that are fire resistant in varying degrees and some of their findings are summarized in our Table 11.15 (columns 3–7) in Chapter 11. On the basis of these plots the most fire-resistant woody species are: *Lonchocarpus laxiflorus, Terminalia glaucescens, Combretum binderanum, C. gueinzii, C. molle Borasus aethiopum* (north of Nile), *Stereospermum kunthianum,* and *Strychnos innocua.* The dominant fire climax grasses are *Hyparrhenia filipendula, H. dissoluta, Brachiaria brizantha, Panicum maximum, Sporobolus pyramidalis,* and *Pennisetum purpureum.*

From Table 11.15 it is apparent that geophyte densities of 60 000–90 000 per square kilometre were present in association with living large trees, and of 150 000–300 000 per square kilometre, after large trees had been eliminated by elephants and fire. These densities evidently persist for a decade or more of annual burning, but most species do not resist the annual burn sufficiently to achieve any net aerial growth from year to year. The aerial photographic transect analysis in 1967 through the former Wairingo woodland (Chapter 11) showed densities of small trees and bushes (1–8 metres crown diameter) lower than 2000 per square kilometre. Indeed none of the eight aerial transects in Murchison Falls Park, South showed densities higher than 5000 per square kilometre, and the highest density of small trees and bushes in the transects north of the Victoria Nile was 11 000 per square kilometre. These densities were exceptional.

This reflects a continued decrease in regeneration but is probably also a result of heavy elephant browsing. The densities of geophytic root stocks may not be significantly different from 1958, but browsing may restrict the aerial growth to the point at which the vast majority do not achieve a crown diameter of 1 metre, and so are not distinguishable on the aerial photographs (Plate 2.7). Certainly in peripheral areas, where elephant usage is lower, but the incidence of fire similar, compared with central areas, there are higher densities of shrubs. It seems clear that the hopes of Buechner and Dawkins (1961) that some of the root coppice, particularly of *Lonchocarpus laxiflorus,* would develop into closed woodland, have not been realized, and that some of the less fire tolerant, or elephant-preferred woody growth has been eliminated over large areas.

Three plots were set up in the grassland of Murchison Falls Park, South in 1965. They had sides of 61 metres (200 feet) each and an area of 0·37 hectare (0·92 acres). One was ditched, one had a fire-break but was open to animals, and the other was open to both fire and animals. Unfortunately the ditched plot was not large enough to carry out burning experiments, but the woody growth in this plot 'has been quite remarkable' (Wheater 1968). In 1967 six similar experimental plots were established in open grassland at Chobe, Murchison Falls Park, North. Three of them were surrounded by an elephant-proof ditch, which has successfully excluded large mammals—except Uganda kob *Adenota kob*, which are able to jump across it, and one penetration of a few hours duration by two bull elephants. A plot within the ditch and one without have been prevented from burning since their establishment. One plot within and one without has been 'early-burned' each year, and one within and one without 'late-burned'.

The difference between the ditched and unditched plots open to large mammals is very marked. Quantitative and qualitative analyses have been made (Spence and Angus 1971), but the differences are obvious from photographs taken in 1969. All three unditched plots appeared to be similar and at a distance were indistinguishable from the surrounding grasslands. Close to, it could be seen that the two plots that were burnt (one early and one late) apparently received greater grazing pressure and use from large mammals than the one that was not burnt. The latter showed a slight increase in the amount of litter and flammable material, but no tree or shrub growth differentiated it from the surrounding grasslands. The late-burned plot showed rather more bare ground than the others.

All the ditched plots showed very much denser growth. The unburned plot was already a tangle of herbs and emergent shrubs and saplings of several trees and shrubs (including *Acacia, Kigelia,* and *Piliostigma*) and the dense mat of dead grass and creepers was such as to render walking awkward. The early-burned plot also showed spectacular sapling growth, though fewer in variety and less dense than in the unburned plot. The late-burned plot showed markedly less tree and shrub growth than the preceding two, but nevertheless it far exceeded any in the unburned, unditched plot. Acacias were the most prominent sapling, and although all had been severely scorched all were alive.

In an unmanaged situation, late burning would hardly occur as an annual event, and it is felt that even one year of early-burning would permit many of the saplings to grow sufficiently to avoid destruction in subsequent late burns. Outstanding in the late-burned plot was a prolific creeper which made a dense mat over the ground and all emergent shrubs or trees. Little if any bare ground was visible in the ditched plots and bare patches, attributed to decayed termitaria, that are so typical of the grasslands, were grown over luxuriantly by the grass *Cynodon dactylon.*

This experiment shows that the absence of elephant permits tree growth in the presence of fire, although the latter will slow down, but not eliminate, tree regeneration. Other herbivores were also excluded, but there can be no doubt that the effective factor was the absence of elephant. Together with the much larger-scale examples of Budongo and other natural experiments these plots make an incontestable case for elephant (at their current densities) as the primary agent in the suppression of woody growth.

A second series of six plots similarly treated was set up in *Terminalia* woodland at Chobe, but we have not been able to visit them. Both sets of plots have been recorded in 1967 and 1969 by staff and students from St. Andrews University (Spence and Angus 1971) and the results of re-recordings, when available, should be of great interest.[†]

Buechner and Dawkins (1961, p. 761) discuss the effects of fire on the Rabongo Forest.

Severe damage, ultimately resulting in mortality, is caused when fire follows fresh debarking before fire resistant cork layers can be formed . . . Large trees along the forest edges, including *Chlorophora excelsa, Cynometra alexandri,* and *Pterygota mildbraedii,* were being killed by the combined action of debarking and burning. As a result of the destruction of both large trees and the understory along the margins of the forest, light penetration increased sufficiently to permit the spread of grasses, notably *Panicum maximum,* into the forest. Sufficient inflammable material is produced to carry the fire from surrounding grasslands ever deeper into the forest.

These authors recommended that fire be controlled and in 1966, Stuart-Smith (1966) reported that there were no recent signs of fire penetrating the forest, and that burning away from the forest edge to maintain a firebreak was being carefully carried out. Our observations in 1967 confirmed this. However, Stuart-Smith also noted that the very open and grassy nature of the forest edge was particularly dangerous as it would allow fire to penetrate right into the forest (Plate 2.4).

As we have seen, the Budongo Forest is expanding where there are few or no elephant and contracting where there is considerable elephant use, although in

† Spence (personal communication) revisited the plots in March 1973. There had been no burning within the plots for 18 months (not even controlled experimental burning), but he concluded that the effects of burning were entirely subordinate to the effects of grazing. In the grassland series, *Acacia seiberiana* on the ungrazed plot had shown a steady growth increment and some individuals were already 26–30 feet high. In three growing seasons the *Combretum* in the vicinity of the woodland plots had been killed by barking; in the ditched plot the *Combretum* growth was very conspicuous; *Acacias* had grown to 22 feet high and *Albizia* had increased to 12–16 feet.

both areas the incidence of fire is similar. Eggeling (1947b, p. 32) remarks:

although fire retards the expansion of the forest, it is by itself unable to stop the process [and, (p. 33)] it is indisputable that wherever they occur in numbers elephants are a limiting factor in the natural development of vegetation . . . North, north-east and north-west of Budongo the same herd, in conjunction with fire, has likewise slowed down (and possibly now prohibits) the spread of the forest. Near Budongo in this area there are numerous high-forest nuclei (many of them based on streams) which are potential spawn for the spread of the forest. Around these nuclei the normal surrounding fringe of colonising and protecting bush, which includes *Caloncoba schweinfurthii* Gilg. and *Acanthus arboreus* Forsk., is so battered and broken by elephants that dry-season fires penetrate to the edge of the forest, killing back all external colonising regeneration and scorching the bases of the larger trees. In places, especially near favourite watering places, these forested patches are steadily decreasing in size. Owing to fire and elephants they are now relics rather than nuclei. Elephants, not fires, are the controlling factor [see also Chapter 11].

This process has continued over the twenty-five years since Eggeling's work, and, as in the case of Rabongo, few of these relics now remain (Plate 2.3).

The Forest Department policy of early burning may have retarded this process, although until 1964 there were no roads into the Kitigo grasslands and it is doubtful if burning was carried out as early as it should have been. Since 1964 the burning has been carried out early, and in 1966 and 1967 was very early— and thorough, as it was carried out by the Game Guards on their patrols. Burning around the Kaniyo and Pabidi Reserves has been much more haphazard, often delayed until late January, owing to shortage of Local Government staff.

Fire in the medium and tall *Hyparrhenia* areas does not appear to frighten the larger animals. Elephant, buffalo, waterbuck, kob, hartebeeste, and warthog can be seen in close proximity to fire. On the direct approach of flames these animals would normally walk away from or around them. In one instance a herd of elephant was seen to cross low flames into the area just burnt. The numerous small streams and swamps act as barriers, across which animals can escape if necessary, and warthog have the additional resort of their burrows. All species will walk over ground over which fire has just passed and on which material is still smouldering. The reaction of animals to fire in the giant *Pennisetum* grassland areas was not observed.

Fires are seldom so extensive, or intensive, as to deprive herbivores of all food at any one time. It is very unusual for more than 80 per cent of the cover to be removed, even in an extensive burnt area because changes of wind, or natural fire breaks, such as swampy ground, short grass areas, or erosion patches, leave some unburnt islands. The lack of grass is of short duration, as even in the dry season grass shoots have appeared within a week of a burn. Swamps and stream banks provide reservoirs of grass and browse which are utilized extensively at this time. They are of particular importance to elephant by enabling them to remain in the grasslands throughout the burning season.

2.5. Summary

The greater part of the elephant range lies between 600 metres and 1200 metres above sea level, drained by a number of rivers, and showing a series of catena sequences depending on geomorphology and soils, which are in general of low productivity. Air temperatures are high with little seasonal variation. Relative humidity averages about 60 per cent and seasonal fluctuations increase away from the influence of Lake Albert. The rainfall pattern is characterized by a short dry season (December–February) followed by a long wet season (March–November) with rainfall peaks in April–May and September–October.

The current vegetation of the area has been described and mapped, the following types being identified: closed forest formations, low forest, woodland, bushland, wooded grassland, bushed grassland, grassland, and swamp. In addition to the Budongo Forest there are small patches of relict forest and gallery forest, but the greater part of the area is now grassland of recent origin. At the periphery of the elephant range, tree and shrub variety and density increases. The dominant woodland tree is *Terminalia glaucescens* with *Combretum binderanum* dominant in the understory.

The grass stratum comprises three main types of fire climax grassland: medium-height *Hyparrhenia* grassland on the lower and drier ground to the west; tall *Hyparrhenia* grassland between 850 metres and 1100 metres; and giant *Pennisetum purpureum* grassland above 1100 metres. Most relict forest patches occur in the *Pennisetum* belt. Heavy grazing by hippopotamus has resulted in extensive areas of grass less than 15 centimetres high, along the Nile. A feature of the grassland is the abundance of geophytic shrubs whose aerial parts are removed annually by the burn, but are rapidly replaced after the burn. Owing to heavy elephant browsing they do not succeed in outgrowing this phase of suppression by fire.

Fire is thus an ecological factor of great significance in this area. The present policy of the National Parks, Game and Forest Department administrations is to burn the grasslands annually, as early as possible in the dry season to prevent more dangerous fires later in the season. The primary and immediate effect of fire is to restrict the dry season food supplies of herbivores, but it also has an important long-term effect on the composition and structure of the vegetation. Evidence as to the respective roles of fire and elephant has been examined and leads to the conclusion that elephants, not fires, are the controlling factor in the disappearance of woodland and forest in the area. This is supported by observations in experimental plots from which elephant, but not fire, have been excluded.

3. Land-use

To our knowledge the only forms of land-use practised in the vicinity of the
North Bunyoro elephant range are subsistence agriculture and limited livestock
husbandry, a small area under progressive agriculture by means of a group farm-
ing scheme, sport hunting, forestry, and tourism. The latter is by far the most
important both in economic terms and in relation to conservation.

3.1. Subsistence agriculture and livestock

Knowledge of early population levels and distribution is scanty and has been
summarized in Chapter 1.

In 1931 the human population of Bunyoro was estimated at 114 700 (Thomas
and Scott 1935). Excluding the game reserve, some 7863 square kilometres
(3036 square miles) of land and swamp were inhabited by people, an average
density of 14·7 per square kilometre (37·7 per square mile). The human population was (and still is) for the most part concentrated in central and south-west
Bunyoro (Atlas of Uganda (1962), map 35). During the 1930s, the Banyoro
natural increase was augmented by large numbers of tobacco growers from West
Nile District, and human expansion radiated out from central Bunyoro, particularly along the roads as they were constructed. It has resulted in continuing and
relentless encroachment on 'traditional elephant grazing grounds'.

Thomas and Scott's (1935) estimate was evidently too high, for the first
modern census in 1948 gave an estimate of 108 380 for the African population
of Bunyoro (East African Statistical Department 1950). This was equivalent to
13·8 per square kilometre (35·7 per square mile) excluding the Game Reserve.
The 1959 census (Anon 1965) gave a figure of 126 875 for the Bunyoro population, which had therefore been increasing at an average rate of about 2 per cent
annually. The over-all population density in 1959 was 16·1 per square kilometre
(41·8 per square mile). However, the National Park (2097 square kilometres,
810 square miles) was created in 1952 and settlement permitted in the Controlled
Hunting Areas (1323 square kilometres, 511 square miles). These areas comprised
the former Game Reserve (3421 square kilometres, 1321 square miles). The average population density, excluding only the Park was thus 13·8 per square kilometre (35·7 per square mile), but over a larger area than in 1948.

In the 1960s political upheaval in the Congo, Ruanda-Urundi, and the Southern
Sudan resulted in the resettlement of thousands of refugees in Bunyoro, the vast
majority engaging in subsistence agriculture. (There is a large resettlement scheme
located just south of the elephant range.) The 1963 Agricultural census (Anon
1965) gave a total population for Bunyoro of 191 517 ± 6423, that is 20·8 per
square kilometre (54·0 per square mile) excluding the National Park. This is a
significantly higher population than that obtained by projecting the 1959 popu-

lation estimate and it seems clear that the rate of increase has accelerated, both
as a result of immigration and a higher natural increment. On the basis of these
figures, the population increased by 50·9 per cent between 1959 and 1963, which
is equivalent to about 10 per cent a year—improbably high, even allowing for
immigration, and much higher than for other Districts in Uganda.

The results of the 1963 census were presented for Bunyoro as a whole (Anon
1965, 1966). The population was not exceptionally young in age structure, showing 41 per cent under 16 years old (as compared with 50 per cent in Ankole and
Kigezi Districts). In 1948, 37 per cent of the Bunyoro population was estimated
to be under 16 years of age.

Two-thirds of the crops are seasonal and the rest permanent, mainly beans,
plantains, cotton, cassava, and maize (Plate 3.1). Cotton was grown as a source
of cash income by 60 per cent of the holders, the rest for subsistence. The total
area of agricultural holdings was 366 000 acres (1479 square kilometres, 571
square miles), that is, 17 per cent of the land area of Bunyoro outside the National
Park. The average holding was 9·05 acres, and the average part of this under cultivation was 3·10 acres. However, in 1959 the land adjoining the elephant range
was cultivated to the extent of only 4·7—5·6 per cent (Atlas of Uganda (1962),

PLATE 3.1. Settlement south of elephant range

map 45). Even now probably no more than 10 per cent of the land in the vicinity of the elephant range is cultivated, but this, with its attendant 'crop protection' policy is clearly sufficient to deny land to elephant.

The Ministry of Agriculture, Forestry and Cooperatives supplied the following information in response to our enquiry about recent developments in the vicinity of the North Bunyoro elephant range:

Probably the most significant from the point of view of your interests is the recent (and continuing) clearance of a tsetse barrier, which runs in a long arc from about half-way along the Hoima-Masindi road, round the north of Masindi to Gulu road. It is largely within this barrier that mechanised 'Group Farms' have been established, and these have proved more successful in Bunyoro than elsewhere in Uganda. In order to keep this barrier from reverting to bush, settlement (including that of some refugees) is being encouraged within it, and this will probably be the main area of activity in the near future. Population movements into this belt are beginning to occur, so that for this area population increase is likely to be high . . . The Government has set up a sugar estate on the Masindi-Butiaba road, and this may lead to considerable developments in the next few years.

(D. M. Pudsey, *in litt.*, 7 June 1968.)

Livestock census results for Bunyoro show very low numbers—17 000 cattle, 6000 sheep, and 104 000 goats, of which about 9000 cattle and 15 000 goats are found near the elephant range (in Bugungu Controlled Hunting Area (Atlas of Uganda (1962), map 55)).

3.2. Sport hunting

Two controlled Hunting Areas, the Bukumi-Bugungu Controlled Area (728 square kilometres, 281 square miles) and the Karuma Falls Controlled Area (596 square kilometres, 230 square miles) adjoin the National Park, accounting for over half its southern boundary (Fig. 1.2); they are the responsibility of the Game Department. These are areas where hunting is restricted and the shooting of certain species limited under the Game Ordinance. A sportsman wishing to hunt must first obtain a Controlled Area permit, from the District Commissioner.

A basic charge is made for this permit, while a *per capita* fee is also payable for each animal taken. The object of this arrangement is to allow proper control of the offtake of game and prevent overshooting, and also to produce revenue from the game areas for the Local Administrations, thus encouraging their interest and co-operation in its continued conservation.

(Atlas of Uganda 1962.)

Unfortunately there is no control over settlement in the Controlled Hunting Areas; in each of the Bunyoro Controlled Areas settlement is rapidly expanding and poaching is very serious. In 1967 some crops were planted in the National Park by settlers from the Bukumi-Bugungu Controlled Area. The intruders were subsequently expelled. We shall see (Chapter 5) that elephant are now almost completely absent from the Bukumi-Bugungu Controlled Area, and this applies also to hippopotamus and crocodile, buffalo, and many other species. The process is at an earlier stage in the Karuma Falls Controlled Area, where elephant and hippopotamus are still very abundant (see Figs 4.8 and 5.2—5.4). Settlement has been retarded here compared with the area to the west of the Park, mainly due to lack of communications, but with the completion of a trunk road from Masindi to Gulu in 1964, dividing the Karuma Falls Controlled Area, ribbon subsistence agriculture and settlement has been rapidly developing and has already had an appreciable effect on the ecology of the area.

From 1946 to 1960 there was a rising trend in the numbers of elephant shot annually by licence holders (from 40 to 170 per year), and subsequently a drop to under 100 per year. By no means all these elephants were shot in the Controlled Areas so this is not a very important source of revenue, and in any case is threatened by the spread of subsistence agriculture and the concommitant elimination of game animals from these areas. Poaching is rife and appeared to be virtually uncontrolled when our field work was being carried out in 1965—7, but as Tener (1964) has pointed out 'the most important single problem in the sustained operation of Controlled Hunting Areas (and Game Sanctuaries) is that of maintaining game habitat in the face of increasing pressure from Settlement, cultivation and grazing'.

3.3.   Forestry

The Budongo Central Forest Reserve, which is located to the south-west of the elephant range, contains about 427 square kilometres (165 square miles) of mahogany forest, 'the largest and richest forest of this type in East Africa' (Philip 1965). The combined Forest Reserves are contiguous with the Murchison Falls National Park to the north and with the Bukumi-Bugungu Controlled Hunting Area to the west. In the south and east it is bounded by dense settlement.

The total area of the Budongo Central Forest Reserve is 474 square kilometres (183 square miles), and is under Central Government Administration. In addition to the forest areas there are 131 square kilometres (51 square miles) of grassland in the vicinity of the forest, also administered by the Central Government. The Budongo Reserve is divided into a number of blocks (see Chapter 5, Fig. 5.9).

The Kaniyo block formerly came under the Bunyoro District Administration as a Local Forest Reserve, but all local Forest Reserves were classified as Central Forest Reserves in 1968. Pabidi Forest is a small block of approximately 207 square kilometres (80 square miles) comprising about 26 square kilometres (10 square miles) of forest and about 181 square kilometres (70 square miles) of grassland. It was formerly a Local Forest Reserve.

The forest is expanding and would probably come to occupy the grasslands if

Block		Area	
		km^2	miles^2
(a) Forest	Biiso	45·8	17·7
	Nyakafunjo	84·7	32·7
	West Waibira	107·5	41·5
	East Waibira	125·9	48·6
	Siba	66·0	25·5
	Kaniyo	44·0	17·0
		474·0	183·0
(b) Grassland	Kitigo	95·1	36·7
	others	36·3	14·0
		131·3	50·7

elephant-use could be controlled. Further details of the Budongo Central Forest Reserve are given by Philip (1965).

Thus, together with the Pabidi Forest, there are nearly 518 square kilometres (200 square miles) (and a potential further 313 square kilometres (121 square miles)) of high forest in or adjacent to the elephant range. Intense management of the Budongo Forest began in 1935 when the first Working Plan (1935—44) was drawn up.

Although this was a very simple plan, it laid down the principles from which there has since been little deviation. Compare the main object of management then—'to provide facilities for profitable exploitation while endangering in minimum the preservation of forest of the existing type'—with the main object today—'to produce economically the maximum sustained yield of hardwood timber, especially the mahoganies', and 'to maintain specimens of the characteristic plant and animal communities'. Thus, at a time when the only agriculture was subsistence agriculture and other forms of land-use were unknown, the Forest Department was laying down an enlightened plan which was to be followed for the next 30 years and is still being followed.

Since 1935, the Working Plans have been revised every ten years and it is perhaps true to say that with the first revision of the Plan in 1947 (1945—54) Budongo changed from being a forest of minor importance to one of inter-national repute. This was largely due to Eggeling's work (1947a, 1947b), which is among the classic tropical ecological studies. Some £200 000 has been spent in Budongo on field operations; most of this considerable sum has gone directly to improving the quality and quantity of timber available for the future. Revenue up to 1968 has amounted to about £650 000, mainly in the form of royalties paid to the Government by the saw-millers, representing a substantial net profit.

However, this does not give a true picture of the present, and future, situation because the trend in expenditure, gross revenue, and net profit is steeply rising. Revenue and expenditure for the first four Working Plans showed a steady increase to a net profit in the 1955—64 Working Plan of over £154 888. For the

9½ years to which this total relates, the average annual net profit was £16 304—nearly £39 per square kilometre (£100 per square mile) of forest (excluding Kaniyo Forest Reserve). The net annual profit over the period of the current Working Plan (1964–74) is expected to be about £116 per square kilometre (£300 per square mile) of forest, but this excludes staff salaries. The annual gross revenue is expected to average £163 per square kilometre (£422 per square mile). This is, in economic terms, a highly favourable use of land compared with the return from other current forms of land-use. However a recent proposal to develop an area of about 5000 square kilometres (2000 square miles) around Murchison Falls National Park for cattle ranching and subsidiary game cropping operations envisaged, at maturity 23 years hence, a net income of about £360 000 per year, or £70 per square kilometre (£180 per square mile) (Anon 1967).

Pabidi Forest has not been under such intense management, partly because it is not so rich, and partly because formerly, being managed by the Bunyoro Kingdom Government, there were not the funds to carry out an intensive programme. However, it is a source of untapped wealth which has a Management Plan dating from 1958. With the availability of funds and its classification as a Central Forest Reserve in 1968, this forest probably also will be developed.

Since 1955, the main aim of forest management has been to grow mahogany (*Khaya anthotheca* and *Entandrophragma* spp.) at the lowest possible cost on a system of sustained yield. Initially it was assumed that natural regeneration of desirable species would not be sufficient to produce a final stand, and from 1938 to 1951 various methods of artificial regeneration were tried in the Biiso and parts of the Siba and Nyakafunjo blocks. These included planting projects involving mainly *Khaya anthotheca*. Owing to labour shortage and serious elephant damage, this artificial regeneration was abandoned in 1951. In 1954, after extensive research trials, it was found that adequate natural regeneration of desirable timber species could be obtained if the canopy was opened sufficiently. It was found that the main non-desirables ('weeds' in forester's language, although up to 180 feet high!), *Cynometra alexandri*, *Celtis* spp., *Lasiodiscus* sp., and others, were susceptible to contact arboricides. It was hoped that a gradual removal of these non-desirable but apparently climax species would maintain the forest in its mixed state and prevent it reaching the climax.

Since 1954 the system of removal of non-desirables by poisoning has continued with some changes in method. In the past few years the policy has tended towards greater opening of the canopy as this would appear to give a much greater regeneration of desirable species; refining now follows immediately after felling; and no help is given to the natural regeneration after felling. No silvicultural work has been carried out in Kaniyo or Pabidi Reserves.

Felling began in Budongo in 1919 and the first licence was granted in 1930. The original felling concentrated on the removal of the large over-mature mahoganies and mvule (*Chlorophora excelsa*). This so-called salvage felling has continued with renewals of the licence up to the present and has resulted in the whole of

PLATE 3.2. Logging operations in Budongo Forest

the Biiso and Nyakafunjo blocks being cut over. Felling at present is being carried out in the Waibira block (Plate 3.2).

Until 1965 the felling limits were 3·8 metres (12·5 feet) girth, at breast height (g.b.h.), or above buttresses (g.a.b.), for mahogany and mvule, and 1·8 metres (6 feet) g.b.h. or g.a.b. for other species. As it was not compulsory to take other species, little attempt was made to cut them, but since 1965 the obligatory felling list has been considerably increased and this has resulted in a greater canopy opening. In the past *Cynometra alexandri* was included as a compulsory species for the millers, but in 1966 it was removed from the compulsory list. At the same time the minimum girth limit of the mahogany and mvule was reduced to 3·5 metres, (11 feet) g.b.h. or g.a.b. It is estimated that it will take another 20—25 years to complete this salvage felling.

In 1964 a conversion felling was started in the Siba block. This is designed to bring the whole of the Budongo Forest onto a uniform management system with an 80 year rotation. Here the felling limits are 2·1 metres (7 feet) g.b.h. or g.a.b. for the mahoganies and mvule, and 1·8 metres (6 feet) g.b.h. or g.a.b. for all other compulsory species. The resulting canopy opening is considerable.

Felling is also being carried out in the Kaniyo Forest Reserve; here the girth limit is 1·8 metres (6 feet) g.b.h. or g.a.b. for all species. Little felling has taken place in Pabidi; there has been occasional felling, mainly when the millers felling in Kaniyo have been short of a species for a particular order.

For many years, then, the Forest Department has carried out a programme of improvement and exploitation, which at no time has been hindered by lack of effort or understanding, but has occasionally been slowed down due to lack of funds. There has been no land shortage in Bunyoro and consequently the forests have never suffered from encroachment by man, but this situation will change very rapidly in the next few years as the population increase continues. There have been no major insect or fungal pests and it would be thought that the problems of the forest are few. But over the years there have been many records of elephant moving into the forest and causing damage. Elephants must have used the forest for centuries, and some earlier estimates of numbers are given in the historical survey in Chapter 1 (see also Chapter 11). In 1944 however, it was noted that damage to young plants was very heavy and it was largely due to this elephant damage that the planting programme was abandoned in 1951.

In 1955 there again appears to have been a build up of elephant numbers, coinciding with the start of the Timber Stand Improvement treatments, and in 1956 and 1957 early attempts at treatment had to be abandoned as the elephants refused to leave the treated areas. Since 1955 the records have shown a continual movement of elephants into the treated areas and in 1963 the damage became really serious. It is difficult to give any one reason for this and it is probably due to a combination of factors, including the progressive contraction of the North Bunyoro elephant range and the fact that the refining and felling operations reached the north-west margin of the forest in 1963. Since 1963 the damage to the young regeneration areas has remained serious (Chapter 11).

A potential annual revenue of some £100 000 is seriously threatened by continued elephant use of the forest. The extent and nature of the damage is discussed in greater detail in Chapter 11, measures already taken to limit the damage are described in Chapter 10, and proposals based on the current investigation are advanced in Chapter 12.

3.4.   Tourism—the National Park

The Murchison Falls National Park, which was created in 1952, comprises an area of about 4033 square kilometres (1557 square miles) of which 2097 square kilometres (810 square miles) lie in Bunyoro. The Park is one of three in Uganda and the National Parks Administration comes under the Ministry of Information and Tourism. The Park has already been described in terms of its general qualities, and an account of its history and administration has been given by Willock (1964). In terms of land-use potential the economic, scientific, and conservation values will become apparent in this report.

This Park is an area of outstanding natural beauty and interest, containing the Murchison Falls (Plate 1.1) and exceptional stretches of the Victoria Nile River, graced by islands and rapids. It has the most spectacular and accessible population of crocodiles left in existence, though grave fears have been expressed for its future (Cott 1968). The launch trip on the River Nile from Paraa to the Falls is a highlight of any visit to East Africa.

In this section we propose to deal briefly with the current and potential economic value of the area to Uganda in terms of tourism. Estimated yields from necessary conservation cropping of several animal species are discussed elsewhere. This present emphasis on economic values does not mean that we are unaware of the aesthetic or scientific values, but we feel that the future of the area will depend primarily on a realization of its economic potential. Already the Falls have been threatened by a hydro-electric scheme (Katete 1968; Anon 1970)

The number of visitors to the Murchison Falls National Park totalled 58 739 in 1970. Since the Park was opened in 1953 the increase in visitors was initially more or less linear (Fig. 3.1) but exponential since 1960.

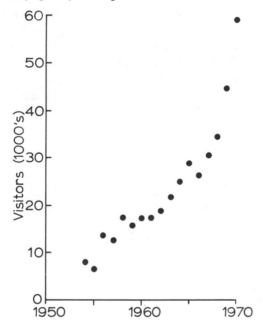

Fig. 3.1. Annual numbers of visitors to Murchison Falls National Park.

The gross and particularly the net value of tourism is difficult to estimate. The report by a firm of consultants (Maxwell Stamp Associates, Ltd. 1966) on tourism in Uganda gives estimates which are unlikely to be seriously in error, but our case would not be prejudiced even if they were in error by a factor of two or more. Unfortunately the report considers data only up to 1964. It states that 'the volume of visitors to East Africa . . . has increased by 68% in the period 1960–64' and 'the rate of growth in the 1960s in Uganda has been greater, however, than the rest of East Africa'. The estimated receipts from tourists in Uganda in 1960 totalled £540 000; in 1961, £649 000; in 1962, £977 000; in 1963, £1 225 000; and in 1964, £1 295 000.

'During the period 1960–4, the rate of growth per annum of estimated tourist receipts has been 24·4 per cent in Uganda, 13·5 per cent in Kenya and 19·7 per cent in Tanzania.' If these rates of growth continued for the next 5, 10, and 15 years the tourist receipts would be as follows:

	Uganda	Kenya	Tanzania
1970	£ 4 798 000	£15 119 000	£ 7 248 000
1975	£14 298 000	£28 477 000	£17 810 000
1980	£42 609 000	£53 638 000	£43 765 000

In 1967 tourism brought in about £14·5 million to Kenya and 'all available statistics point to the fact that tourism is growing' (Mitchell 1968, p. 100). In 1970 tourism brought in K £18·5 million to Kenya (Njiri 1971)—more than predicted. The 1964 trend has also continued in Murchison Falls Park (Fig. 3.1), and on the basis of these rates of growth and in terms of proportional land area, the estimated receipts for Murchison Falls Park, South are approximately £1·4 million in 1970, £4·2 million in 1975, and £12·5 million in 1980! The possibility of tourist saturation or decline makes it perhaps unwise to accept the later predictions without reservations.[†]

Katete (1968) stated that

Currently, the Murchison Falls Park attracts no less than 70 per cent of the country's tourist business, valued at U.S. $9 000 000 annually. It is forecast to rise to $15 000 000 by 1974. If Murchison Falls Park lost its attractiveness as a tourist resort consequent upon disturbances caused by the hydro-electric scheme, 70 per cent of the $15 000 000 income would be at stake, giving an annual loss of the order of $10 million, possibly more.

On the basis of these figures, published by the late Director of Uganda's National Parks, Murchison Falls Park, South accounts for 37 per cent of the tourist business, that is £1·4 million in 1968 and £2·3 million in 1974. This represents for 1968—70 a gross annual yield of £667 per square kilometre (£1730 per square mile).

The consultants estimated that 25 per cent of tourist expenditure is on items imported into Uganda. Thus, net foreign exchange return to the economy from tourism will be 75 per cent of the potential receipts quoted above.

These are not direct returns to the National Parks, whose actual receipts from tourism are negligible in comparison, but mainly to service industries connected with hotels and transport. In 1967 the direct revenue to the Murchison Falls National Park from tourist receipts was less than £40 000. Proportional to area this represents £22 000 to the South bank or £10·5 per square kilometre (£27 per square mile). On an area proportional basis the expenditure on the southern section was only £47 000, or about 3·4 per cent of the estimated gross receipts from tourism in Uganda.

† Since this was written there has been a change of Government and General Amin banned tourists from Uganda.

3.5.   Summary

In terms of yield per unit area, the National Park, as a basis for tourism, is by far the most important to Uganda, followed by forestry as the most important form of land use in the areas bordering the elephant range. On an area proportional basis the National Park gross yield was about £667 per square kilometre (£1730 per square mile) in 1968–70 and could increase, but the net yield is difficult to estimate. The forest yields some £163 per square kilometre (£422 per square mile) gross, £116 per square kilometre (£300 per square mile) net and it is thought that grasslands within the forest reserves would in time be replaced by forest if elephant numbers could be controlled. This compares with about £28 per square kilometre (£73 per square mile) under subsistence agriculture, and £69 per square kilometre (£180 per square mile) under cattle and game, if a high productivity ranching and game cropping scheme could be implemented. The current return from sport hunting alone is negligible.

4. Mammals and birds

Like other areas in western Uganda, the Murchison Falls National Park shows an impoverished fauna (in numbers of species) of grazing herbivores. This can perhaps be accounted for by the fact that there was formerly little grassland, and a much greater extent of closed canopy woodland and forest, as well as thickly bushed grassland. In this Chapter the more important species will be described briefly, in terms of their distribution and relative abundance (or where known, their absolute abundance). Descriptions and coloured illustrations of mammal species are given by Dorst and Dandelot (1970); the birds are described and illustrated by Mackworth-Praed and Grant (1952, 1955).

4.1. Mammals

4.1.1. *Sample counts of large herbivores*

In 1969 we carried out sample counts in order to estimate the populations of large mammals in North Bunyoro. The area sampled comprised the Murchison Falls National Park, South and the Karuma Falls Controlled Hunting Area. Our objective was to be able to attach confidence limits to the estimates, and in the case of elephant, to provide confirmation of the reliability of the total counts of elephant carried out in 1966 and 1967 (described in Chapter 5).

A method of stratified random quadrat sampling from an aircraft was used, based on 10 square kilometres quadrats; it is described and discussed in Appendix A and the estimates for the six species that were counted are set out in Table 4.1.

For elephant we chose a high-density stratum containing 136 quadrats of which 38 (or 28 per cent) were sampled, and a medium-density stratum of 134 quadrats of which 31 (or 23·2 per cent) were sampled (Fig. 4.1). This stratification was derived from the results of complete counts in 1966/67 described in the next chapter. The buffalo stratification used was the same (Fig. 4.3), but the elephant high-density stratum was the buffalo medium-density stratum and vice versa. The strata chosen for the hartebeest, kob, waterbuck, and warthog were the same—a low-density stratum of 178 quadrats of which 34 (or 19·1 per cent) were sampled; a high-density stratum in the north of 82 quadrats, of which 27 (or 32·9 per cent) were sampled, and a second high-density stratum in the south west of 10 quadrats, of which 8 were sampled (Figs 4.2—4.6). Thus there was some fortuitous weighting for higher density. For buffalo the peripheral stratum was also re-stratified to allow for a third stratum in which direct observations had suggested this species was present in low densities. It contained 54 quadrats of which 11 (or 20·5 per cent) were sampled, but this further stratification did not improve the precision of the estimate, for the standard error was higher than when only two strata were used, and this was in turn higher than the standard error for the unstratified analysis (Table 4.1). This suggests that the stratification for buffalo did not reflect the actual distribution of the species in the area at the time.

Table 4.1

Population estimates for six large ungulates in North Bunyoro elephant range
(Random sample quadrats counted from the air centre, 26—28 May 1969)

	$\hat{Y}$	S.E.	S.E. as %	Density km^{-2}
Elephant				
unstratified	9461	1457	15·4	3·50
2 strata	9364	1368	14·6	3·47
cf. total count August 1967	7913	—	—	2·93
Buffalo				
unstratified	14 291	2498	17·5	5·29
2 strata	14 871	2640	17·7	5·51
3 strata	14 725	2683	18·2	5·45
Hartebeest				
unstratified	4644	667	14·4	1·72
3 strata	3751	497	13·2	1·39
Uganda kob				
3 strata	2581	449	17·4	0·96
Waterbuck				
3 strata	1171	210	17·6	0·43
Warthog				
unstratified	3969	445	11·2	1·47
3 strata	3610	384	10·6	1·34

Notes. S.E.=standard error
Y = estimated population of animals

It is interesting to compare the standard error for the various species' estimates (Table 4.1). The warthog and hartebeest stratified samples gave the lowest standard errors, respectively 10·6 per cent and 13·2 per cent of the population estimate. The stratified count for elephant was next at 14·6 per cent, and the stratified counts for kob, waterbuck, and buffalo were very similar at 17·4 per cent, 17·6 per cent, and 17·7 per cent of the population estimates. These standard errors are undoubtedly much higher than they would have been if it had been possible to allocate the number of sampling units per stratum proportionally in each stratum for each species. However, considerations of cost inevitably make the design of sampling programmes for multi-species estimates less than optimal.

Siniff and Skoog (1964) sampled 30 per cent of the total units in the area studied, as compared with our 26 per cent; they were concerned with a single species, and they were also able to allocate sampling effort proportionally. Their standard error was consequently smaller (9·6 per cent of the population estimate), and a similar or better value could be obtained for the species counted in the

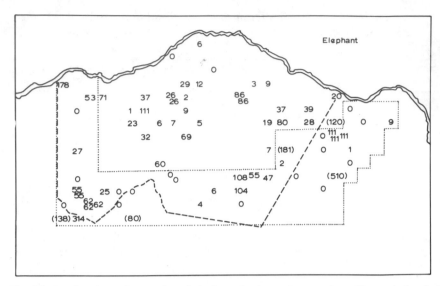

Fig. 4.1. Results of sample counting of elephants in the random quadrats. Figures in brackets –large herds seen during the counting outside the random quadrats. Density strata indicated by dotted lines.

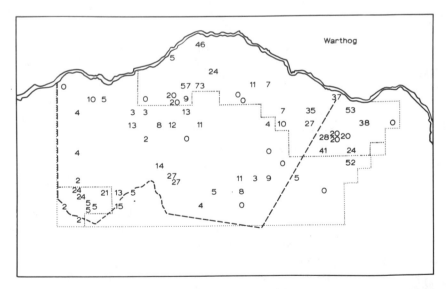

Fig. 4.2. Results of sample counting of warthog in the random quadrats. Density strata are indicated by dotted lines.

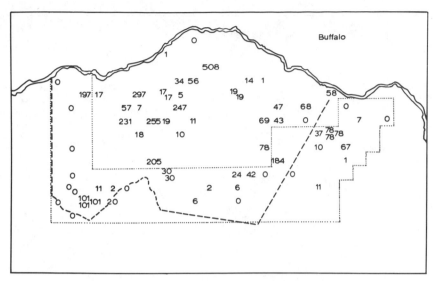

Fig. 4.3. Results of sample counting of buffalo in the random quadrats. Density strata are indicated by dotted lines.

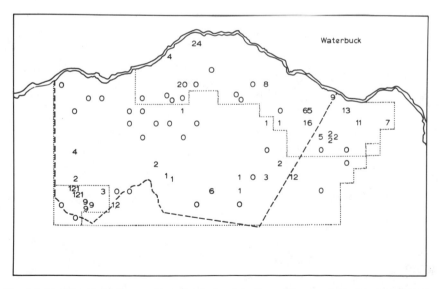

Fig. 4.4. Results of sample counting of waterbuck in the random quadrats. Density strata are indicated by dotted lines.

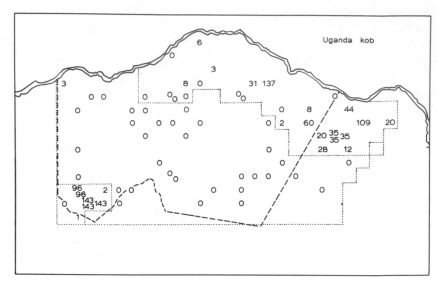

Fig. 4.5. Results of sample counting of Uganda kob in the random quadrats. Density strata are indicated by dotted lines.

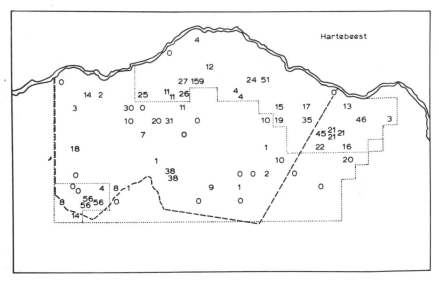

Fig. 4.6. Results of sample counting of hartebeest in the random quadrats. Density strata are indicated by dotted lines.

Murchison Falls National Park, South (M.F.P.S.) if considerations of cost were
not so restricting.

The present counts may also be compared with the results of Watson, Parker,
and Allan (1969) in the Mkomasi Reserve. For five strata combined the standard
error was 17·6 per cent of the estimated population of 5705 elephant. In one
large stratum (in which sampling covered 25 per cent of the stratum), sub-
stratification gave a standard error that was 24 per cent of the estimated population. Jolly (1969) presents the results of estimates based on counting equal
sized quadrats, representing 27 per cent of the area sampled for three species.
The standard errors of the unstratified estimates ranged from 17·3 per cent to
27·9 per cent of the estimates, and when analysed by four arbitrary strata, 17·3–
23·6 per cent of the estimates. Even arbitrary stratification (which is a permissible
procedure) can reduce the variance of the estimate. On comparison with other
estimates made in East Africa the variance of our estimates is quite low.

The use of uniformly sized quadrats in the present count has eliminated two
of the sources of error discussed by Watson *et al.* (1969). The actual counting
of animals is an unknown source of error, although by concentrating on counting
in small quadrats we hope that it has been minimized. Certainly this source of
error should be less than in complete counts, but there are probably more animals
than the estimates indicate. The vegetation is considered to be fairly uniform
from the point of view of counting elephant, although for other species long-grass
areas may have affected the results by exaggerating the relatively low densities of
antelopes, buffalo, and warthog in the long-grass areas.

Comparison with the total count of elephant in August 1967 (Chapter 5) shows
that this estimate is about 18 per cent higher. A comparison of methods made by
Watson *et al.* (1969) showed that an estimate (from random strip sampling) was
27 per cent higher than a complete count (not 21 per cent as they stated).

4.1.2. *Hippopotamus*

The hippopotamus (*Hippopotamus amphibius* L.) is an animal which is aquatic
in habit during the day (Fig. 4.7) and a close grazer on land at night (Plates
4.1 and 4.2). There is a body of unpublished work on this species in the Queen
Elizabeth and Murchison Falls Parks, some of which we propose to summarize
here, because of its bearing on the vegetation trends and on the elephant problem.
Aerial counts of hippopotamus (Plate 4.2) and surveys of habitat deterioration
(see Chapter 2, Plate 2.8) were made in April and November 1964, and in April
1967 (Laws and Parker, unpublished), the latter partly financed by Wildlife
Services Ltd. These covered the Victoria Nile River from the Karuma Falls in the
east to Murchison Falls—a river length of about 88 kilometres (55 miles) allowing
for bends, and each count occupied 10–11 hours counting time (Table 4.2).

Habitat surveys in April and November 1964 suggested that the vegetation
was badly overgrazed throughout the area within hippopotamus grazing range,
serious effects being noted up to 5 kilometres (3 miles) from the river. The average

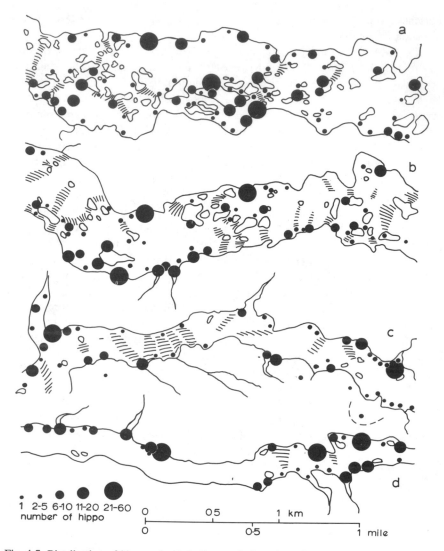

Fig. 4.7. Distribution of hippo schools in four typical reaches of the Victoria Nile (November 1964). Their location is shown in Fig. 4.8. Rapids are indicated.

width of the hippopotamus grazing zone is about 3 kilometres (2 miles) but varies seasonally—expanding in the dry season as the quality of the vegetation deteriorates, and contracting during the rains as grazing improves. In the Queen Elizabeth Park individual hippopotamus travel up to 10 kilometres (6 miles) from the lake shore, and one seasonally occupied wallow is 7·2 kilometres (4·5 miles) from the lake. The area affected by hippopotamus overgrazing above the Murchison Falls represents about 8 per cent of the elephant range in North Bunyoro and if we

PLATE 4.1. Hippos and young on bank of River Nile

include the overgrazed areas below the falls, the total hippo grazing area is about 10 per cent of the elephant range.

In analysing the counts the river was arbitrarily divided into 8 kilometre (5 mile) sectors, numbered 1—11 from east to west (Fig. 4.8). There were sections where overgrazing appeared to be much worse and where soil erosion was well advanced, especially near water. Possible competition between elephant and hippopotamus is indicated by the spatial distribution of elephant densities discussed in Chapter 7. Thus, a postulated build-up in hippopotamus populations within the National Park has possibly contributed to the problem by tending to restrict the elephant range.

The aerial counts in April 1964 (Sections 1 and 2) and November 1964 (Sections 3—11) totalled 10 142 hippopotamus in 1184 schools, averaging 8·6 per school (Table 4.2, and Fig. 4.8). The estimated grazing density (based on an average grazing zone of 3 kilometres (2 miles)) on either side of the river was 19·2 per square kilometre (49·7 per square mile); range for the eleven sections 9·4—26·5 per square kilometre (24·3—68·6 per square mile). In the more intensive and extensive studies in the Queen Elizabeth Park (Laws 1964, 1968a) it had been found that the average hippopotamus grazing densities were 17·4 per square kilometre (45 per square mile). Although this is a much more fertile area than Murchison Falls Park, the management programme for the Queen Elizabeth Park aimed at reducing the hippopotamus population to an estimated optimal density of 7·7 per square kilometre (20 per square mile).

PLATE 4.2. Hippo school in backwater of River Nile

In view of the widespread habitat deterioration it was therefore recommended
that a cropping programme should be undertaken in the Murchison Falls Park
above the Murchison Falls, aimed at producing initially a grazing density of
11·6 per square kilometre (30 per square mile) in Sections 1—5 and of 9·7 per
square kilometre (25 per square mile) in Sections 9—11. Sections 7 and 8 would
be left as control areas. Section 7 showed less than half the average density of
hippo per square kilometre (9·4 per square kilometre, 24·3 per square mile) and
Section 8 showed 17·7 per square kilometre (45·8 per square mile). It was recommended that reduction towards the recommended levels be carried out as quickly
as possible by taking a total of 4130 hippopotamus (2830 in Sections 1—6 and
1300 in Sections 9—11). Separate quotas were given for the individual sections,
and it was intended that the cropping schedule should be revised in detail as
further information became available.

It was pointed out that after this initial cropping operation further reduction
cropping would be necessary, followed by annual cropping to maintain the reduced
population level, either indefinitely, or until the population stabilized at a lower
level.

In the 29 months between the counts 2811 hippopotamus were cropped by
Game Management (Uganda) Ltd. from Sections 1—6 and 9—11, under contract
to the Trustees of the Uganda National Parks. The second count in April 1967 gave
a total of 8462 hippopotamus in 1209 schools, averaging 7·0 per school (Table 4.2
and Fig. 4.8). The difference between the counts was greatest in the first two
sections where most animals were cropped; the over-all difference was 1680 so
the net increment in this period was 1131. (The actual figures are given here
although, owing to the possibility of missing hippopotamus in concealed locations

Table 4.2

Results of hippopotamus counts above Murchison Falls, 1964 and 1967

Section	Grazing area (km²)	1964 Number	1964 Density (km⁻²)	1967 Number	1967 Density (km⁻²)	Difference between counts	Number cropped	Net increment
1	66·6	978	14·7	661	9·9	− 317 }	961	83
2	55·2	1460	26·5	818	14·8	− 642 }	496	426
3	55·2	1297	23·5	1227	22·2	− 70	417	443
4	44·0	1086	24·7	1112	25·3	+ 26	345	81
5	45·8	1015	22·2	751	16·4	− 264	325	33
6	43·0	975	22·7	683	15·9	− 292	Control	135
7	45·3	424	9·4	559	12·3	+ 135	Control	−37
8	41·4	731	17·7	694	16·8	− 37	126	−118
9	46·9	964	20·6	720	15·4	− 244	95	22
10	39·1	632	16·2	559	14·3	− 73	46	144
11	45·8	580	12·7	678	14·8	+ 98		
Total	528·3	10 142	19·2	8462	16·0	−1680	2811	1131

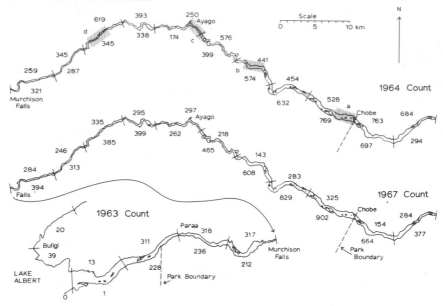

Fig. 4.8. Summary of results of the 1963 survey, and 1964 and 1967 counts of hippopotamus. The boundaries of the counting sectors are shown. Details of the shaded blocks, a–d, are given in Fig. 4.7.

or deep water, both counts are likely to have given minimal figures; the larger sources of error will operate in the same direction for both counts.) The estimated average grazing density in 1967 was 16·0 per square kilometre (41·5 per square mile), range for the eleven sections 9·9–25·3 per square kilometre (25·6–65·5 per square mile).

Assuming that the counts are accurate, the net increment could be explained by the operation of three possible factors. First, increased recruitment to the population over two years, induced by the cropping; this would probably comprise two components—increased natality and reduced natural mortality. Research on hippopotamus population dynamics has shown that natural regulatory factors do operate (Laws 1968a, 1968b); a net increase in recruitment of 5–7 per cent a year in response to heavy cropping is quite possible and could account for most of the estimated net increment of 1131. Secondly, immigration to the area, which can only have come from below Murchison Falls; and thirdly, the possibility of more accurate counting, because the level of the river has progressively fallen since the floods of 1961/62 and the banks have become clearer of overhanging vegetation. We believe the first to be the primary factor operating, but substantial immigration may have occurred.

From July 1967 the National Parks Administration has undertaken the cropping operations and, for a variety of reasons, including a fall in market demand, the rate of population reduction has fallen. Between the second count in April 1967, and 31 December 1968, 809 hippopotamus were cropped. A further 253 were taken up to 31 March 1969. Hippopotamus counts should be made at least annually in future. For our present purposes it is sufficient to note that the average grazing density of hippopotamus in a postulated 3 kilometre (2 mile) wide riverine strip above the Murchison Falls averaged about 16 per square kilometre (41 per square mile) in April 1967. Outside the National Park and Karuma Controlled Hunting Area the hippopotamus population density is virtually zero, owing to the prevalence of poaching activities.

Unfortunately, there are no reliable counts for the numbers of hippopotamus in the Victoria Nile below the Murchison Falls. In July 1963 Laws and Savidge (unpublished) carried out an aerial survey of hippopotamus distribution on the Victoria Nile, above and below the falls, within the Murchison Falls Park (Fig. 4.8). The aircraft time available for this count was severely limited. It amounted to 7 hours for some 121 kilometres (75 miles) of river, compared with 10½ hours for 88 kilometres (55 miles) of river counted in 1964. The respective counting intensities are thus 17·2 kilometres per hour (10·7 miles per hour) and 8·3 kilometres per hour (5·2 miles per hour). Thus the later count was about twice as intensive as the 1963 survey, and on comparing them the number counted is found to be closely related to counting intensity. For the comparable area above the falls, 4377 hippopotamus were recorded, compared with 10 142 in the 1964 counts, a ratio of 1 : 2·3.

In the 1963 survey (Fig. 4.8) a total of 1695 hippopotamus were counted below the Falls (including those in wallows on the north bank) and applying the above ratio an estimate of 3898 is obtained for the actual population below the falls in 1963. Of those recorded in this survey, 677 were on the south bank of the river, which is here much wider in general than above the falls and contains virtually no islands. It is assumed that the schools on the south bank graze at night in North Bunyoro, and the north bank schools in Acholi. Applying the ratio as above to the survey count suggests an estimated population of 1557 hippopotamus on the south bank, between the Falls and the western boundary of the Murchison Falls Park, in 1963. Owing to heavy poaching there are virtually no hippopotamus west of the Park boundary and in Lake Albert (Fig. 4.8).

The numbers of hippopotamus below Murchison Falls may now be much less than the estimate based on the 1963 survey. Immigration from below the Falls has been mentioned as a possible factor contributing to the net increment in hippopotamus numbers above the Falls between 1964 and 1967. In 1969 Parker and Watson (1969), in studying the crocodile population by aerial photographic transects, covered some 85 per cent of both banks of the river between Paraa and the Falls, and only 749 hippopotamus were seen. Parker was surprised at the large numbers seen below Paraa (i.e. in addition to the 749 counted above Paraa), and although this was a subjective impression, unsupported by counts, it suggests a possible displacement of the population downriver as well as upriver. However, even if there were only 1500 hippopotamus below the Falls in 1969 it does not invalidate the general conclusions presented here. Further counts of hippopotamus would however, be valuable.

In terms of grazing density, calculated as above, there is an area of 73·8 square kilometres (28·5 square miles) within 3 kilometres (2 miles) of water on the south bank below Murchison Falls and so the estimated grazing density in 1963 was 21·1 per square kilometre (54·6 per square mile). On the north bank the corresponding area is 80·8 square kilometres (31·2 square miles) and the density was 26·9 per square kilometre (69·0 per square mile). These estimates exclude the very low-density sections of shore to the west (Fig. 4.8). The values are similar to the densities recorded in 1964 in Sections 3–6 above the Falls (22·2–24·7 per square kilometre; 57·3–63·9 per square mile). The eastern half of the upper river, within the Park, which these sections comprise, contains the widest reaches and is most comparable with the hippopotamus habitats along the lower river (Figs 4.7 and 4.8).

We conclude, therefore, that on the south bank of the Victoria Nile some 337 square kilometres (130 square miles) are overgrazed by some 6000–7000 hippopotamus at an average over-all grazing density of 17·8–20·8 per square kilometre (46·1–53·9 per square mile). The average hippopotamus is estimated to weigh 1000 kg (2200 lb) (Laws 1964, 1968a, b), so that, in terms of standing crop biomass this average density represents some 17 000–20 000 kg per square kilometre (99 000–116 000 lb per square mile) over about 10 per cent of the North Bunyoro elephant range. Within this riverine area the standing crop biomass of hippopotamus is at least six or seven times that of elephant.

After man and elephants, the hippopotamus populations have been the most important biotic influence on the habitats in the study area. The capacity of hippopotamus to create areas of short grassland, to maintain them at moderate grazing densities, and to overgraze them at high densities is of great importance both to the other herbivore populations (especially antelopes such as Uganda kob, *Kobus* (*Adenota*) *kob*, waterbuck, *Kobus defassa*, and hartebeest, *Alcelaphus bucelaphus*, which are restricted to short-grass areas) and to elephant.

Furthermore, the hippos are instrumental in creating areas of thicket. This they achieve by their grazing activities, which lead to the production of short-grass areas and therefore reduce, or in some areas eliminate, fire as an influence on the vegetation, thus allowing woody growth to increase. In addition, by their habit of making faecal depots along their trails, especially at the base of bushes, they preferentially manure the periphery of thicket clumps and probably stimulate their enlargement.

It appears that, within the Murchison Falls Park, the distribution of deciduous thicket along the banks of the Victoria Nile (see Chapter 2, Fig. 2.1 Plate 2.8), corresponds to the present areas of high hippopotamus densities within the Park, that is, below the Murchison Falls and in the eastern sections of the upper river. The prevalence of thicket on the Butiaba Flats, the Bugungu Controlled Hunting area, and the south-west part of the Park is possibly partly related to former hippopotamus distribution, and to overgrazing by domestic livestock, but probably also related to edaphic and climatic factors.

Finally, in making and maintaining wallows, the hippopotamus improves the amount and distribution of standing water available to other species. This is not an important function of the species in North Bunyoro, where the population is largely confined to the River Nile, but is important on the north bank of the river below the falls.

4.1.3. *Other large mammals*

Bushpig (*Potamochoerus porcus* (L.)) occur in forests and thickets but although they are probably relatively common, they are not often seen because they are nocturnal. Warthog (*Phacochoerus aethiopicus* (Pallas)) are common throughout the grassland and are particularly numerous in the National Park. The warthog population estimate obtained by sample counting was 3610 ± 768 (probability levels, p = 5 per cent), but because of the long grass over much of the area and their habit of going down burrows, it is considered that this figure may be very low and unrepresentative. It indicates a mean density of 1·29 per square kilometre (3·3 per square mile) as a minimal figure. The apparent density was highest in the northern stratum (2·3 per square kilometre, 5·8 per square mile) and lower in the central stratum (0·9 per square kilometre, 2·3 per square mile) and in the south west (1·1 per square kilometre, 2·8 per square mile). The data are presented in Fig. 4.2. The greatest densities occur in the limited short-grass areas at the top of the catenas, and in the short-grass areas due to hippopotamus grazing. Giant forest hog (*Hylochoerus meinertzhageni* Thomas) are present in the Budongo Forest, probably in small numbers.

Buffalo (*Syncerus caffer* (Sparrman)) occur everywhere except near dense settlement, but are particularly numerous in the National Park (Plate 4.3). The estimate, based on unstratified random quadrat sample counting from the air, gave a figure of 14 291 ± 4996 (p = 5 per cent), which indicates a mean density of 5·3 per square kilometre (13·7 per square mile). When analysed by strata (Fig. 4.3), the mean density in a central stratum was found to be 7·8 per square kilometre (20·3 per square mile) and in a peripheral stratum, 3·2 per square kilometre (8·3 per square mile). (These strata correspond to the medium- and high-density strata described later for elephant and imply an inverse correlation between elephant and buffalo densities.) Observation suggested that the south-eastern part of the area held the lowest densities of buffalo. When this substratum was analysed separately it was found to have a mean density of 2·5 per square kilometre (6·5 per square mile) compared with a density for the rest of the peripheral stratum of 3·5 per square kilometre (9·1 per square mile).

Grimsdell (1969) found an unexpectedly low reproductive rate in a low-density buffalo population north of the Victoria Nile (Aswa-Lolim Game Reserve), compared with a high-density population studied in the Queen Elizabeth National Park. He suggested that at low densities, buffalo are not able to utilize the long-

PLATE 4.3. Buffalo herd in grassland

grass habitat and that unless heavy grazing pressure, often by hippopotamus, leads
to maintenance of areas of short- or medium-height grassland, buffalo growth and
reproductive rates remain low. We have no data on these parameters of the North
Bunyoro buffalo populations but the recent random quadrat counts suggest that
buffalo prefer medium-height grassland, tending to avoid the areas heavily grazed
by hippopotamus and also the long-grass areas in the south-east (Fig. 4.3). However inferences about buffalo distribution made from a single count must be
treated with caution, since there may be large seasonal differences in distribution.
Also, the lower peripheral densities may reflect an edge effect due to poaching
disturbance, particularly in the west.

Little is known of the buffalo using the forest areas. Observations by Forest
Department staff suggest that there may be a 'resident' buffalo population in the
Budongo Forest and a peripheral population that occupies the forest edge by day
and feeds in the surrounding grasslands at night. A recently observed phenomeon
in Budongo is that the grass tracks, old loading bays, and grassed glades are kept
cropped short. This is apparently due to a herd (or herds) of buffalo which have
penetrated the forest, although restricting their movements to the grassed areas
created by human activities. They do not penetrate undisturbed high forests, but
are confined to the felled and treated areas and to the grass verges of forest roads.
Observation is extremely difficult, but small herds have been seen in the vicinity

of the Budongo Sawmill, and recent droppings from very large herds have been seen just after dawn in the Nyakafunjo and Biiso blocks (see Chapter 5, Fig. 5.9) (indicating that they spend the night in the forest). Tracks made by herds estimated to number 100 or more have been observed at all times of the year. The slight damage to the forest caused by buffalo is discussed in Chapter 11.

Apart from some breaking of stems and compaction of soil the peripheral herds do no apparent damage. Observation is difficult but herds of up to 50 have been seen in the fringing forest, and herds of 300 or more have been counted in the grasslands.

Oribi (*Ourebia ourebi* (Zimmermann)) occur but are nowhere common. Reedbuck (*Redunca redunca* (Pallas)) are seen singly or in pairs in the open grass-land Bushbuck (*Tragelaphus scriptus* (Pallas)) are found throughout the range, in both forest and grassland except in medium *Hyparrhenia* grassland. Typically this antelope is associated with forest, woodland, and thicket, but in the open treeless grassland of the tall *Hyparrhenia* zone (and possibly in the giant *Pennisetum* areas) it has remained in small numbers in areas from which all arboreal cover has disappeared.

Attwell (1970, p. 190) has commented on a similar change in habit in the Zambezi Valley. 'Bushbuck, usually species of thick bush and forest, commonly use clumps of the coarse perennial grass *Vetiveria nigritana* as refuge, in the absence of other cover—particularly in the dry season when thickets have been cleared by pressure of other species.' In Murchison South, bushbuck are therefore mammalian indicators of the former extent of woodland and gallery forest. These individuals frequent long-grass areas and are only evident after the grass is burnt each year. Our impression is that there is still a considerable degree of ecological separation between the bushbuck and reedbuck, the former using the thicker, longer-grassed habitats in valleys and fairly steep slopes and the latter tending to be found in more open country.

Waterbuck (*Kobus defassa* (Ruppell)) are common in the National Park and occur elsewhere in the grasslands (Plate 4.4). Their population was estimated at 1171 ± 420 ($p = 5$ per cent), by means of the stratified random quadrat sample count from the air. This is equivalent to an average density of 0·43 per square kilometre (1·1 per square mile). The mean densities in three strata (Fig. 4.4) were 3·4 per square kilometre (8·8 per square mile), 0·7 per square kilometre (1·8 per square mile) and 0·15 per square kilometre (0·39 per square mile). They tend to be concentrated in short-grass areas on the top of the catenas, in the zone heavily grazed by hippopotamus and in the south-west corner of the area.

Uganda Kob (*Kobus* (*Adenota*) *kob* (Erxleben)) are also concentrated on the hippopotamus-induced short-grass areas above the Murchison Falls, and in the south-west of the area (Fig. 4.5) on the top of the catena (Plate 4.5). A stratified random quadrat sample count from the air indicated an estimated population of 2581 ± 898 ($p = 5$ per cent). This is an average density for the total area sampled of 1·0 per square kilometre (2·6 per square mile). However, the two strata con-

PLATE 4.4. Defassa waterbuck, male

PLATE 4.5. Uganda kob, male

taining kob averaged 7·8 per square kilometre (20·2 per square mile) and 2·2 per square kilometre (5·7 per square mile).

Jackson's hartebeest (*Alcelaphus bucelaphus* (Pallas)) are common but separately distributed throughout the grassland, again mainly concentrated in areas of short grass. This is probably the most abundant antelope in the area; a stratified random quadrat sample gave an estimate of 3751 ± 994 ($p = 5$ per cent), corresponding to an average density of 1·4 per square kilometre (3·6 per square mile)' The mean densities in three strata (Fig. 4.6) were 2·4 per square kilometre (6·2 per square mile), 2·4 per square kilometre (6·2 per square mile) and 0·9 per square kilometre (2·3 per square mile).

Duiker (*Sylvicapra grimmia* (L.)) are common in the woodlands and wooded grasslands, but much less frequent in the open grasslands. Red and yellow-backed duikers (*Cephalophus natalensis* A. Smith, and *C. silvicultor* (Afzelius)) occur in the Budongo Forest, as does the blue duiker (*C. monticola* (Thunberg)). The giraffe (*Giraffa camelopardalis rothschildi* Lydekker), black rhinoceros (*Diceros bicornis* (L.)), and square-lipped rhinoceros (*Ceratotherium simum* (Burchell)), occur north of the Victoria Nile, the latter recently introduced, but are not present south of the river.

As regards carnivores, lion (*Panthera leo* (L.)) are relatively common in the National Park and Karuma Controlled Hunting Area, but infrequent elsewhere; they do not occur in the forest. Leopard (*Panthera pardus* (L.)) are ubiquitous; serval (*Felis serval* Schreber) occur throughout the grasslands, and golden cat (*Felis* (*Profelis*) *aurata* Temminck) have been recorded from the Budongo Forest.

Spotted hyaena (*Crocuta crocuta* (Erxleben)) are common throughout the grassland areas and also occur in the forests. They are particularly numerous in the National Park where on several occasions nocturnal packs of up to a dozen animals were seen. The frequency with which young elephant were found with amputated tails and trunk wounds attributed to hyaena leads us to believe that they may be major predators of elephant calves.

Of the primates, chimpanzees (*Pan troglodytes* Blumenbach) are numerous in the Budongo Forest, where Reynolds (1965, p. 207) estimates the population to number 1500 ± 500, and occur in Pabidi Forest. They have also been infrequently reported from Rabongo. Baboon (*Papio anubis* J. P. Fischer) occur in moderate numbers throughout the forests, woodlands, and wooded grassland. They also occur in smaller numbers along the banks of the Victoria Nile bordering the grassland. Vervet monkeys (*Cercopithecus aethiops* (L.)) occur in the woodlands, wooded and bushed grasslands, and gallery forests, but not in true forest or grassland. Blue monkeys (*Cercopithecus mitis* Wolff) are common in Budongo and Pabidi Forests (but have not been recorded from Rabongo). The red-tailed or white-nosed monkey (*C. ascanius* (Audebert)) is common in Budongo and Pabidi Forests (and occurs in Rabongo). Black mangabeys (*Cercocebus albigena* (Gray)) also frequent Budongo.

Colobus monkeys (*Colobus abyssinicus* (Oken)) are common in Budongo,

PLATE 4.6. Colobus monkeys in riverine forest

Pabidi, and Rabongo Forests, and occur in most gallery and relict high forest patches (Plate 4.6). Although it is essentially a forest animal, this species will cross open country from one patch of forest to another. A single individual was seen travelling across open, recently burned grassland near Rabongo Hill 6·4 kilometres (4 miles) from the nearest patch of forest.

4.1.4. *Small mammals*

There has been very little work on the smaller mammals of North Bunyoro. A. L. Archer (personal communication) has collected at least 38 species of insectivores, bats, primates, lagomorphs, rodents, and carnivores in the Bugoma Forest, Bunyoro. Most if not all of these species occur, or formerly occurred, in North Bunyoro.

4.1.5. *Standing crop biomass*

Compared with other grasslands in western Uganda (Queen Elizabeth National Park, Toro Game Reserve) those of North Bunyoro appear to carry surprisingly sparse ungulate populations other than elephant, buffalo, and hippopotamus. The dominance of the relatively non-nutritious and fibrous tall *Hyparrhenia* and *Pennisetum* species may be a contributory cause, for few ruminants are adapted

Table 4.3
Comparison of average biomass figures for areas in the Murchison Falls Park, South (see elsewhere in this book) *and the Queen Elizabeth National Park* (Field and Laws 1970).

| Species | Unit weight (kg) | Biomass (kg/ha) | | | | |
| | | Murchison Falls Park | | Queen Elizabeth Park | | |
		Riverine	Long grass	Long grass	Short grass/ thicket	Short grass
Elephant	2234†	44·68	86·01	–	–	–
	1700	–	–	31·45	35·78	9·75
Hippopotamus	1000	190·00	0·00	0·00	192·85	29·90
Buffalo	395	30·81	12·72	18·64	56·48	68·41
Uganda kob	65	5·07	1·43	0·66	2·83	41·90
Waterbuck	160	5·44	0·24	0·59	5·74	1·26
Hartebeest	136	3·26	1·22	–	–	–
Topi	100	–	–	0·00	0·00	37·86
Warthog	50	1·12	0·46	0·00	1·03	1·03
Total		280·38	102·08	51·34	294·81	190·11
Other than elephant, hippopotamus, buffalo		14·89	3·35	1·25	9·60	82·05
% elephant, hippopotamus, buffalo		94·7	96·7	99·1	96·7	56·8

† Estimate for M.F.P.S. from Table 10.2

to feed on them. The dominant grasses are edaphic-fire climax species and the productivity rating of the soils is low-medium.

We have compared the standing crop biomass of the larger herbivores of North Bunyoro with data available for the Queen Elizabeth National Park. In Table 4.3 biomass estimates per unit area for the dominant herbivore species in the Murchison Falls National Park, South (M.F.P.S.) are presented for comparison with estimates recently published for three habitat types in the Queen Elizabeth Park (Field and Laws 1970). The unit weights used in calculating the M.F.P.S. biomasses are those given by Field and Laws (1970), with the exception of elephant (for reasons given in Chapter 10) and hartebeest, for which the unit weight is taken to be 136 kg. This is a figure given by Foster and Coe (1968) for a closely related subspecies of *A. buselaphus*. The elephant unit weight in M.F.P.S. is in fact substantially higher (2234 kg) than the figure used in the Queen Elizabeth Park calculations (1700 kg) owing to the reduced recruitment (discussed later) and the consequent excess of older and larger animals in the population. In making the calculations for M.F.P.S. it has been assumed that elephant densities average 2·0 per square kilometre in the riverine zone and 3·85 per square kilometre in the long-grass areas. These values are derived from the stratified random quadrat sample counts modified by the results of complete counts. An over-all hippopotamus density in the riverine zone of 19 per square kilometre is assumed and the densities of other species are derived from strata means calculated in the random quadrat sampling analysis and presented earlier.

We find that on a unit-area basis, if habitat type is taken into account, the two areas have surprisingly similar standing crop biomasses. Thus the M.F.P.S. riverine zone (supporting probably about 280 kg per hectare) resembles in parts the short-grass/thicket areas of Queen Elizabeth Park (supporting 295 kg per hectare) and in parts the short-grass areas of that Park (supporting 190 kg per hectare). The short-grass study areas of the Queen Elizabeth Park support much lower hippopotamus densities than the short-grass/thicket areas of that park, or the M.F.P.S. riverine zone, because they are situated well away from the lake shores or large rivers. In these areas hippo numbers may be limited to some extent by the area of the wallows they use. The long-grass study area in the Queen Elizabeth Park has a substantially lower standing crop biomass (51 kg per hectare) than the long-grass areas of M.F.P.S. (102 kg per hectare)

When similar habitat types in the two parks are compared species by species, the similarities are particularly striking. Biomasses of elephant, hippopotamus, waterbuck, and warthog in the riverine part of M.F.P.S. and the short-grass/ thicket areas of Queen Elizabeth Park, are particularly close, and buffalo and Uganda kob are quite similar in this respect. The main discrepancy between the long-grass areas is due to the greater unit weight and high peripheral elephant population in the M.F.P.S. and possibly also to seasonal reduction in standing water in that part of the Queen Elizabeth Park.

Over-all, however, proportionately more of the Queen Elizabeth Park is short-grass/thicket or short-grass habitat and the average standing crop biomass per unit area for the park as a whole is higher than for M.F.P.S. where only about 10—20 per cent of the area comprises the more productive habitat types.

Even so, the biomass in the long-grass areas of M.F.P.S. compares favourably with other, drier areas of East Africa. Lamprey (1964) reported an estimated year-round average biomass of 122·5 kg per hectare for a small part of the Tarangire Reserve in northern Tanzania, which was a dry-season concentration area. Foster and Coe (1968) recorded a long-term average biomass of 63·0 kg per hectare for the Nairobi National Park, Kenya.

The forests, in contrast to the grasslands, carried rich and varied faunas though with low standing crops. Representatives of these faunas still survive in the relict strips of gallery forest and relict patches of high forest, and above all in the Budongo Forest. In the National Park, however, unless the present degradation of these forest remnants is halted, it is certain that the forest animals associated with them will disappear, and when this happens the diversity of the biota within the National Park will be considerably reduced. This is particularly disturbing, because the forest is being managed for timber production and, as we shall see (Chapter 11), its ecology is changing in the process.

4.2. Birds

In addition to the mammals there is a diversity of invertebrates, reptiles, amphibia, and birds, both in the forest and grasslands. Of these groups only the birds are well-known from a faunistic aspect, but provide an example of the potential loss of species as the wooded habitats progressively disappear. There are 410 species currently listed in the Murchison Falls Park check-list. The forests, gallery forest, and relict forest patches provide a complete habitat for 14 species, that is, 3·4 per cent of the total check-listed; they provide a partial habitat for 27 species (6·6 per cent). Thus 41 observed species (10 per cent of the total observed check-list) are completely or partly dependent on the forest habitat. The woodland provides a complete habitat for 35 species (8·5 per cent of the total). The woodland also provides a partial habitat for 127 observed species (31·0 per cent).

Thus, of the 410 species observed and recorded in the check-list, 12 per cent are completely dependent on forest or woodland and a further 38 per cent partially dependent on the wooded habitats, together comprising half the total observed. Clearly, from a consideration of this important group alone, any further reduction in the area of wooded habitats is to be viewed with alarm. These figures relate to the entire Park and many woodland species are now confined to the area north of the Victoria Nile (M.F.P.N.). If the trend of woodland disappearance could be reversed and the area of wooded habitat increased, recolonization is still possible. However, a similar trend from woodland to grassland is apparent in M.F.P.N., and outside the National Park the increasing human population is destroying habitats on which many species depend.

4.3. Summary

The general status of elephants and other mammals in the area has been established. After elephants, probably the most important is the hippopotamus population, which has been the subject of a management cropping programme since 1965. Prior to management some 14 000 hippos were using the riverine areas in the northern and southern sectors of the Park. Up to March 1969, 3873 had been removed by cropping, but the grazing density in North Bunyoro in 1967, based on aerial counts, was still about 19 per square kilometre, representing a standing crop biomass of about 19 000 kg per square kilometre in the riverine zone. In North Bunyoro some 10 per cent of the elephant range is affected by hippopotamus overgrazing and there is competition there between hippopotamus and elephant in favour of the former species; within the riverine zone the standing crop biomass of hippopotamus was at least six times that of elephant. This large hippopotamus population has an important effect on the habitats, and influences the distribution of other species, including bushpig, warthog, giant forest hog, buffalo, oribi, reedbuck, bushbuck, hartebeest, waterbuck, Uganda kob, duikers, several carnivores, and seven primate species. At least 38 species of smaller mammals occur in North and West Bunyoro. Many of these are partly or entirely dependent on wooded habitats. Aerial counts to estimate the numbers of the more important species have been made and some 40 000 individuals of seven species of large herbivores were present in the area in 1969. Their standing crop biomass per unit area has been calculated at some 280 kg per hectare in the riverine zone of short- or medium-height grass and thicket, and at 102 kg per hectare in the medium- or tall-grass areas away from the River Nile. The former value is closely comparable with estimates for other similar areas in Western Uganda, but higher than for drier regions of East Africa.

Of the other faunal groups only birds are well known, in terms of occurrence rather than abundance. Of 410 species currently listed as occurring in the National Park, 12 per cent are completely dependent on the forest or woodland and a further 38 per cent partly dependent on wooded habitants. Many woodland species are already extinct in the southern sector of the Park, where the change to grassland is most advanced.

5. Elephant numbers

5.1. The grassland and wooded grassland range

5.1.1. *Aerial counts*

More than a hundred routine observation flights were made during the course of the two-year cropping programme and provided a valuable background of experience for three 'complete' aerial counts of elephants. A population estimate with confidence limits has already been given in Chapter 4.

The purpose of these counts was to determine if possible, not only total numbers of elephant—population size—but also their detailed distribution, movements, and group-size frequency distributions. For this reason 'complete' area counts were made on 16—20 November 1966, 16—20 February 1967, and 11—14 August 1967. Additional counts would have helped in clarifying possible seasonal changes, but were not possible owing to shortage of funds. The total cost of these three counts was £750, excluding the salaries of pilots and observers. Actual counting time totalled 65 hours, averaging 21·7 hours per count.

The procedures adopted for carrying out these counts are described in detail in Appendix A. We are well aware of the inadequacy of only three counts as the basis for calculations of population size. As a result it should be appreciated that the following analysis contains an element of speculation that we would have wished to avoid. Nevertheless our procedures and conclusions follow the course of the simplest explanations and it should be borne in mind that one of us (I.S.C.P.) was living in the area for two years and working with elephant daily. This provided a chain of continuity and insight into the area and the pattern of elephant distribution which, even if unrecorded at the time, was of considerable importance. The correctness of our information is borne out by the success of the cropping operation in 1966 and 1967 when we always knew where to go and where male or female elephants would be found.

The total numbers counted in Blocks 1—12 (Fig. 5.1) in November 1966 and February and August 1967 were 7779, 8713 and 7913 respectively (mean 8135), which are in reasonably close agreement. These totals are all well within the confidence limits of the estimated population in a similar area in 1969, obtained by stratified random quadrat sampling (Chapter 4). The confidence interval for that estimate (p = 5 per cent) was 6628—12100. To obtain from them an estimate of the actual population size it is, however, necessary to take into account a number of factors which affected the count results.

Thus Block 12 (Fig. 5.1) was counted only in the third count; variable numbers were hidden in the Budongo and other forests during the counts; some 900 elephants were cropped or shot on control during the period of the counts; and the influence of variable recruitment has to be considered. It is also possible

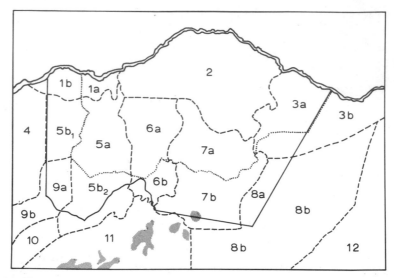

Fig. 5.1. Elephant counting Blocks 1–12. Forest patches are shaded. Blocks 1, 3, 5–8, and 9 are subdivided, following natural features, approximately to define medium- and high-density strata. This is related to proposals made in Chapter 12; the counting sub-blocks were different.

that the counting efficiency increased slightly after the first count because the pilot for the second and third counts (I.S.C.P.) was much more familiar with the area and with elephant distribution patterns and had worked in the area for nearly two years. The pilot during the first count (A. D. Graham) has considerably less experience of the area. (See Appendix A for a discussion of the importance of the pilot as opposed to observers in aerial counting.) Let us now consider these factors in turn and attempt to evaluate their effect on the population estimates.

Although we had confidence in the accuracy of the counting method adopted, there was an increase of some 800 animals between the totals for the first and second counts, when in fact a substantial decrease (due to elephant entering the forest) was expected. Assuming that the difference did not reflect counting errors, the only area from which this increase could have come was that east of the Karuma-Kiryandongo-Masindi Port Road (Block 12).

The Game Warden, Masindi, had information that elephant had been in this area at the time of the count and that there had been movement across the road dividing it from the Karuma Controlled Hunting Area. It was therefore decided that this area should be included in the third count, and in the August 1967 count it was found to contain 679 elephant, in one large herd. The tracks of this herd showed up clearly from the air making it possible to determine that it had recently come out of the Karuma Controlled Hunting Area (Fig. 5.4). Although there can be no final proof, the large difference between the first and second counts could be explained if the animals comprising this herd were in Block 12 during the

November 1966 count, but were in the adjacent block(s) during the February 1967 count.

During the November count there were only four large herds (of more than 100 animals) in these blocks (Fig. 5.2) numbering 273, 189, 147, and 108, totalling 717. There were six large herds in the south-east parts of Blocks 3, 7, and 8 during the February count (Fig. 5.3) numbering 448, 452, 540, 142, 154, and 115, totalling 1851. In the August count there were four large herds in Blocks 3, 7, 8, and 12 (Fig. 5.4) numbering 728, 679, 250, 118, totalling 1675 (Plates 5.1–5.4). There is fairly close agreement between the last two counts as to the numbers of elephant aggregated in large herds, averaging 1763, compared with only 717 in large herds in the November count. This would agree with our view that some 1000 elephant were missed during the first count because they were in Block 12 and therefore outside the area counted.

This pattern is identical with the seasonal movement involving 600–1000 elephants, known to the Game Department for many years and repeatedly referred to in their annual reports.

Large herds have been recorded before in our counting Block 8; which is contiguous with Block 12; thus, a herd of about 900 was seen on 1 June 1958 at the headwaters of the Titi River, and another similar-sized herd was seen on 14 May 1959 close to the Rere Hill (Buechner *et al.* (1963), pp. 50–1). Buss and Savidge (1966, p. 802) report that 'a large herd (possibly 1000) had moved into a woodland area east of Rere Hill in June 1963.'

Beuchner *et al.* (1963, p. 49) present further observations which have a bearing on this postulated movement:

the additional increment from March to June, 1958, . . . seems to have resulted mainly from ingress across the Masindi-Mutunda road. The observation of a herd of about 1000 elephants migrating northwards close to Rere Hill on May 14, 1958 [*sic*], supports the probability of immigration along this pathway. However, elephants may also have moved into the study area from the 250-square-mile tract of uninhabitated heavily wooded grassland between the southern boundary of the study area and the northern extent of the cultivated lands [i.e. in our Blocks 8 and 12]. Because of the extreme difficulty of sighting elephants in the dense arboral vegetation of this area, no systematic counts were made. A fortuitous observation of 300 elephants in a single herd on July 18, 1957, suggests that the area could conceal substantial numbers of animals.

For many years elephant have moved into the general area of our counting Block 12 from Block 8, in April–July, returning to the National Park area in November. Thus in August and November substantial numbers could be expected in Block 12 (and were found when the block was counted in August). They would not be expected to be there in February. This movement out of the Park into Block 12 appears to be correlated with seasonally improved water availability outside the Park. Buechner *et al.* (1963, p. 49) remark that, 'in that portion of the study area east of the Park rain-storms drop less moisture than within the

PLATE 5.1. Part of herd of 340 elephants in M.F.P.S. Note dead trees.

PLATE 5.2. Herd of 206 elephants in M.F.P.S.

PLATE 5.3. Large elephant herd in grasslands near Rabongo.

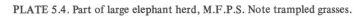

PLATE 5.4. Part of large elephant herd, M.F.P.S. Note trampled grasses.

Park where Rabongo Hill forces storms to rise and release rain. The extreme eastern portion of the study area, therefore, is also drier than the Park. The grasses are burned earlier, and the elephants move into the Park during the long dry season'. Probably a combination of earlier burning, owing to human settlement, and a seasonal cycle of surface water availability is responsible for this movement.

Seasonal variation in the numbers uncounted within the forest canopies would also affect the totals, and it is necessary here to anticipate the conclusions reached later (Section 5.2). There, indices of relative seasonal abundance of elephant within the Budongo Forest are discussed (dropping and track counts, and numbers shot on control), and estimates of the number of elephant using the forest (1000–1500) are given.

Taking the lower estimate (which we consider more likely), applying it to a graph showing seasonal changes in one index of numbers of elephants in the forest (monthly numbers shot on control), assuming that the peak index value equals 1000, we have estimated the numbers expected to be in the forest in November, February, and August as 360, 860, and 340 respectively.

There are no reliable data for Pabidi or Rabongo Forest, but the numbers would have been much smaller. During the first count it was established that there were some elephant in the Pabidi Forest; restricted observations through the canopy did not indicate many and we arbitrarily estimated a maximum of 100 (on the basis of 3·9 per square kilometre (10 per square mile) of the forest). In the second count, aerial observation did not reveal any elephant in Pabidi, suggesting that there had been a reduction; let us accept 50 as a maximal estimate. In August, Pabidi Forest again held only small numbers of elephant. The numbers within the Rabongo Forest are negligible in this context, although of great importance in their destructive effects on this small relict forest patch.

Between the first and second counts approximately 97 elephant were shot on control in the area by the Game Department. Between the second and third counts approximately 230 were shot on control and 600 cropped in the National Park by Game Management (Uganda) Ltd (Table 5.1).

Table 5.1

Data considered in a first estimate of the size of the North Bunyoro elephant populations

	November 1966	February 1967	August 1967
Aerial count	7779	8713	7913
Missing in uncounted area	1000	–	–
In Pabidi Forest	100	50	50
In Budongo Forest	360	860	340
Cropped since first count (cumulative)	–	97	927
Totals	9239	9720	9230

As regards recruitment to the population, this is probably at least balanced by deaths, as the population has been declining (Chapter 10); in any case it is considered to be very small. Thus from a consideration of the areas under a smoothed curve of monthly birth frequencies for the Murchison Falls Park, South, derived from Fig. 9.8 (Chapter 9), we expect about 20 per cent of the total births to occur between November and February and about 39 per cent between February and August. Assuming, for the purpose of the present discussion, that the natality rate was 5 per cent, total births to a population of 9000 would be 450 a year, of which about 90 and about 175 are expected to be born in November–February and February–August respectively.

No adjustment has been made for the different pilots in the first and two later counts although this may have contributed to the higher counts. Even without this adjustment the results are remarkably consistent, with a range of no more than 5·2 per cent of the mean estimate.

The conclusions about the population size are summarized in Table 5.1. The mean of the three estimates is 9396 which suggests a total population in November 1966 of about 9400, of which 325 ± 75 are considered to be resident in the Budongo Forest. The over-all population had been reduced, by control shooting and cropping, to about 8500 by the end of 1967, it being assumed here that natality and mortality were equal. A stratified random quadrat sample in 1969, excluding the forest area gave an estimate of 9364 ± 2736 (Table 4.1).

5.1.2. *Distribution and movements*

Buss (1961, p. 144) noted a strong tendency for elephants to congregate during the dry season in the marshes along the shore of Lake Albert and along the south banks of the Nile below Murchison Falls. A wet-season aerial count in May 1959 showed few elephant in these areas. He concluded that these dry-season concentrations resulted in local over-utilization of some food plants, particularly along the Lake Albert shore, and that elephants dispersed in the wet season to the 'better and more extensive food supplies on the open savannas . . . I believe this water-dry season relationship is very important in governing some of the food habits and migratory behaviour of the elephant in Uganda'. However, Buechner *et al.* (1963, p. 36) remark that their observations in 1957 to 1959 'did not substantiate an earlier hypothesis that elephants migrated into the Park during the dry season in January and February and emigrated with the long rains in May and June. Although migratory movements were related to rains, they did not follow an annual cycle'.

There is no valid evidence for the movement of North Bunyoro elephants over ranges of more than 20 miles, and even this is now unusual. We do not believe that long-range movements have ever been regular or frequent, even under natural conditions. Wing and Buss (1970, p. 35) give a record of the supposed movement of an adult female elephant over a distance of 115 miles between Semliki Plains (south of Lake Albert) and Igisi Hill. This is on the basis of a cow elephant marked in March 1961, which it was claimed was the same animal as one shot on 6 December 1963. One of the team which marked the animal in 1961 recognized four rectangular holes 'spaced equidistant along the edge of her left ear' when she had been shot. We are not prepared to accept this as valid evidence that it was the same animal, but even if it were such a movement would be exceptional and individual.

It would appear certain from our observations that major seasonal patterns are no longer an important feature of elephant behaviour in the area, probably due to increasing concentration within a smaller area and more uniform habitat deterioration. However, as we shall see, a movement of elephant from the Nile banks in Block 1, was probably induced by burning; and it seems probable that the movement of elephant into Block 12 during the wet season may be related to availability of water. Also there is a seasonal movement of part of the peripheral population into the Budongo Forest in the dry season.

5.1.2.1.   *Distribution.* It is again worth emphasizing the point that the information on distribution provided by the aerial counts was borne out by many routine reconnaissance flights and by the actual cropping activities in 1965, 1966, and 1967.

The results of the counts are presented in Figs. 5.2–5.4 and Tables 5.1–5.3. In the figures the distribution of elephants is plotted according to seven group size categories.

Considering the November 1966 count first (Fig. 5.2) the distribution of single animals and small herds (number of animals, $n = 1-5$) at first sight appears to be more or less random, although detailed analysis indicates a clumped distribution. There is a marked tendency for large herds to be clumped, particularly in the peripheral part of the elephant range, and it can be seen that, in general, there is a wide zone (5–13 kilometres, 3–8 miles) between the peripheral elephant groups and human settlement. The majority of elephant counted were within the National Park and only a quarter of the number counted (24·7 per cent) was outside the Park boundaries. The area east of the Karuma-Kiryandongo road was not counted because it was thought that human settlement along the road constituted a barrier to elephant movement.

In the results of the February 1967 count (Fig. 5.3), the over-all range of distribution is very similar, but elephant have moved into the northern part of the Karuma Controlled Hunting Area. The distribution of small groups ($n = 1-5$) again appears to be fairly random, if anything less clumped than in November, but the distribution of larger herds appears to be more clumped, especially at the periphery of the range. Concentrations on the headwaters of the Titi and Weiga Rivers are noticeable. Over a quarter of the elephants counted (27·8 per cent) were outside the National Park boundaries. Again there is, for the most part, a wide unoccupied zone between elephant and human populations. The area east of the Karuma-Kiryandongo road was again not counted.

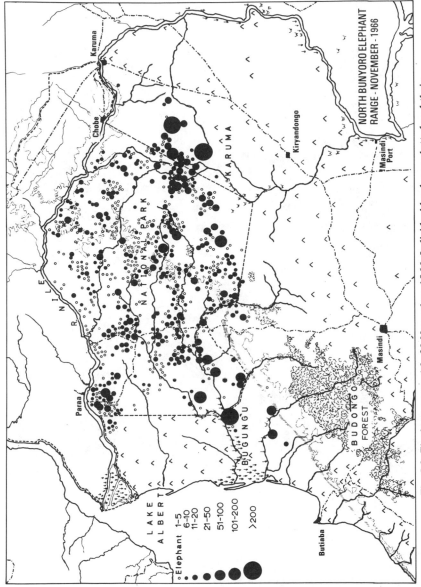

Fig. 5.2. Elephant count, 16–20 November 1966. Individual herds are plotted and their sizes indicated. Distribution of human settlement is indicated by ⋀.

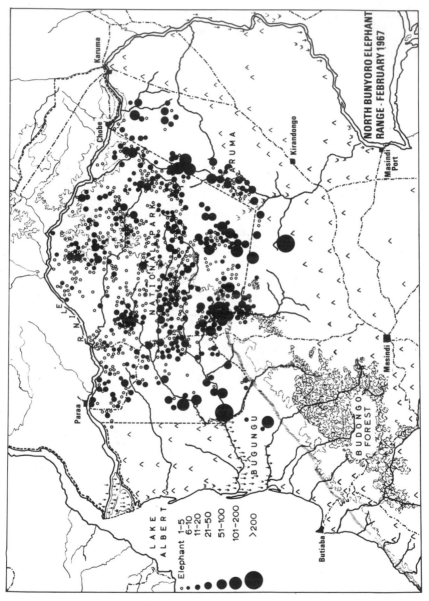

Fig. 5.3. Elephant count, 16–20 February 1967. See caption to Fig. 5.2 for key.

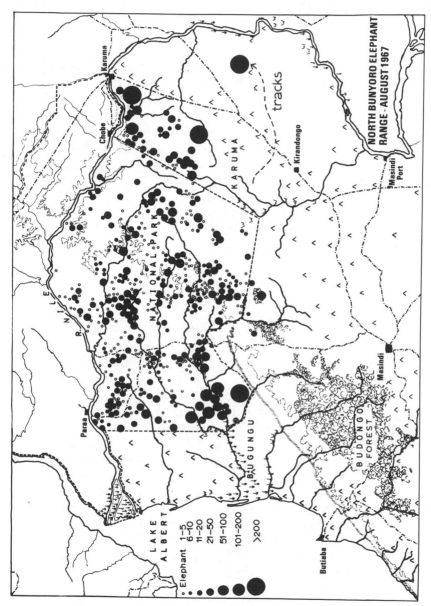

Fig. 5.4. Elephant count, 11–14 August 1967. See caption to Fig. 5.2 for key.

In the August 1967 count (Fig. 5.4) the area east of the Karuma-Kiryandongo road was counted for the first time (for reasons which were given above). Elephants appeared to have moved from the south-east corner of the range, to concentrate in the northern part of the Karuma Controlled Hunting Area. Nearly a third of the numbers counted (31·5 per cent) were outside the National Park boundaries. There appear to be more medium- and large-sized groups, with perhaps a more clumped distribution. Small groups ($n = 1-5$) are virtually missing from the north-east corner of the National Park, between the Zoila River and the River Nile.

Between the February and August counts 423 elephant were cropped in Block 2 (Fig. 5.1), mainly to the north of the Zoila River, but also between the Zoila and Joliya Rivers; and 112 were cropped in the northern half of Block 7. It seemed probable that the virtual absence of small herds in the northern part of Block 2 was caused by cropping in the immediate vicinity, and by the cropping to the south which may have created a potential 'vacuum' and drawn elephants from the north of the Zoila. Large herds again tend to be peripheral in distribution; one very large herd ($n = 679$) was located east of the Karuma-Kiryandongo road near the River Nile; its tracks were still visible in the tall grass and showed that it had recently moved from the area in the vicinity of the headwaters of the River Titi. (The track path is shown in Fig. 5.4.)

In all three counts it was noticeable that elephant were absent from the Lake Albert shore, from the Bugumu Controlled Hunting Area and from the Butiaba Flats.

The density distributions and group size distributions during the three counts are analysed and discussed in Chapter 7.

5.1.2.2.   *Analysis by counting blocks.* In Table 5.2 the results of the actual counts, tabulated by individual blocks, are presented. There are considerable differences within blocks between the three counts, which could be due to counting errors, to local or general movements, to cropping or control shooting in the intervals between counts, or to a combination of these factors. It is unfortunate that there are so few counts, but a more detailed, though speculative, analysis suggests that there may be two or four main systems in relation to the elephant populations within the over-all area covered.

Thus a more consistent pattern emerges when neighbouring blocks are combined. If the counts for Blocks 2 and 7 are combined, and the third count adjusted for the number cropped (Table 5.3) the results are in very close agreement, the range of the estimate for this area being only 5 per cent of the mean. This suggests a very stable resident local population occupying an area of some 1165 square kilometres (450 square miles), which we consider to be the 'heartland' of the North Bunyoro elephant range.

Next, Blocks 3, 8, and 12 have been combined and give a mean of 2431 elephants over the three counts with a range of 43 per cent of the mean. When adjusted (Table 5.3) the new mean is 2786 and the range is only 16 per cent of

Table 5.2

Numbers of elephant counted and cropped by blocks

Block	November 1966	February 1967	August 1967	Cropped (1)	Cropped (2)
1	575	288	282	–	–
2	1069	987	831	–	423
3	953	1246	1238	–	65
4	0	0	0	–	–
5	930	1013	1899	–	–
6	.666	1417	505	–	8
7	1413	1461	1003	–	104
8	905	1274	998	–	–
9	1205	589	366	–	–
10	20	0	13	–	–
11	143	438	99	97	230
12	–	–	679	–	–
Total	7779	8713	7913	97	830

Notes. (1) Cropped between November and February
(2) Cropped between February and August

Table 5.3

Adjusted elephant population estimates (excluding forest residents)

Blocks		November 1966	February 1967	August 1967	Mean
1, 4, 5, 6 combined	count	2071	2718	2686	2492
	adjusted	2671[1]	–	–	2692
2, 7 combined	count	2482	2448	1834	2254
	adjusted	–	–	2369[2]	2432
3, 8, 12 combined	count	1858	2520	2915	2431
	adjusted	2858[3]	–	2980[4]	2786
9, 10, 11 forest combined	count	1368	1027	478	957
	adjusted	1403[5]	1659[6]	1005[7]	1356
Totals	count	7779	8713	7913	8135
	adjusted	9414	9345	9040	9266

Notes. (1) One or two large herds, totalling *ca* 600 possibly missed in Block 4, tracks seen
(2) 535 elephant cropped between 23 February and 25 May 1967
(3) 1000 probably missed because Block 12 not counted
(4) 65 elephant cropped between 23 February and 25 May 1967
(5) 35 plains elephants estimated to be in Budongo Forest
(6) 97 elephants cropped between November and February; 535 plains elephants estimated to be in Budongo Forest, probably includes *ca* 400 from Block 8
(7) 327 elephants cropped since November; and large herd of *ca* 200 not seen in Block 10 or 11, probably at forest edge.

the mean. The argument for having missed some 1000 elephants because Block 12 was not counted in November 1966 was given above. It is believed that the peripheral animals are more mobile and have a less random density distribution, due to a (hypothetical) behavioural density-regulating mechanism having broken down in these peripheral areas. Apart from this the other major discrepancy in the adjusted totals for these blocks is in the February count. If some 400 elephants moved into Budongo Forest in February from Block 8, as seems likely, then the range of the further adjusted estimates would be very small (2858–2980 or 4 per cent of the mean).

If adjusted estimates for Blocks 9, 10, 11, and the Budongo Forest are considered together (Table 5.3), then even allowing for a seasonal influx of 400 in February from outside these areas (probably mainly from Block 8, as suggested in the previous paragraph), the totals are not in very close agreement, the range being 33 per cent of the mean. One large herd of 200 was seen close to the Forest in December 1966 and April 1967 but did not appear in Block 11 in any of the counts. We assume that either it or a larger group was missed during the August count or was hidden under the canopy at the forest edge. It may be pointed out that these interpretations are in close agreement with the numbers estimated to frequent the Budongo Forest on a seasonal basis, and it would be difficult to accept a markedly higher seasonal influx on the basis of these figures.

This leaves Blocks 1, 4, 5, and 6 to be considered. Unadjusted count totals give a mean of 2492 and a range which is 26 per cent of the mean. In view of the close agreements between the combined totals for the second and third counts (unadjusted), it seems likely that some 600 elephants may have been in Block 4 during the November 1966 count, as one or more large herds, but were missed in this count. This block contains some dense thicket, and recent elephant tracks were seen in it during the count, but no elephant were observed. Block 4 was not searched as thoroughly as it should have been because of the human settlement there; adjusting in this way would give a mean of 2692 and a range only 1·2 per cent of the mean; but this is speculative.

We may also profitably compare the variation in the totals within some individual blocks. Block 1 was severely burnt in late January 1967 and about half the elephant present in November had evidently moved out by February (Table 5.2), probably to Block 6, and had not returned by August 1967. Although the River Nile forms the northern boundary of Block 1, providing water and riparian grazing and thicket, the competition afforded by a high hippopotamus population (density 23 per square kilometre, 60 per square mile) may have been sufficient to cause the elephant to move. This is one of the few sectors of the Park in which there are no streams or swamps other than along the River Nile.

The most likely origin for the influx of elephant to the forest from the west which is discussed later, is from the block below the Rift Valley Escarpment,

PLATE 5.5. Elephant trails climbing the escarpment above the Butiaba Flats.

containing the Weiga swamps (Block 9). Between the first two counts Block 9 apparently lost some 600 elephant; the block immediately above the escarpment (Block 11), which surrounds the Budongo Forest, had gained some 300. Movement up and down the escarpment between these two blocks is well documented (Buechner *et al.* 1963) and well-worn tracks (Plate 5.5), traversing the escarpment at the time of the second count, indicated considerable recent elephant movement. It therefore seems reasonable to assume that some 600 elephant moved up the escarpment and the balance (300) between this number and the 300 counted outside the forest, were in the forest or at the forest edge. Forest Department records supported this.

Throughout the dry season of 1958—9 elephant were concentrated between the Budongo Forest and the Park boundary (the northern half of Block 11). 'Each morning that I visited the area during this period there were many fresh droppings on the road and many freshly made trails crossing the road, attesting further to the presence of many elephants' (Buss 1961, p. 144). At the beginning of the rains (late March 1959) 'many of the elephants above the escarpment were congregating into large herds preparatory to their emigration from the area'. Buss saw four herds above the escarpment of at least 100 elephants each, all travelling west towards the Butiaba Flats between 18 March and 23 March; on 25 March nearly 400 elephants were seen travelling down the Waisoke River.

'Although we had made bi-weekly safaris to Butiaba Flats searching for elephants after January 6, 1959, and conducted an aerial reconnaissance over this area
on February 26, 1959, these were the first elephants that we recorded between
the Sonso and Weiga Rivers on Butiaba Flats since December 10, 1958.' By mid-
April very few elephants were seen above the escarpment and numbers on the
Flats were at the pre-dry season level.

Beuchner *et al.* (1963, p. 50) concluded that 'about 1500 elephant can be
accounted for in the Butiaba Flats-Budongo Forest migration'. Elsewhere (p. 49)
they remark that 'southwest of the Park, on Butiaba Flats where the elevation
is somewhat lower, the area is drier, burning of the grasslands here occurs earlier
in the year, and patches of unburned grass are infrequent. These conditions seem
to be related to the Butiaba Flats-Budongo Forest migration'.

It seems probable that the herd of about 200–300 discussed above and later
represents the survivors of the large herds which were formerly found on the
Butiaba Flats. Control shooting, which increased greatly after 1957, has undoubtedly been largely responsible for their decline.

In this connection it is of great interest that in the past decade there have
been large numbers (over 200 recorded in one year) of deaths each year below
the escarpment in the Izizi-Weiga area. Data on elephant deaths represented by
found ivory in several areas in the west of the Park which are regularly patrolled
by rangers, are presented in Fig. 10.1 and 10.3 (Chapter 10). These deaths
are seasonal and have been attributed by some investigators to disease or to
poisonous plants, but in several (unpublished) investigations no reliable evidence
as to the cause of death was obtained. It is now suggested that the deaths in these
areas represent animals wounded in the intensive control shooting operations in
and around the Budongo Forest. Shooting elephant within the forest is a difficult
and hazardous operation, due to the closed nature of the vegetation, especially in
the young regeneration areas within the forest. The Game Guards are instructed
to aim for the heart, or if the whole animal is not visible, where they think the
heart is. This technique must produce a high percentage of wounded animals,
some mortally wounded, that die later.

The first recorded deaths from suspected 'disease' in 1958 were related to an
intensification of the control shooting programme centred on Budongo Forest
(Chapter 10, Fig. 10.1). Equally suggestive is the fact that the deaths are seasonal
in incidence, occurring mainly in January to April, when control shooting is at its
height (Figs 10.2 and 10.3); and that the area where the majority of carcasses
are found—the Weiga swamp—is just below the escarpment and the most likely
area for wounded elephants to make for. A fuller discussion of this question will
be found in Chapter 10.

A probable seasonal movement pattern from Block 8 through Block 11, to
enter Budongo Forest from the north-east is discussed below. The movement

between Blocks 3, 8, and 12 has been described, but it is worth emphasizing that the elephant involved are usually in very big compact herds (see below).

Frequent reconnaissance flights over all areas through the period 1965–7 did not suggest that any large-scale movement, not indicated by the three counts, occurred. No movement of the population as a whole took place, and the movements that were recorded or inferred involved only small sections of the elephant communities at any one time. The spatial scale of the movements was very small, the greatest displacement being only 29 kilometres (18 miles). This further emphasizes and underlines the integrity of differing group structures.

During the three elephant counts a minimum of 68·5 per cent of those counted were resident within the Park boundaries (in August) and the remaining 31·5 per cent mainly within the Karuma Controlled Hunting Area; none were counted in the Bugungu Hunting Area (although it is suggested that some 600 were there in November 1966). Comparison of the 1966–7 counts with the distribution maps given by Buechner *et al.* (1963) relating to 1957–9 indicate a very marked contraction in the range of elephant distribution over the intervening decade (Fig. 1.4). Similarly Buss (1961, Fig. 1) collected 71 elephants for his study in areas where very few elephant occur today. As a result the elephant population is in direct contact with man only in limited areas of its periphery, and for the greater part there exists a buffer zone of neutral ground. This appears to be a consequence of the interaction with man, leading to the aggregation of the peripheral elephant communities into very large herds, so that they are much less continuously distributed than the 'central' populations (Chapter 7).

It is not claimed that these are more than minimal estimates of numbers, although for the resident elephants in Blocks 2 and 7 the reproducibility of the counts was evidently within ± 5 per cent of the mean. We have no means of estimating the extent of bias, though it is likely to result in a lower, rather than a higher, estimate than the true value for the population size. The analysis suggests a total population in November 1966 (excluding the forest residents) of about 8200–9300 elephants and we consider the higher part of this range to be more likely. It agrees reasonably well with the earlier estimate of 9400 for the total population including the forest residents, and with the estimate, based on sample counting of 9364 ± 2736 (excluding the forest) for 1969. Further counts would provide material for testing some of our suggestions, but it now seems unlikely that they will be made.

It should be noted that the boundaries of the counting blocks were selected by reference to physiographical features of the range, rather than to the social configuration of the elephant populations. Nonetheless there appears to be quite good evidence for assuming that there is a central, more or less resident, population with much less stable, comparatively mobile, peripheral populations, which now (or in the recent past) move seasonally into the periphery of the range which is much more heavily wooded than the main range of the elephant herds. These peripheral 'populations' are characterized by high densities and by the presence of a number of large herds and by a relatively discontinuous distribution (Figs 5.2—5.4). Let us now consider the organization and composition of the large herds. The distribution pattern of elephant densities throughout the range is considered in Chapter 7.

5.1.3.   *Large herds*

During the aerial counts in 1966—7 and frequently during the course of reconnaissance flights in 1965—7, a number of herds in excess of fifty individuals was seen in North Bunyoro. These large groups were classifiable into two categories, and appear to have differing origins.

1. Groups with members scattered, appearing as an 'approximation' of smaller herds and showing little co-ordination as a unit, but separated by a larger gap from other elephant groups.

2. Large groups whose members were in very close proximity to each other and showed a considerable degree of co-ordination as a single unit. (Fig. 5.5, Plates 5.1—5.4).

Such groups are undoubtedly the origin of many of the tales of elephant migrations. The former were recorded throughout North Bunyoro elephant range and seemed to be genuine random aggregations. Their formation is apparently due to chance encounter of a number of smaller units; or through smaller herds being drawn together by physiographic conformation of the habitat; or an 'island' of good forage, perhaps after localized rain, or of vegetation remaining after a burn. They have little permanence, often appearing as a herd for as short a period as an hour or less. Although seemingly a herd at such a time, the term is perhaps not applicable and the aggregation better described as a 'close concentration'. These 'close concentrations' generally number less than 100 individuals, with the largest recorded in our study being 240. When they are disturbed the lack of co-ordination is immediately apparent as they readily divide and subdivide into their small component units.

The herds in the second category are entirely different. The pronounced individuality of family units or extended families is almost entirely submerged within the larger group, although sometimes they can apparently be discerned. All members appear to act as one co-ordinated unit. Such herds frequently number several hundreds and have been recorded numbering up to 1200 individuals (Buss and Savidge 1966). When disturbed these herds behave as do family units, by bunching tightly, and forming huge phalanxes (Fig. 5.5, Plate 5.2). Splitting of these huge groups probably occurs mainly due to the sheer unweildiness of such a formation, or during directive movement.

Analysis of the composition of two large herds in North Bunyoro (by means of aerial photography) indicated that their age structures were similar to that of the general population (Laws 1969b) in that they showed reduced recruitment. It is suggested below that the formation of large herds may be partly or wholly

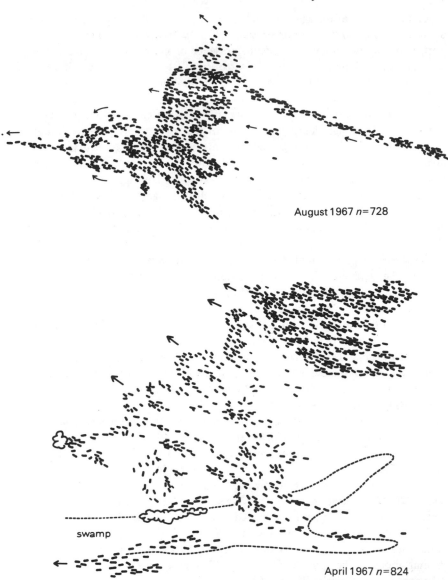

August 1967 *n*=728

April 1967 *n*=824

swamp

Fig. 5.5. Patterns in very large herds (drawn from aerial photographs—individual animals shown).

due to the shooting of matriarchs on control operations. Old females may thus be reduced in numbers or absent from the large herds. Unfortunately we have no direct evidence to support this hypothesis; their presence or absence is not detectable by the method of obtaining the age structure of a sample based on age/length keys applied to aerial photographs (Laws 1969b), which gives only a general indication of the age structure. The female growth curve levels off after about 25 years, and the matriarchs would, if present, form only a very small proportion of the total numbers. Thus the presence or absence of matriarchs in the large herds is an important point which requires further investigation. It could perhaps be resolved by intensive aerial or ground observation.

The co-ordinated herds occur only around the periphery of the elephant ranges in North Bunyoro (Figs 5.2–5.4) and show a considerable degree of permanence. Although fluctuations in size of the large groups evidently occur (probably through division or aggregation into similar herds rather than by attrition or addition of small units and individuals), such herds can always be found in the southern part of the Karuma Controlled Hunting Area, near Rere Hill, in the south-east corner of Murchison Falls Park, and in the vicinity of the Weiga River and to the west of the Park (Figs 5.2–5.4). The two largest of these herds counted (on photographs) in 1965–7 contained 824 and 728 individuals (Fig. 5.5).

We should emphasize that in the course of many daily reconnaissance flights covering the elephant range, large herds were never seen in the central areas of the range, but invariably, when our visitors wanted to see the large herds it was possible to find them around the periphery of the range.

Wing and Buss (1970) describe the movements of four large herds observed on the Butiaba Flats between 1958 and 1963. These numbered 870, 1240 (870 + 370), 1000, and 600, and were tracked over periods of 39, 31, 11, and 25 days respectively. During these periods they remained for the most part within an area of less than 130 square kilometres (50 square miles) between the Weiga and Bubwe Rivers (see Chapter 1, Fig. 1.3).

The herd of 870 elephants was first sighted on 18 July 1963 and it had split into three groups by 22 July, which were tracked until 25 July. During this period it was restricted to a movement of about 16 kilometres (10 miles) up and down the Waisoke River and to about 6·5 kilometres (4 miles) south of this river. The second herd included a recognizable 'crossed-tusk' female and numbered about 370. It was seen on 28 July moving south towards the Waisoke River, where it joined the first herd and moved south to the Sonso River. Between 31 July and 18 August, the herd numbering about 1240 elephants (including the 'crossed-tusk' female which was seen on several occasions) was frequently seen 'milling about on the upper Sonso'. Up to 27 August it was seen on several occasions on the Waisoke River and by 28 August it was north of this river and split into two groups which moved north and south respectively. The latter group (about 750 elephants) later split into several groups and the 'crossed-tusk' cow was seen in a family unit of 12 animals. Thus these two herds wandered in an area of less than 130 square kilometres (50 square miles) for nearly six weeks.

The third herd of about 1000 was first observed on 24 October 1958 south of the Sonso River and its movements were traced from the air. By 31 October it had reached the Waisoke River and split into two equal-sized groups; these then dispersed into smaller groups on 3 November and headed up the Weiga River.

The fourth herd of about 600 was followed from 26 October to 5 November, during which time it 'meandered' in a small area on the Butiaba Flats between the Waisoke and Bubwe Rivers. This herd had been seen by Game Guards in the northern part of the area for two weeks before. By 5 November it was heading north towards the Park boundary. It was therefore in an area of less than 130 square kilometres (50 square miles) for a period of at least 3—4 weeks.

These observations, together with those of Buechner *et al.* (1963) and the Game Department, provide evidence of the former occupation of Butiaba Flats (south of the Waisoke River) by very large herds of elephant. The aerial observations of Buss and Savidge (1966) and ourselves indicate that elephants are now rarely seen south of the Waisoke River. The observations described by Wing and Buss (1970) also provide evidence of very restricted ranges for these herds over fairly long periods. These authors also give details of considerable disturbance to which one of the herds was subjected. Five bulls were shot out of the fourth-described herd and the herd was 'chased with an airplane to obtain photographs'. They also note that 'at least 20 calves had been live-captured from the herd during the previous dry season for commercial sale'. In the capturing technique used the animals were chased by men in vehicles and this causes very great disturbance. It is also relevant that much of the control shooting in and around the Budongo Forest in recent years has probably involved animals comprising these herds.

Brooks and Buss (1962, p. 46) noted that 'a widely known movement of elephants to Butiaba Flats south of the Butiaba-Masindi road was arrested in the late 1930s'. The movement
occurs between April and September [and the route] follows the western edge of Budongo Forest into the southern part of the forest and across the Masindi-Butiaba road into the Siba Forest (in the Waki triangle). Although this movement was arrested before World War II by intensified control operations, elephants have re-established their movements over this route since 1957.

The recent resumption of elephant migrations temporarily arrested in Bunyoro District probably is a direct consequence of the increase and intra-specific competition of elephants in Murchison Falls National Park.

Wing and Buss (1970) subsequently comment 'the drastic restriction of the main migratory routes from Butiaba Flats where these large herds congregated, and their continued circuitous meanderings over rather protracted periods, whether they were severely harassed or left relatively undisturbed, suggests restraint of attempted migration'.

We do not believe there is valid evidence for true migration in these elephants and in our opinion the large herds represent not gatherings for frustrated migrations, but interactions with human interests as a direct result of the restriction of range over a long period. Our frequent reconnaissance flights showed that large herds could be found throughout the year at the periphery of the elephant range. They were especially noticeable and could be seen at a great distance in the open grass-lands in the south-east of the National Park.

The occurrence of these massive herds has been recorded from near Rere Hill and in its general area over an extended period (Anon (1949), p. 9; (1955), para. 388; Buechner *et al.* (1963)). Incomplete descriptions in many of the Game Department Reports suggest that some such herds have frequented this area since 1925 and formed the bulk of the 'migratory' beasts reputed to move seasonally from the former Game Reserve to the Kafu River and back (Chapter 1). There are reports, extending over many years, of massive herds west and south-west of the Park (Anon (1947), para. 42; (1955), p. 57, para. 377; Beuchner *et al.* (1963)).

Records of elephant concentrations shown on the maps presented by Buechner *et al.* (1963), Buss and Savidge (1966), and Buss and Wing (1967) indicate that the main concentrations were to the east and west of the elephant range. Comparison with the results of the present study (Figs 5.2–5.4) shows a considerable contraction of range, especially in the south-west, where control shooting has been heaviest.

There may have been an increase during the past few years in the numbers of large herds in the North Bunyoro population. Buechner *et al.* (1963) recorded large herds of 1000, 1000, 900, 376, and 400 (pp. 42 and 50), mainly to the east of the area (near Rere Hill) and to the west (on Butiaba Flats). Buss and Savidge (1966, pp. 795, 801, 804) record herds of 1240, 430, 300, and 260, the first three in these areas. In all counts they carried out (in 1957–9) only 15 herds contained more than 200 individuals, an average of 1·25 per count. In the four counts carried out in 1963–4, four such herds were sighted, an average of 1 per count. In our three recent counts there were 13 large herds containing over 200 elephants, an average of 4·33 per count. This apparent increase in frequency of large herds since 1963–4 is probably a consequence of the continued progressive contraction of the elephant range (see Chapter 1, Fig. 1.4), especially as a result of the refugee resettlement scheme in this period, which has taken up an area of land on the southern boundary of the elephant range.

North of the River Nile, Buss and Savidge (1966, p. 805) observed that 'near the east central edge of the Elephant Sanctuary a concentration of 1295 elephants formed and reformed into different sized groups during a 25 minute period on May 10, 1964. To classify such concentrations into groups of meaningful size was not feasible'. The occurrence of similar herds ranging in size up to 1000 individuals or more, is known from other localities in Uganda. Thus, Pitman (Anon 1928) records a huge herd in the region of the Kafu River; this reference has already been quoted in Chapter 1. In 1934 R. J. D. Salmon, Game Ranger, observed three herds estimated to number 1000, 700, and 700 elephants respectively in north-western Buganda (Anon 1934, p. 11).

Similar herds have also been recorded from the Tsavo ecological unit, Kenya. One of us (I.S.C.P.) has seen the following herds in the area east of the Tsavo National Park, between August 1960 and January 1963: 200, 200, 1000, 1000,

300–400, 300, 200, 1000, 500, 666, 100, and 200 west of the Tsavo National Park in March 1957. Laws and Watson (unpublished) have observed herds of 650, 250, 400, 700, and 1300 in the eastern part of the Mkomasi Game Reserve, Tanzania; 1000, 250, 560, and 400, near McKinnon Road, Tsavo National Park; and a concentration of 300 near Kibwezi, Kenya. These groups represent re-groupings of three peripheral populations in the Tsavo ecological unit and are not related to migrations but exist throughout the year (Laws 1969b). In the Serengeti National Park, Tanzania, Lamprey, Glover, Turner, and Bell (1967) record 15 herds of over 100 elephants, including 3 numbering over 400 individuals, from three counts in 1965, 1966, and 1967.

All these herds have one factor in common. They are on the peripheries of elephant populations which are in contact with expanding human populations or activity, and there are grounds for believing that they result from the displace-ment of communities, rather than as 'a prelude to intended migration' (Wing and Buss 1970, p. 36). They are apparently not related specifically or causally to environmental differences. This interpretation is supported by the following comment on Salmon's observations of large herds in Buganda (see above). 'At present the big herds prefer the southern part of the area, and that is where the human population is increasing.' A further quotation from another Uganda Game Ranger, who shot elephant intensively from 1900 to the 1930s is 'heavy shooting of elephants does not tend to break up herds. On the contrary, with heavy shooting the tendency is for elephant herds to join up together for self protection, until, in open country, one sees ponderous herds' (Anon 1933, p. 44). (This has also been the experience during heavy cropping of hippopotamus in the Queen Elizabeth Park (Laws, unpublished).) Bere (1961) remarks, 'the tendency is for these great concentrations to occur in valleys in dry weather and may in some way indicate a population surplus to the normal carrying capacity of the area'.

It seems possible that the very large herds may result from a breakdown or change at high densities in a hypothetical elephant behavioural mechanism promoting dispersal on the lines suggested by Wynne-Edwards (1962), possibly based on an heirarchical or territorial pattern. There is at present no evidence in support of this suggestion, but a parallel density related behavioural difference has been observed in populations of topi and Uganda kob in the Queen Elizabeth Park (personal observation) and Uganda kob in the Murchison Falls area and in the Semliki Flats (Buechner 1961; Leuthold, 1966). For the kob single territories are prevalent in low-density populations, but high-density populations are charac-terized by a number of territorial breeding grounds with single territories interspersed between them. Further discussion relevant to this point will be found in Chapter 7.

As a 'rule of thumb' in formulating management policies on limited information, it can be taken that the presence of such large herds indicates a displaced popu-lation, or clan, and artificially high densities. We consider that displacement lead-ing to formation of large herds will certainly result in very serious habitat damage in the absence of management action (which may involve reduction cropping and control of burning (Laws 1970b)).

5.2.   The Budongo Forest

Owing to the closed nature of the habitat, it is much more difficult to study the forest elephants, and aerial counts or direct ground counts are not possible. In order to obtain an estimate of the numbers of elephant using the forest it was therefore necessary, first to examine their movements and distribution throughout the year (by means of several indices of abundance) and then to attempt to relate these indices to changes in the numbers of elephants in the grasslands.

It was formerly thought that the main movement of elephants in relation to the forest was up from the Butiaba Flats into the forest (Buss 1961) and this may well have been the case until recent years, but these herds have now been greatly reduced by control shooting since 1958. Little weight was formerly given to the fact that the distance between the south-east boundary of the Murchison Falls Park and the north-east margin of the forest was only 14·5 kilometres (9 miles) and that the Pabidi Forest occupied part of this zone. It now appears that most of the elephant moving into Budongo in recent years came from this direction.

5.2.1.   *Dropping counts*

In 1964 a pilot study was initiated by the Forest Department with the object of establishing the origin of the elephant entering the forest, the parts of the forest they used, and the seasonal pattern. This initial study continued from September 1964 to August 1966. It made use of the extensive network of roads throughout the forest (see Chapter 11, Plate 11·3) and involved counting (on the fifteenth day of each month) the number of elephant droppings per 201 metres (220 yards) of road, over a total of 84·1 kilometres (52·8 miles) of forest road (Fig. 5.6). The combined dropping mass was counting, not the individual boluses. A concurrent record was kept of the rainfall. Droppings were cleared at each count so the monthly count represented the number accumulated since the previous count. According to Wing and Buss (1970, p. 21) some 94 per cent of droppings produced in a month should be easily recognizable and a further 4·5 per cent barely recognizable.

The dropping index (number of droppings per 220 yards per month) (Fig. 5.7) varied considerably from month to month, but showed a definite pattern, with a marked peak in the dry season (January—March), clearly indicating that more elephants used the forest in the dry months than in the wet season. There was a small subsidiary peak in July—August.

The increase in January was very abrupt. At this time the local people carry out grass burning and there is a definite relation between the grassland burning and elephant movement. In Fig. 5.8 the average monthly dropping indexes and (forest) rainfall figures for the two year period have been compared to demonstrate more clearly the inverse relationship between rainfall and elephant use of

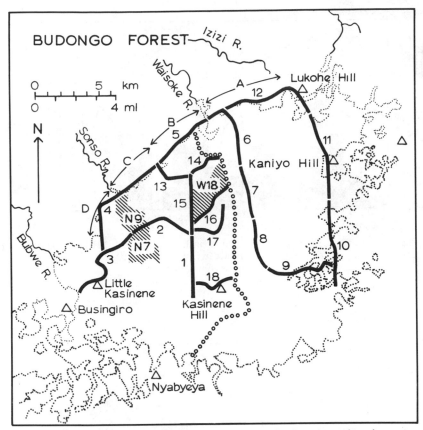

Fig. 5.6. Budongo Forest showing road sectors (1–18) for dropping and track counts; compartments sampled in damage study; road Sectors (A–D) for counts of damaged *Terminalia* trees outside forest. Treated areas are all west of line of circles; dotted line indicates forest edge.

the forest. The peak of elephant numbers in January (as indicated by dropping counts) is clearly correlated with the lowest monthly rainfall, and the combined January–March peak (which accounts for 56 per cent of the droppings counted annually) follows the peak of the dry season. Similarly the secondary peak in elephant numbers coincides with the July minimum in rainfall. Conversely the lowest numbers using the forest are related to, or closely follow, months of high rainfall.

We believe the secondary peak in the dropping counts also represents a real influx of elephant to the forest. Evidently the average level of about 0·1 droppings per 220 yards per month represents the contribution of the 'resident' elephant population and the peak level of 0·645, the seasonal visitors plus 'residents'. Smoothing (in three-month running averages) gives a peak of about 0·5 droppings per unit length of road for the January–March period, suggesting

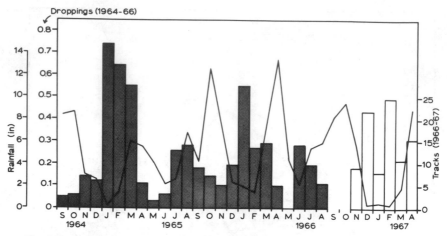

Fig. 5.7. Results of dropping and track counts in Budongo Forest, 1964–7. Shaded histogram–monthly dropping index; unshaded histogram–monthly track counts. The rainfall recorded at Nyabyeya is shown for comparison.

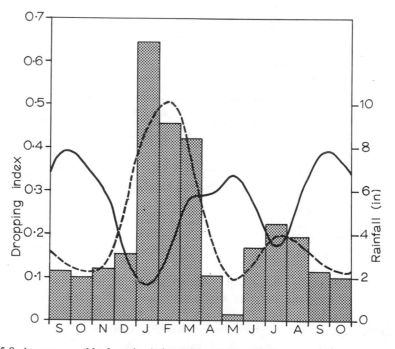

Fig. 5.8. Average monthly dropping index (1964–6). Broken line–smoothed dropping indices; continuous line–smoothed monthly rainfall.

a ratio of 'resident' to seasonal occupation of 1:4. The very low value for droppings recorded in May suggests a possible movement of 'resident' elephants out
of the forest in this month, which would thus occur at a time when nutritive
conditions in the grassland are probably optimal. There was not a similar dispersal
of residents out of the forest in October–November, but the grasses are taller
and coarser then (Chapter 2).

Although the over-all picture was one of increased elephant movement into
the forest associated with decreased rainfall, there were considerable variations in
the counts on the different roads in the forest. The area from the River Waisoke
to Lukohe Hill, in the north, and along the eastern boundary of the Forest
Reserve was found to show most elephant movement. In contrast, movement
across the road between the Sonso and Waisoke Rivers was limited, and only one
large herd crossed into the forest early in the dry season. Large numbers of droppings were recorded in the young regeneration areas and it was noticeable that the
numbers in Budongo Compartment W 21 (Fig. 5.9) rose sharply after felling and

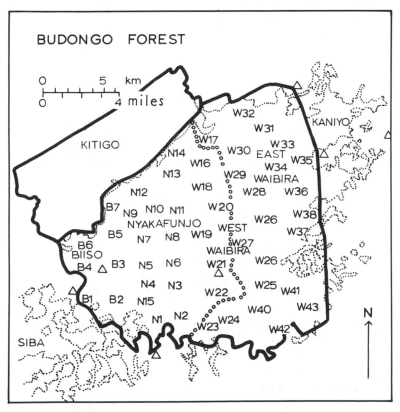

Fig. 5.9. Budongo Forest Reserve, showing forest blocks mentioned in text. The location
of compartments is indicated; forest edge is indicated by dotted line; line of circles represents eastern boundary of treated areas.

treatment (see Chapter 11, Plate 11.3). Very few droppings were recorded in the older treated areas of Biiso and Nyakafunjo.

A controlled shooting scheme in 1966 (with the objective of deterring elephant from entering the forest between the River Waisoke and Lukohe Hill) resulted in a shift of the main movement to the eastern boundary of the reserve, as reflected by the dropping counts. It did not, however, result in a decrease in the numbers of herds entering the forest.

5.2.2. *Track counts*

Although it provided valuable information, the pilot study based on dropping counts was incomplete because it did not cover the area of unfelled and untreated forest, and with the opening up of roads into this forest it was decided to extend the investigation. In November 1966 a new series of counts began.

It was decided to use the number of tracks, rather than droppings, as an index, because it had been noted that when crossing an open track, elephant tended to defecate, and it was felt that tracks would give a truer picture of elephant movement. There is, however, a tendency to assume that there were more elephants present than was really the case. This study again involved the use of the forest roads which were divided into eighteen sections (Fig. 5.6). In each section the numbers of tracks per mile of road were counted, over a total of 99 kilometres (61·5 miles) of roads.

Each counting operation lasted three days with, as far as possible, eight days between successive operations. On the first day the roads were brushed clear of any tracks made since the previous count; on the second day a count of new tracks was made; this was repeated on the third day and the results of the two counts averaged. After each count old tracks were obscured so that they would not be recounted.

Fifteen such counts were carried out over the period from 28 November 1966 to 25 April 1967. The average monthly numbers of tracks have been incorporated in Fig. 5.7, for comparison with the dropping count data of the previous two years, and with the current rainfall. It shows a much more variable pattern than that shown by the dropping count study, probably because it represents only about 8 days movement per month, whereas droppings accumulated over a month. Also it includes areas of unfelled and untreated forest. These areas are regarded by us as transit zones, between forest edge and young regeneration areas (see below), and so the track counts give a more detailed picture of movements within the forest (Table 5.4).

During the track counts a note was made of the estimated sizes of herds entering and leaving the forest, and also the direction of movement. The results showed quite clearly that the elephants tended to enter the forest in large herds, but left the forest in small herds; it would therefore appear that the large herds break up after entering the forest. The large herds are probably composed of smaller herds, aggregated, possibly under the influence of some behavioural

Table 5.4

Budongo Forest: number of elephant tracks counted per mile (2·6 km)

Section	Nov.	Dec.			Jan.			Feb.		Mar.			Apr.			Total
	1	1	2	3	1	2	3	1	2	1	2	3	1	2	3	
1	0·33															0·33
2				0·83							0·84					1·67
3														0·29		0·29
4	1·77		0·46	0·23			0·15			0·15	0·39		0·69	4·54		8·38
5		0·62														0·62
6		0·24		0·82			0·24	0·70	5·06	1·17	0·24					8·47
7			0·93			0·77					0·92					2·62
8	0·15	0·46			0·77		0·62			0·62	0·92				1·75	4·62
9				0·50					2·50	0·83	2·25	0·25	0·16			7·25
10		3·67	4·17	2·00	1·00											11·83
11	1·71		1·00	2·00	0·29											5·00
12		0·74		0·15	0·15				1·03		0·59				0·15	2·81
13					0·50						1·00					1·50
14					2·86				2·28				1·43			6·57
15								1·00								1·00
16		0·40	0·20	0·20	0·60			1·40								2·80
17		0·31		0·15				0·31				0·46				1·23
18							0·60									0·60

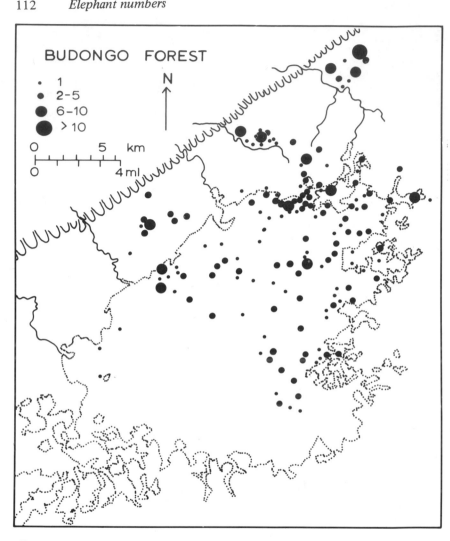

Fig. 5.10. Location of elephant groups shot on control operations in the Budongo Forest and its vicinity, 1966–7. Forest edge indicated by a dotted line; the position of the escarpment is shown.

stress. Where the herds break up after entering the forest is not known, but an observation made in the forest on 21–2 February 1967 suggests that herds retain their initial large size until they pass through the untreated and unfelled forest, and then split up into smaller feeding groups. See also Fig. 5.10.

Analysis of the number of tracks shows two main axes of movement. One is due to a large group moving up from the Butiaba Flats into the forest across Sections 4 and 2 (between the Sonso and Waisoke Rivers) and the other is from the Murchison Falls National Park at the north-eastern boundary of the forest (Sections 6–12). These two patterns appear to be quite distinct.

Buechner *et al.* (1963) concluded that about 1500 elephants were involved in the movement from Butiaba Flats to the Budongo Forest. There are few elephants now left using the Butiaba Flats (probably a result of heavy control shooting and human settlement). Movement from the Butiaba Flats was noted in 1965, 1966, and 1967, during the early part of the dry season (November) and on each occasion over 200 elephants were counted entering the forest. Once they had entered the forest, however, contact with them was lost. It is unlikely that they continued as a large group, and no record was made of such a group leaving the forest.

In mid-April 1967, a second large movement was recorded near this same place. There are several possible explanations. There may have been two separate herds involved, which is unlikely. The first herd may have broken up on entering the forest, passed through into the young regeneration areas, and left the forest by the eastern border: passing round the forest during February and March, it eventually re-formed on the Flats, to enter the forest again when conditions on the Flats deteriorated. This seems very unlikely. Another possibility is that a large herd moved up from the Flats, remained at the edge of the Forest, and left by the same route but in smaller herds, to re-form and re-enter the forest when conditions outside deteriorated. The latter explanation seems most likely as little movement was recorded across road Sections 1 and 15. The dry season of 1966–7 was very severe with only 25 millimetres (1 inch) of rain falling from mid-November to mid-March, so that there was little grass growth after the December burn until the rains started in April.

This second large movement probably represents the survivors of the former Butiaba Flats population of some 1500. They do not figure in any of the aerial counts, possibly having entered the forest before the November and February counts, but they should have been noted in the August count. It seems possible that the control shooting during 1967 may have virtually eliminated them. Observation during future years should confirm whether or not this is so. There is probably now little contact between animals entering the forest from Butiaba Flats and those entering from the Murchison Falls Park.

The second movement pattern from the Murchison Falls Park across the eastern boundary of the forest is quite distinct. The elephants enter across road Sections 10, 11, and 12 (Fig. 5.6) during the early dry season. On the basis of observations made in the forest and its vicinity, many remain at this stage in the forest edge, but some penetrate the forest into the young regeneration areas. The elephants alternate between grassland and forest during this period, but as the dry season progresses so the time spent in grassland is reduced. Instead, elephants alternate between the forest edge and the young regeneration areas, so that by the middle of the dry season this movement back and forth between the edge and regeneration areas is maximal. By the end of the dry season the movements have virtually stopped and the animals are in the young regeneration areas. A fall of rain will encourage elephants to move into the grassland during the dry season. Thus, after a month of no rain from mid-February, during which time no tracks leaving the forest were recorded, 7 millimetres (0·27 inch) of rain fell; within a few days quite a large movement of elephant into grassland was recorded. This again happened during March on two occasions when, after falls of 7 millimetres (0·27 inch) and 10 millimetres (0·40 inch) of rain, movements of elephant into the grasslands were recorded.

Buechner *et al.* (1963, p. 47) comment on elephant movements in relation to the forest as follows:

during the period from late December to late March, the daily rhythm consisted of crepuscular and nocturnal movements to forage in open wooded grasslands surrounding the Budongo Forest on the west, north and east, with diurnal return to the high forest. The areas of wooded grassland most favoured were: (1) the 3-mile wide strip between the Budongo Forest and the Escarpment; and (2) the area between the Budongo and Pabïdi Forests. Failure to observe elephants in these areas during the height of the dry season probably resulted from their daytime preference for the forest.

They suggest that these movements were related to feeding.

There is no evidence to suggest that elephants remained in the unfelled and untreated forest; little movement occurred across Sections 1 and 15 (Fig. 5.6); they passed across Sections 6, 7, and 8 to reach Sections 14, 16, and 17 (the young regeneration areas) and there they stopped.

At the start of the rains there is movement towards the forest edge and away from the young regeneration areas, so that by May there were very few elephants in the forest. Although numbers in the forest drop during the rains from May to November (which is also the peak mating season (Laws 1969a)), some elephants are still in the forest. At this time there is probably a plentiful supply of food available outside the forest and the presence of a local resident population inside tends to support other evidence that there may be a forest elephant, *L. a. cyclotis,* population in Budongo (Chapter 8).

A study of the frequency of movement across roads by elephant, but not necessarily the numbers involved in the movements, gave the results summarized in Table 5.5.

As expected, Sections 6, 7, and 8 were apparently among the busiest, with elephants crossing them on nearly all count periods except the end of the dry season. Movement back and forth over Section 4 tends to confirm that the herd which moves up from Butiaba Flats remains in the forest edge, though split into smaller herds. Movement across Sections 10, 11, and 12 is mainly in the early dry season or after a fall of rain (Table 5.4). Movement across Sections 1 and 15 into the Biiso and Nyakafunjo Blocks is virtually non-existent.

The main elephant movement is into Compartments W 16, W 18, W 19, W 20,

Table 5.5
Local frequencies of elephant movements across roads in the Budongo Forest

| Section | Crossing recorded | | Section | Crossing recorded | |
	Occasions	Percentage of possible recordings		Occasions	Percentage of possible recordings
8	9	60	17	4	27
4	8	53	14	3	20
6	7	47	13	2	13
7	6	40	2	2	13
10	6	40	3	2	13
12	6	40	5	1	7
9	5	34	18	1	7
16	5	34	1	1	7
11	4	27	15	1	7

and the treated part of W 21 (Fig. 5.9); there is a smaller movement into Compartments N 12 and N 13 by the elephants moving up from the Butiaba Flats: why is there no movement into Compartments N 8, N 11, and N 13 from the Waibira side? To answer this we must consider the condition of the forest; the Waibira compartments have been felled in the past six years; they have not developed a closed canopy, nor are they being allowed to, because the herbaceous climber tangle (see Chapter 11, Plate 11.3) is being maintained by continual elephant trampling, and breaking of leading shoots of emergent species. Damage did occur in the Nyakafunjo Block at one stage, but to get there now elephants would have to pass through the young regeneration areas of the Waibira. They probably find enough food in these regeneration areas to hold them there, so that the Nyakafunjo and Biiso Blocks are being protected by the 'front line' of young regeneration in the Waibira Block. These compartments of the Nyakafunjo and Biiso blocks, where felling and treatment did not produce such a marked canopy opening as in the Waibira block, will soon be at a stage where little further elephant damage can be done to them, as they will have closed canopy and will have outgrown the successional danger period when the breaking of leading shoots occurs.

The felling plan for Budongo lays down that the order of felling after Compartment W 22 will probably be Compartments W 23, W 24, W 42, W 40, W 25, W 27, W 26, W 28, W 29, and W 30 (Fig. 5.9). Thus it will be some time (10 years) before those compartments at present bearing the brunt of the elephant attack are succeeded by a new 'front line'. It would seem to be desirable to modify the felling plan so as to advance this 'protection'.

Fig. 5.10 shows the spatial distribution of elephants sampled on control shooting between 1966 and 1967. This distribution does not conflict with the other evidence for two main movements into the forest, a major one from the north-east and a minor one from the west.

5.2.3.   *Number of elephants using the forest*

To put elephant use of the Budongo Forest into perspective, as regards the contribution of these areas to the welfare of the elephant populations of the Murchison Falls National Park, we have attempted a rough estimate of the numbers of elephants that the forest may support. It was not possible with the limited funds and time available to make a precise estimate.

During the shooting operations in the period August 1966 to April 1967, 99 herds were observed and their size recorded.

Herd size	*Number observed*
1	6
2–5	15
6–10	23
11–20	19
21–50	31
51–100	2
over 100	3

This indicated that the average size of the herds was about 25, though this is heavily weighted by the five large herds. However aerial counts showed that the mean herd size in the peripheral high-density zone of the elephant range was 22·5. During the period December 1966 to April 1967, tracks of a total of 128 herds were counted entering or leaving the forest.

Assuming that all animals that entered the forest left it again during these months and did not re-enter, it would appear that approximately 1600 elephant entered the forest during this period (64 × 25). However, if large herds break up after entering the forest and the animals leave in smaller herds, the mean herd size should be less than 25; if we exclude the five large herds the average size was 8; and from aerial counts of a large number of groups in the grasslands the mean group size was 12. During the track counts in the forest, 101 groups were observed averaging 15·8 per group. When analysed according to their location in the forest the mean group size for 32 groups observed on the five peripheral sections (4, 5, 10, 11, and 12; Fig. 5.6) was 24·7, whereas for 69 groups observed in the other (internal) sections it was only 11·7.

The average size of the peripheral groups is the same as for the 99 groups recorded in the surrounding grasslands, during the shooting operations, so these observations confirm that elephants enter the forest in larger herds, averaging 25 animals, but break up into smaller groups within the forest. Five groups observed during the track counts contained 100 or more elephants and these were all peripheral to the forest in location. Furthermore, it was concluded above that there is much movement back and forth within the forest, and it seems probable that many herds cross and recross the peripheral forest roads during this season, possibly following a diurnal pattern (Buechner *et al.* 1963). On this basis, therefore, probably far fewer than 1000 elephant use the forest seasonally. With an average group size of 12 the estimated maximum number would be *ca* 770 (64 × 12).

This order of size estimate receives some support from the aerial counts carried out in the areas outside the forest, and discussed above. The discrepancy between the aerial counts covering Blocks 9, 10, and 11 suggested that only about 300 elephants moved into the forest from these blocks between November 1966 and February 1967; ground observations showed that some 200 elephants entered the forest during the early part of the dry season from the Butiaba Flats in 1965, 1966, and 1967.

It has also been postulated, on the basis of the aerial counts, that some 400 elephants moved in from the north-east, from counting Block 8, between the first two aerial counts. In view of the consistency otherwise shown by these aerial counts, it would be difficult to accept a much higher figure than about 600—1000 for the number of elephants moving into the forest from Blocks 8—11 during the dry season.

An alternative approach to this problem is to consider the area available to elephant and to apply hypothetical elephant densities to this area to estimate the total numbers of elephants using the forest. The felled and treated areas of the Budongo Forest amount to some 41 square kilometres (16 square miles) and there are some 155 square kilometres (60 square miles) of untreated forest between them and the main elephant concentrations. Even if the treated areas (on a year-round basis) supported some 7·7—15·4 elephants per square kilometre (20—40 per square mile), that is, some two or four times the density supported by the surrounding grasslands (which is highly unlikely), they would only support some 300—640 elephants. Even on a seasonal basis it is unlikely that the treated forest areas would support more than this in one month.

The untreated areas (forest edge and closed forest combined) used by elephant can hardly support, on a seasonal basis, an average of more than 3·9 per square kilometre (10 per square mile), that is, a maximal population of 600 elephants. A density of 3·9 per square kilometre (10 per square mile) is very high, even for productive woodland or the forest edge, which are the elephants' preferred habitats: since the forest edge represents a small fraction of the area of untreated forest, and in view of the infrequency of encounters with elephants within the forest, 600 seems too high a figure. Wing and Buss (1970, p. 24), on the basis of eight dropping counts in the Kibale Forest, obtained an average estimate of approximately 3·0 elephants per square kilometre (7·9 elephants per square mile); the range over the eight counts being 1·9—3·8 per square kilometre (5·0—9·8 per square mile). They considered these values unacceptably high and adjusted them downwards. In other areas (not forest) where densities as high as these occur (e.g. Murchison Falls Park, South periphery, Queen Elizabeth National Park, Lake Manyara National Park) the land is overpopulated and serious habitat deterioration is occurring.

On the basis of the evidence presented above, we conclude that between 1000 and 1500 elephant use the forest, the greater part of this use being seasonal, and a lesser amount due to a small 'resident' population. In an attempt to establish the relative sizes of the 'resident' and seasonal use of the forest we have examined two indices of forest use by elephants, the monthly dropping counts (Fig. 5.8) and the monthly numbers shot (Chapter 10, Fig. 10.2).

Considering the dropping counts first, the maximum counts (January–March) average 180, the minimum counts (April–December) average 33, giving a ratio of 5·5:1 between maximum and minimum use. The maximum and minimum numbers shot (expressed as three-month running averages) over the six year period were 153 and 51 respectively, giving a ratio of 3:1. The actual ratio is perhaps nearer 4:1, because dropping counts did not cover the untreated and unfelled forest, and some shooting took place outside the forest (Fig. 5.10), possibly exaggerating the apparent numbers in the forest during May–November.

Applying this to the estimates of total use (1000 and 1500) and rounding off, we get estimates of 750–1100 and 250–400 for the seasonal and 'resident' populations of the Budongo Forest. These values are not at variance with the independent estimates of numbers entering the forest seasonally from the grasslands.

5.3.   Movements between grasslands and forest: conclusions

It appears that there are two routes of elephant movements into the forest, from Murchison Falls National Park and from the Butiaba Flats (Plate 5.5). These movements produce peak numbers of elephants in the forest during the dry season from mid-November to mid-March. In addition there is a small resident group present in the forest throughout the year, which may move out temporarily in May, returning in June. This is supported by earlier observations: 'during May–June, 1958, and again in May, 1959, about 500 elephants were observed in the wooded grasslands peripheral to the Budongo Forest, indicating greater diurnal activity. Apparently there is not a complete exodus of elephants from the Budongo Forest to the Butiaba Flats and Park during the long rains' (Buechner *et al.* 1963, p. 48). The 'residents' would appear to feed almost exclusively in the forest and not to rely on the grasslands to any great extent, except possibly in May.

The majority of elephants that move from the grasslands remain in the forest edge. Those that do penetrate into the forest proceed directly to the young regeneration areas. Towards the end of the dry season, particularly if it has been severe, the elephants remain in the young regeneration areas, but at other times there is a considerable movement back and forth between the forest edge and the young regeneration areas.

Very little movement was noted in the Biiso and Nyakafunjo blocks and it appears that these blocks are now relatively free from elephant use and consequent damage. Nonetheless this situation could rapidly change if the elephant population or its local densities increased, or if the young regeneration areas were made unavailable to elephant.

It is not possible as yet to state accurately how many elephants are in the forest at any one time. It would seem probable that no more than about 925

± 175 entered the forest from the grassland during the period December 1966 to April 1967. It is also probable that a small resident population (of about 325 ± 75 animals) remains in the forest virtually the year round, making a probable total of about 1200 elephant dependent on the forest to a greater or lesser extent; it is considered very unlikely that this total exceeds 1500 animals.

5.4. Summary

The size, distribution, and movements of the elephant population have been studied by analysing the results of three 'complete' counts of the grassland and wooded grassland range, and by means of dropping and track counts in the Budongo Forest. The total numbers counted outside the forests averaged 8135 (range 7779–8713), but various factors influencing the results must be taken into account. These include undercounting, movements between counting blocks and into the forest, and the shooting of some 900 elephants during the period of the study. When allowance is made for these factors it is concluded that in November 1966 the total population was at least 9400, including some 300 forest residents. The total population is thought to have been reduced to at least some 8500 by the end of 1967. A stratified random sample count in 1969 gave an estimate of 9364 ± 2736 (confidence interval for probability $p = 5$ per cent), excluding those elephants in forests at the time of the count.

Numbers in the central part of the range showed a very stable pattern over the period of the study, but the peripheral blocks to the east and south-west indicated a much more variable pattern. This is considered to be due to seasonal movements in relation to the Budongo Forest and the more wooded country at the periphery of their range. Elephant in the peripheral part of the range were more mobile than in the central area. They were at higher densities and often in very large herds. Two categories of these are distinguished: 'close concentrations' which generally number less than 100 animals, and coordinated 'large herds' containing up to 1000 or more. The age structure of large herds is similar to that of the general population, though there may be a lower proportion of matriarchs. They occur only on the periphery of the range, appear to be permanent or semi-permanent, and can always be found in certain areas. There is evidence of an increase in the numbers of 'large herds' in the past decade which is probably related to the continuing contraction of the elephant range. Observations indicate that they may remain in an area of no more than 100 square kilometres for over a month, which implies very intensive habitat use. Occurrences of large herds in other elephant populations show that they are invariably on the periphery of elephant populations that are in contact with expanding human populations or have been displaced from areas they formerly occupied. It is suggested that this involves a breakdown of, or change in, the behavioural mechanisms promoting dispersion.

Elephant numbers and distribution within the Budongo Forest show similar seasonal patterns within three successive years, with a marked influx in the dry season, clearly related to extensive grassland burning at this time. These investigations indicate a ratio of resident to seasonal populations of 1:3 and it is estimated that the resident and seasonal populations number about 300 and 900 respectively. Elephants enter the forest mainly from the north-east and south-west; the latter route was formerly more important, but as a result of intensified control shooting is now minor. Elephant tend to enter the forest in large groups, which break up into smaller groups when inside. The residents appear to feed almost exclusively in the forest and the majority of seasonal immigrants near the forest edge.

6. Sampling the elephant population

6.1. The cropping method

In sampling the elephant population we attempted to remove all sources of bias. This presents difficulties in a mobile animal such as the elephant, but we believe that the method has been successful. For practical and economic reasons it is not possible to treat an elephant population as if we were designing a vegetation survey or a small-mammal trapping operation, and randomize the quadrats or trap lines, so we attempted to randomize the method of collection. It was also particularly important in a National Park to minimize disturbance, and indeed only in this way could such intensive cropping be carried out. These requirements were met by taking complete population units, whether an individual or a group. In this way we obtained a cross-section of the population largely (or perhaps entirely) free from bias, which also simplified subsequent analysis.

Elephants are mobile and herds rapidly change position, so a light aircraft was used to reconnoitre the area and locate the herds. They were then approached on foot and shot at close range (about 10–15 metres), using heavy rifles (0·375, 0·404, 0·416, 0·570 calibre). In the attempt to avoid bias the first unit encountered in the chosen area in each operation was taken, whether it was a single animal, a bull herd, a family unit, or a family herd (Chapter 7). A group had to be small enough to be taken in its entirety and dealt with in the hours of daylight.

As a rule most groups were killed between about 0700 and 1000 hours local time. In practice the maximum size of a group was about 15, although one herd of 29 was taken (Plate 6.1). The average herd size taken was 12. Another requirement was that the animal or group of animals had to be in a favourable locality for hunting, in relation to long grass, bush, and so on, which can reduce the chances of success, particularly when there are small calves present. It had also to be possible to reach the locality of the shooting with lorries so that the carcasses could be utilized.

Although the killing was repugnant to us—as it must be to anyone who has observed elephant groups in the wild—it was necessary for the reasons given above, and discussed elsewhere in this book. The method of killing was humane and very successful and it usually took only 45–90 seconds after the first shot, to drop a complete herd. Of the 800 elephants cropped in this way in North Bunyoro, only on one occasion did a small group—part of a larger group—escape, and these were untouched. This is in marked contrast to the 'poaching' and 'control shooting', formerly and presently practised (Chapters 1 and 10), which still accounts for the deaths of several thousand elephants annually in East Africa. Ivory exports are increasing and 'more elephants are being killed annually than at any time before' (Watson, Bell, and Parker 1972).

In analysing the aerial counts we divided the elephant range into some 300

PLATE 6.1. Cropping an elephant family unit in M.F.P.S. grasslands.

quadrats of 10 square kilometres (3·9 square miles) and in testing for bias of the sample in respect of elephant density, we have deemed the mean densities counted per quadrat to represent the population, and the densities in the quadrats in which the elephant were cropped, to represent the sample density distribution. Some 800 elephants were taken in the Murchison Falls Park, South (185 in November 1965, 15 in February and March 1966, 600 between 23 February and 25 May 1967). The sample came from 56 quadrats, of which all but five were located in the medium-density stratum, comprising 155 quadrats, based on the aerial counts. In terms of numbers of elephant cropped, 749 (94 per cent) came from the medium-density stratum.

The mean elephant density for the three aerial counts was 1·9 per square kilometre (4·9 per square mile) and 3·8 per square kilometre (9·8 per square mile), in the medium- and high-density strata respectively. The mean density of elephants in the actual quadrats from which the cropped sample was taken was 2·32 per square kilometre (6·00 per square mile); the mean for the five in the high-density stratum was 2·33 per square kilometre (6·03 per square mile). The two subsamples are therefore comparable and relate to a medium-density eleph-ant population. Weighted means were also calculated (taking into account the numbers cropped in the separate quadrats) and give an identical mean.

The frequency distribution of densities for the quadrats sampled was analysed and compared with the density distribution of all quadrats in the medium-density stratum. A significance test showed that the two distributions are not significantly different ($\chi^2 = 1 \cdot 21$, 4 degrees of freedom, (d.f.) $p > 87$ per cent). Thus, sampling was not biased with respect to elephant densities in the medium-density stratum. The density distribution, by quadrats, in the high-density stratum was different and this stratum has effectively not been sampled.

The sample was, however, biased in respect of group size, for there was a limit to the size of herd that could be dealt with in a day. Reasons have been given for regarding the larger herds (up to 50–100) as aggregations of smaller groups (Laws 1969b; see also this book, Chapter 7), although 'large herds' (of more than 100 animals) may be qualitatively different. However, the photographic analysis of age structure by means of age/length keys (see Appendix B) does not support the view that they are appreciably different. For both medium- and high- density strata, herds of more than 50 elephants comprised only 2·9 per cent of the total number of herds, and herds of more than 100 animals only 1·2 per cent. But in terms of numbers of elephants these classes comprised 36·6 per cent and 26·1 per cent respectively of the total population. For the medium-density stratum how-ever there were only seven herds of more than 50, comprising 4·6 per cent of all elephants in this stratum.

The frequency distribution of group sizes for the population as a whole (based on the aerial counts in the medium-density stratum) and for the group sizes represented in the sample, are compared in Table 6.1. This shows that both small and very large groups are under-represented in the sample, and groups of 11–15 over-represented. The under-representation of small groups is probably due to a tendency to take family units, rather than bull herds, and larger family units, rather than very small ones whenever a choice presented itself. There were economic reasons for the tendency to select an optimum group size.

We have no means of knowing whether the sample was biased with regard to other unknown factors, but with the method adopted we feel that the bias should have been negligible, and we assume that the sample is representative of the popu-lation occupying the medium-density stratum of Murchison Falls National Park, South.

These comments do not apply to the sample ($n = 303$) from the Budongo Forest and its vicinity. It was collected by Game Guards under the distant supervision of the District Forest Officer (R.C.B.J.) and the Game Department Biologist (P. Martin); it does not represent complete herds, and younger animals (up to *ca* 4 years) are probably under-represented. Thus, in the grassland they tend to be hidden at certain seasons in the tall grass, and in the forest are less likely to be seen at all times, than adults. With this important reservation the method of control shooting was essentially unselective. The spatial distribution of the sample taken in and around the Budongo Forest is illustrated in Chapter 5, Fig. 5.10.

When the distribution pattern of the August 1967 count is compared with that of the February 1967 count (Figs 5.3 and 5.4), a relative scarcity of elephant north of the Zoila River in August is apparent. It is tempting to ascribe this to

Table 6.1

Comparison of group sizes sampled and counted in the medium-density stratum

	Sample				Aerial counts		Summary	
Group size	Bull groups	Family units	Total	%	Total	%	Sample (%)	Count (%)
1	12	6	18	17·5	335	25·1		
2	11	3	14	13·6	147	11·0		
3	4	1	5	4·9	110	8·2	43·7	57·1
4	3	2	5	4·9	83	6·2		
5	2	1	3	2·9	88	6·6		
6	4	6	10	9·7	72	5·4		
7	1	1	2	1·9	83	6·2		
8	1	1	2	1·9	52	3·9	21·3	22·1
9	–	3	3	2·9	41	3·1		
10	–	5	5	4·9	47	3·5		
11	1	7	8	7·8	36	2·7		
12	–	5	5	4·9	43	3·2		
13	–	7	7	6·8	23	1·7	24·4	10·6
14	–	4	4	3·9	28	2·1		
15	–	1	1	1·0	12	0·9		
16	–	–	–	0·0	19	1·4		
17	–	2	2	1·9	20	1·5		
18	–	1	1	1·0	13	1·0	5·8	5·9
19	–	3	3	2·9	14	1·0		
20	–	–	–	0·0	13	1·0		
>20	–	5	5[1]	4·9	58[2]	4·3	4·9	4·3
Total	39	64	103		1337			

Notes. (1) Largest group 29
       (2) Largest group 58

the effects of cropping, for quite large numbers were taken in that area. We have therefore attempted to establish the effect, if any, of intensive cropping operations on the distribution of elephants, confining the analysis to an east-west zone in that part of the range in which cropping took place, but extending southwards to the periphery of the elephant range.

Densities of elephant represented in the three counts, and intensity of cropping, by 10 square kilometres quadrats, have been analysed by ranks related to distance south from the Victoria Nile. The results are presented in Table 6.2. It can be seen that there are large differences between the average densities of the first two counts and the third count. The distribution of sampling intensity is skewed with a peak near the river. However, the discrepancies between the two sets of counts are lower in the region of cropping (*ca* 1·0 per square kilometre) than further south (*ca* 1·5–2·0 per square kilometre). It therefore appears that seasonal differences in eleph-

Table 6.2

Elephant density and sampling intensity per 10 square kilometre quadrat in 18 ranks south of the Victoria Nile, central area

Quadrat rank	Count density			Sampling intensity
	Average N + F	A	Average (N + F) − A	
1	19·4	13·2	6·2	2·4
2	17·8	8·7	9·1	9·6
3	21·4	8·8	12·6	18·8
4	23·7	12·6	11·1	11·0
5	32·1	22·4	9·7	4·4
6	30·6	26·2	4·4	3·4
7	32·8	29·2	3·6	5·1
8	33·0	23·4	9·6	5·3
9	33·9	19·2	14·7	1·8
10	28·9	16·3	12·6	2·4
11	32·7	19·3	13·4	2·0
12	39·2	18·6	20·6	0·0
13	44·3	22·1	22·2	0·0
14	30·5	12·2	18·3	0·0
15	18·3	5·3	13·0	0·0
16	28·7	6·9	21·8	0·0
17	50·6	11·2	39·4	0·0
18	27·8	10·3	17·5	0·0

Notes.   Data from three counts, November (N) February (F) August (A), and distribution of 597 elephants cropped between the February and August counts.

ant distribution (compounded by possible errors in counting) have obscured any effect of cropping on distribution due to removal or disturbance. See also the remarks on seasonal change in group size.

In any case we consider that disturbance due to cropping was negligible, a conclusion supported by our continued air and ground observations during the cropping, and from the fact that it was possible to take nearly 600 elephant during a period of only three months, in a very restricted area (*ca* 430 square kilometres, 170 square miles). The numbers cropped averaged about 1·4 per square kilometre (3·6 per square mile) over-all, and 3·0 per square kilometre (7·8 per square mile) in the quadrats actually sampled.

The density distributions suggest a shift towards the north in August notwithstanding the cropping there, whereas the higher densities in November–February are to the south. It is likely that this is related to the vegetation and rainfall patterns in time and space. Except in the immediate vicinity of the Nile, where competition between elephant and hippopotamus is intense, woody vegetation is more abundant to the south, illustrated by the aerial photographic transects S 5 and S 6 (Chapter 11). The higher densities there occur in the dry season (November/February) when nutritional conditions are less favourable in the grassland. Conversely the increasing density in the grassland occurs in August, which is a wet month, when nutritional conditions are less limiting there. Clearly this pattern can only be confirmed (or rejected) when the results of more counts spread over the whole year are available, but is in line with the seasonal movement into the Forest already demonstrated.

As well as the 1200 elephants cropped in M.F.P.N., three additional samples, each of 300 elephants collected in a similar way are available for comparison. They were cropped in the Tsavo National Park, Kenya (T.N.P.) in August 1966 and the Mkomasi Game Reserve (East), Tanzania (M.K.E.) in March-April 1968 and in the Mkomasi Game Reserve (Central) (M.K.C.) in May 1969, at the request of the Trustees of the Kenya National Parks and the Tanzania Game Department respectively.

6.2.   Information recorded and material collected

After death a serial number was written on the tusks with a felt marker pen, and later they were permanently numbered using a metal punch. The same number was given to a *pro forma* sheet relating to that elephant (Plate 6.2). Date, location, sex, and herd composition were recorded. The location was also plotted on a 1:125 000 scale map of the area.

Other information recorded included body measurements, tusk measurements (Plate 6.3), organ weights, reproductive status, pathology, and any interesting anomalies. A large quantity of material was collected for subsequent study, including as a routine, blood, milk, urine, eye lens, stomach contents, histological

PLATE 6.2. Dealing with dead elephants. *Terminalia* woodland behind, M.F.P.N.

PLATE 6.3. Elephant ivory arranged by elephant groups as cropped, T.N.P.

material, and lower jaws for age determination. All records were entered on *pro forma* field data sheets and a duplicate copy was made of each. One set of all records is held by Wildlife Services Ltd., and one set by R.M.L.

Full details of records, material collected, and its fixation and treatment are given in Appendix B.

6.3.   Age determination

The key to the analysis of the material obtained is the availability of a simple, rapid, and reliable method of age determination. Laws (1966) described thirty age groups related to the progress of eruption and wear of the six teeth on each side of the lower jaw.

The correct identification of the teeth in wear and erupting is critical (because only two teeth in the series of six are visible at any one time) and several methods of checking the identification were described, the most useful of which involves comparing a length/width plot (or the width alone) of the tooth in question against a graph showing the scatter of length/width for each of the mandibular teeth in the series M_1–M_6. In a more detailed later study (Laws, unpublished) of a larger sample in which the sex was known, it was shown that when data differentiated by sex are plotted, for each sex there is no overlapping between the scatter clusters representing successive teeth in the series M_1–M_5, though there is overlap between M_5 and M_6. Hanks (1969a) has also shown this is true of female elephant in Zambia. In the unpublished study the developmental process and chronology of tooth development has been described and figured.

Chronological ages were assigned to the relative age groups and checks on their validity presented. An important piece of the evidence concerned the presence of ridges on the tooth roots, which were shown to follow an annual (seasonal) pattern in the early years, and presumably later. The chronological ages assigned were not arbitrary, but were based on these assumed annual increments. A correlation between eye-lens weight and age has been demonstrated (Laws 1967b) and there were no significant differences between samples from two very dissimilar habitats. In the present study ages were estimated in the field with cleaned mandibles, using the Figs 1–7 of Laws (1966) as a guide. Ages were allocated to the nearest year or half-year or less, by interpolation between the groups figured. Very occasionally the dental age varied bilaterally; in these cases the average of the two estimates of chronological age was taken.

The presence of abnormal seventh molars, which are visible in 10 per cent of elephants in which erruption of M_6 is complete or almost complete, has been described (Laws 1966, and unpublished). In estimating the age of such animals the M_7 is discounted and the age assigned as if the M_6 were the last tooth. As a field check, shoulder heights were plotted against age and for any anomalous points the jaw was re-examined. The few anomalous results were immediately re-examined and usually, but not invariably, assigned alternative ages. Subsequently plots of other age-dependent characters (tusk size, organ weights, reproductive parameters etc.) showed remarkable consistency (Laws 1967a, 1969a, 1969b, unpublished; Laws and Parker 1968; McCullagh and Lewis 1967; this book) and independent internal checks of certain parameters also support the general validity of the ages assigned.

Some additional support for the validity of the method comes from three known age elephants, although only one was a wild animal.

1. The captive female African elephant 'Dicksie', recently died in the London Zoo, aged 27 years. Short (1969) examined the dentition and estimated her age, on the basis of the above criteria, as 28 years.

2. In October 1971 one of us (R.M.L.) was able to examine the jaw of the male elephant 'Peter Pan' which died in the Brookfield Zoo, Chicago. The fourth mandibular tooth was fully in wear and his age was therefore estimated at 15 years. He was received in the Zoo on 5 July 1957, when he was said to be six months old and died on 28 May 1969. Thus, if the estimated age on arrival was correct he was about 12½ years old at death. If the estimate of age on arrival was low, which is quite possible, then the estimated age would be closer to the true age.

3. The wild male elephant 'Moonflower' and his mother 'Dustbin Nellie' were well known from their regular visits to Paraa Lodge, Murchison Falls National Park. After death his lower jaw was recovered (Plate 6.4). The Park records indicate that 'Moonflower' was born about January—February 1961 and he was shot in August 1969, having become a nuisance, aged 8 years and 6 or 7 months. The age based on our criteria is 8—9 years (Laws 1966, group VIII, Fig. 3)— very close to the known age.

Other age criteria for the African elephant are available (Johnson and Buss 1965; Krumrey and Buss 1968; Sikes 1966a, 1968a) but are not very suitable for application in the field and are different in each case from those employed in the present study. We believe that Johnson and Buss (1965) may have placed too great reliance on the body growth of captive animals (which may be anomalous) in assigning ages to dental stages. Sikes' (1966a) method assumed that the number of lamellae is constant for each tooth in the series, whereas Laws (1966) showed that there was considerable variation and overlap. Also she did not assign chronological ages, being more cautious than us.

Only future work can provide the information needed to calibrate the methods and to decide on which is the most reliable. Thus, although we feel reasonably confident that our age estimations are valid, the results we describe below (Chapters 8, 9, and 10) are subject to the necessary reservation that final proof of the chronology assigned to the age groups is lacking.

6.4. Summary

Information and material was obtained from 2000 elephant cropped in the National Park and some 300 shot on control operations in the vicinity of the Budongo Forest as well as 900 examined from three populations in Kenya and

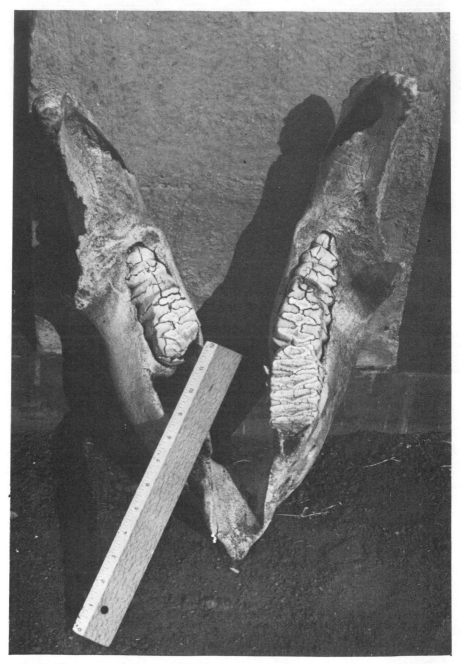

PLATE 6.4. Lower jaw of 'Moonflower', born January/February 1961, died August 1969, aged 8½ years (photograph R. J. Wheater).

Tanzania. The results presented here relate mainly to 800 cropped in the southern sector of the Murchison Falls Park in 1965, 1966, and 1967.

The techniques used in sampling the elephant populations have been described. A possible source of bias was the selection of particular classes of animals, but this was virtually eliminated by taking complete population units (individuals or groups) which also minimized disturbance to the survivors. The method was successful and humane; sampling was confined to the medium-density zone and was not biased with respect to elephant densities there, but biased towards lower group sizes. Since larger groups have been shown to be aggregations of smaller groups it is assumed that the sample was representative of the population in the medium-density zone. However, in the Budongo Forest sample, young animals were under-represented.

Individual ages were determined from replacement and wear of teeth. Information recorded included body measurements, body weights, tusk weights and dimensions, stomach fill, and organ weights (including brain, kidneys, heart, lung, spleen, thyroids, adrenals, mammary glands, ovaries, uterus, conceptus, embryo or foetus, testes, seminal vesicles, prostate, and bulbo-urethral glands). Placental scar counts were recorded and observations made on hearts and aortae. Material collected included histological material from reproductive and endocrine organs, eye lenses, stomach samples, whole blood, serum, milk, depot fat, urine, and lower jaws. Sperm smears, ovaries, and female tracts were examined in the field for reproductive status.

7. Distribution and social organization

For various reasons, planned observations on elephant behaviour were not part of the programme described in this book, but in the course of the field work various manifestations of elephant behaviour were observed and are described where relevant. There is available another source of factual quantitative information on the organization of elephant populations, namely observations on distribution, densities, and social structure, which will be discussed in this chapter.

7.1. Elephant densities

7.1.1. *Over-all distribution*

The broad spatial distribution of elephant numbers during the three aerial counts has been presented in Chapter 5 and we can now examine the distribution in terms of densities. In order to transform the raw data to density data, an overlay grid of 10 square kilometre (3·9 square mile) quadrats, covering the elephant range, was constructed, using the 1:125 000 map. The numbers recorded in each quadrat in each of the three counts were extracted from the map and converted to densities per square kilometre. They were also summed over the three counts for each quadrat, and converted to mean densities.

The number of quadrats covering the elephant range (as indicated by distribution during the three aerial counts) is 290, but in determining the area occupied by the elephant populations three discrete occupied quadrats (each with a single large herd in one count), to the south-east and south-west, have been excluded and a correction has been made for the area of the quadrats overlapping the Victoria Nile (most of which are appreciably less than 10 square kilometres in area). A quadrat with zero density in all three counts has been included only if it is surrounded by quadrats which show positive occurrence during at least one count.

The estimated area of the elephant range is therefore 2727 square kilometres (1053 square miles). To this must be added the area of the Budongo Forest Reserve (excluding Siba and Kitigo, now effectively outside the elephant range, 364 square kilometres (141 square miles)), and a corridor of about 100 square kilometres (39 square miles) running from north-east to south-west, connecting the National Park and Budongo Forest. This gives a range of approximately 3200 square kilometres (1235 square miles). Thus, for a combined population of 9400 elephants the average density was about 2·9 per square kilometre (7·5 per square mile); by the end of 1967 it was probably down to about 2·7 per square kilometre (6·9 per square mile), due to cropping and control shooting. The stratified random sample count indicated a mean density of about 3·5 per square kilometre (9·0 per square mile).

This is very much higher than previously reported for this and other large elephant populations in Uganda and elsewhere. Thus, for the North Bunyoro population, 1963/64, the estimated average density was 1·7 per square kilometre (4·5 per square mile); for the Tangi-Karuma area, 1963/64, 1·1 per square kilometre (2·8 per square mile); for Queen Elizabeth National Park, 1963—4, 0·8 per square kilometre (2·2 per square mile) (Buss and Savidge 1966), 1966, 1·9—2·3 per square kilometre (5—6 per square mile) (count of 3884 exclusive of the Maramagambo Forest, in September 1966 (Field 1966)); for Tsavo National Park, East 0·5 per square kilometre (1·4 per square mile) (Glover 1963); for Tsavo National Park, 0·7 per square kilometre (1·9 per square mile) (Sheldrick, unpublished), 0·9—1·4 per square kilometre (2·3—3·5 per square mile) (Laws 1969b); Kruger National Park, 0·12 per square kilometre (0·32 per square mile), range in several subareas 0·01—1·33 per square kilometre (0·02—3·44 per square mile) (Pienaar, Wyk, and Fairall 1966); Luangwa Valley, Zambia 0·07—0·30 per square kilometre (0·17—0·78 per square mile) (Patton 1968), 0·5—1·4 per square kilometre (1·3—3·6 per square mile) (Food and Agriculture Organization 1968). Over smaller areas higher densities have been reported; in the Kibale forest (560 square kilometres, 216 square miles) 3·1 per square kilometre (7·9 per square mile), (Wing and Buss 1970), and in Lake Manyara National Park (91 square kilometres, 35 square miles of dry land) over 4·6 per square kilometre (12 per square mile) (Douglas-Hamilton 1972). Even so, subareas of comparable or greater size in the North Bunyoro elephant range have higher densities of elephants than these.

Let us examine the homogeneity of the density distribution over that part of the elephant range which lies outside the Budongo Forest, in terms of average use. In the discussion below it is assumed that the three aerial counts provide accurate data on actual numbers of elephant. This is not strictly true, but is probably a reasonable assumption in view of the close agreement between the three counts (taking movements, cropping etc. into account) and the stratified random sample estimate.

The densities per quadrat are shown for the August 1967 count and for the three counts combined in Figs 7.1 and 7.2. Clearly there is a wide range of densities, as might be expected, but in general quadrats with high densities lie on the periphery of the population as a crescent, surrounding a central zone, characterized by medium densities. This high-density zone corresponds to the distribution of large herds and concentrations (Figs 5.2—5.4). In the further analysis the data have been classified in two strata, a medium-density stratum and a high-density stratum, the boundary between them having been fixed by reference to the density pattern and to the distribution maps. This boundary is arbitrary, and high and medium densities in fact intergrade along it. However, as we shall see, the elephant populations in the two strata defined by it show different characteristic properties. For the moment it is sufficient to note that the mean densities of elephant differ and that the group size frequencies also differ in the two strata. The average density for the medium-density stratum is 1·9 per square kilometre

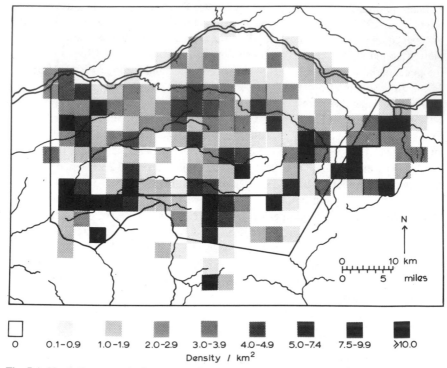

Fig. 7.1. North Bunyoro elephant range showing elephant densities per 10 square kilometre quadrat, August 1967 aerial count. National Park boundary and boundary between medium- and high-density strata are shown.

Density / km²: 0   0.1–0.9   1.0–1.9   2.0–2.9   3.0–3.9   4.0–4.9   5.0–7.4   7.5–9.9   ⩾10.0

(4·9 per square mile); for the high-density stratum 3·8 per square kilometre (9·8 per square mile).

The frequency distribution of densities per quadrat for the three counts are presented in Tables 7.1 and 7.2. The differences between the individual monthly density distributions (χ^2) are highly significant ($p < 1$ per cent) as might be expected from the differences between the count totals. The data from the three counts can be combined in two ways. First, by adding the calculated density distributions for each of the three counts and dividing by three; and secondly, by summing the separate counts per quadrat, taking the mean and converting these means to densities. The former gives a smoother hypothetical average instan- taneous population density distribution; the latter an estimate of approximate distribution of elephant usage per quadrat over a period of time (the combined period of the counts). Obviously a larger number of counts would lead to greater accuracy, particularly for the latter estimates.

All distributions when compared with the theoretical Poisson distributions were clearly non-random. This was also suggested by the track densities over the aerial transects (Chapter 11), and is to be expected from the social organization

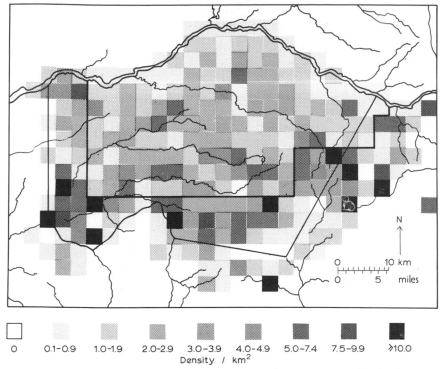

Fig. 7.2. North Bunyoro elephant range showing mean elephant densities for the three aerial counts. National Park boundary and boundary between medium- and high-density strata are shown.

of elephant communities; the spatial distribution of herds is also strongly clumped (see below).

We have mentioned that the density strata have been arbitrarily defined. An earlier analysis taking a slightly more peripheral line of demarcation between the two density strata gave an even higher mean density (4·0 per square kilometre, 10·4 per square mile) for the peripheral crescent. In fact there appears to be a density gradient from the River Nile southwards. Mean densities per quadrat were calculated by summing the total number of elephant counted within each quadrat during the three counts and reducing this total to an average density. For the ranks of squares located 1, 2, 3, . . . 18 quadrats south of the River Nile, mean densities were calculated from the original density figures. Eight peripheral columns have been omitted because they introduce uncharacteristically high densities near the Nile, where the crescent of high densities approaches the river (Fig. 7.2).

The results are presented in Fig. 7.3. It can be seen that there is an increase in elephant density as we progress southwards from the river, from about 1·1 per square kilometre at the Nile banks rising to a peak of about 4·5 per square

Table 7.1

Elephant densities per 10 square kilometre quadrat during three aerial counts; medium-density stratum

Density /10 km²	November 1966		February 1967		August 1967		Combined average (1)		(2)	
	No.	%	No.	%	No.	%	No.	%	No.	%
0	25	16·1	16	10·3	47	30·3	29·3	18·9	5	3·2
1– 5	18	11·6	18	11·6	11	7·1	15·7	10·1	8	5·2
6–10	17	11·0	17	11·0	13	8·4	15·7	10·1	24	15·5
11–15	20	12·9	21	13·5	19	12·3	20·0	12·9	22	14·2
16–20	14	9·0	16	10·3	13	8·4	14·3	9·2	26	16·8
21–25	12	7·7	14	9·0	12	7·7	12·7	8·2	21	13·5
26–30	12	7·7	11	7·1	6	3·9	9·7	6·3	17	11·0
31–35	4	2·6	9	5·8	6	3·9	6·3	4·1	6	3·9
36–40	8	5·2	6	3·9	8	5·2	7·3	4·7	7	4·5
41–45	5	3·2	7	4·5	2	1·3	4·7	3·0	2	1·3
46–50	4	2·6	4	2·6	4	2·6	4·0	2·6	6	3·9
51–55	5	3·2	1	0·6	0	0·0	2·0	1·3	5	3·2
56–60	1	0·6	1	0·6	1	0·6	1·0	0·6	3	1·9
61–65	2	1·3	3	1·9	5	3·2	3·3	2·1	2	1·3
66–70	0	0·0	1	0·6	1	0·6	0·7	0·5	1	0·6
>70	8	5·2	10	6·5	7	4·5	8·3	5·4	0	0·0
Total	155		155		155		155·0		155	

Notes. (1) Separate density distributions added
(2) Separate counts per quadrat summed and densities calculated

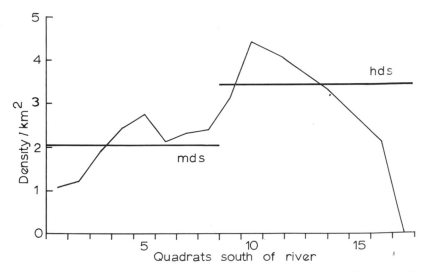

Fig. 7.3. Mean elephant densities at increasing distances from the Victoria Nile (see text). Mean values for medium- and high-density strata (mds and hds) are indicated.

Table 7.2

Elephant densities per 10 square kilometre quadrat during three aerial counts;
high-density stratum

Density /10 km^2	November 1966		February 1967		August 1967		Combined average (1)		(2)	
	No.	%	No.	%	No.	%	No.	%	No.	%
0	54	40·9	47	35·6	59	44·7	53·3	40·4	8	6·1
1– 5	14	10·6	11	8·3	7	5·3	10·7	8·1	17	12·9
6–10	12	9·1	7	5·3	8	6·1	9·0	6·8	17	12·9
11–15	3	2·3	8	6·1	7	5·3	6·0	4·6	13	9·8
16–20	2	1·5	7	5·3	9	6·8	6·0	4·6	6	4·6
21–25	4	3·0	6	4·6	5	3·8	5·0	3·8	6	4·6
26–30	3	2·3	9	6·8	5	3·8	5·7	4·3	10	7·6
31–35	3	2·3	3	2·3	3	2·3	3·0	2·3	7	5·3
36–40	6	4·6	3	2·3	1	0·8	3·3	2·5	7	5·3
41–45	3	2·3	1	0·8	2	1·5	2·0	1·5	6	4·6
46–50	2	1·5	2	1·5	1	0·8	1·7	1·3	4	3·0
51–55	2	1·5	3	2·3	1	0·8	2·0	1·5	7	5·3
56–60	3	2·3	2	1·5	2	1·5	2·3	1·7	3	2·3
61–65	1	0·8	0	0·0	2	1·5	1·0	0·8	4	3·0
66–70	2	1·5	1	0·8	2	1·5	1·7	1·3	2	1·5
>70	18	13·6	22	16·7	18	13·6	19·3	14·6	15	11·4
Total	132		132		132		132·0		132	

Notes. (1) Separate density distributions added
(2) Separate counts per quadrat summed and densities calculated

kilometre and then declining again. There is a considerable smoothing effect
inherent in the treatment, but a step between medium- and high-densities is
apparent. The average density over the first eight rows of quadrats is 2·06 per
square kilometre and for the next nine, 3·46 per square kilometre, values which
approximate to the over-all means for medium- and high-density strata presented
above. These density levels have been inserted in Fig. 7.3.

It seems likely that the low densities (< 1·5 per square kilometre, < 4 per
square mile) near the Nile banks reflect competition with hippopotamus, for the
average range of hippopotamus grazing is about 3 kilometres (2 miles) inland from
the river. Along the stretch of river bounding the area to the north, hippopotamus
grazing densities averaged at least 16 per square kilometre (41 per square mile)
in April 1967 above the Murchison Falls and an estimated 21 per square kilometre
(55 per square mile) below the Falls in 1963 (Chapter 4). In terms of standing
crop biomass these are equivalent to average elephant densities of 9 per square
kilometre and 12 per square kilometre respectively, in addition to the elephant
densities already recorded. Thus the riverine strip is very heavily used. Hippopotamus create short-grass areas, utilized by antelopes and other herbivores, but
unsuitable for elephant feeding. The aerial observations and photographic tran-

sects indicated that widespread erosion commonly extended to 5 kilometres (3 miles) inland from the river.

The significance of large herds in North Bunyoro and in other elephant ranges has already been discussed in Chapter 5. The common factor wherever they occur is that they are at the periphery of the elephant range and adjacent to areas of human settlement or other activity; they result from displacement of elephant populations or 'clans'. In North Bunyoro the same common factor is involved in their distribution and the high-density stratum (and distribution of large herds) cannot be shown to be specifically related to more favourable environmental conditions—at first sight a possible alternative. Thus, in North Bunyoro, high densities and large herds are associated with a wide range of physiographic situations and soil types; with a wide range of rainfall (762—1270 mm, 35—50 in annually); and with a wide range of vegetation quality and quantity, comprising open grassland, wooded grassland, woodland and bushed grassland, and swamp. Nor are they closely related to the distribution of standing water.

The medium-density stratum probably represents a situation which is undoubtedly closer to the natural relation between elephant social organization and environment than in the high-density stratum. Even here, in view of the now almost complete habitat conversion (Chapter 11), and the continued decline of the population (Chapter 10), the densities obtaining (1·9 per square kilometre, 4·9 per square mile) are evidently too high to permit the woody vegetation to survive or expand. Even more so is this the case in the high-density zone.

Extrapolating from these results suggests a possible management application of the findings on density distributions. In view of the smaller mean group size in low-density populations one might find the long-term average density frequency distributions in such a population to approach more closely a random (Poisson) or more regular distribution. In estimating optimum elephant population densities (carrying capacities) for a series of areas it would be extremely useful if one could eliminate the variables related to habitat type, rainfall, etc. Thus, the optimum carrying capacity in terms of elephant for *Commiphora* bush characteristic of the low-rainfall zones of East Africa is probably less than the optimum for *Terminalia* woodland characteristic of wetter zones. If similar data on a number of elephant populations of varied densities in different habitats can be obtained, the density-- frequency distributions might prove to be useful in establishing empirically whether (in a more or less uniform habitat or habitat stratum) the elephant population exceeds carrying capacity.

7.1.2.   *Group and single animal density distributions*

In the previous section we examined the density distribution of elephants over the range in terms of numbers of animals per unit area. Let us now look at the density distribution in terms of population units or groups, per unit area, irrespective of group size. Taking the same boundary between the medium- and high-density strata, the average numbers of groups per quadrat are 2·91 and 1·71 for the respective strata (range 0—13 per 10 square kilometre quadrat within each stratum), that is, 0·29 and 0·17 groups per square kilometre. In this analysis, single animals, being discrete population units, have also been classed as groups.

The frequency distributions of group densities by count and by strata are presented in Tables 7.3 and 7.4. The August distribution for the medium-density stratum is markedly different from the earlier two counts, showing in particular a very much higher proportion of zero records. This discrepancy is similar to that shown by the earlier elephant density distributions (Tables 7.1 and 7.2) and may be due to the cropping of nearly 600 animals in this stratum between the last two counts. This may also have slightly affected the results for the high-density stratum, which indicate an appreciably higher number of quadrats of zero elephant density for this count. It is, however, possible that natural seasonal changes are also involved.

At any one time the spatial distribution of elephant groups is strongly clumped. In Table 7.5 the 'instantaneous' frequency distributions for the three counts have been summed to produce a combined 'instantaneous' distribution pattern. Negative binomial distributions have been fitted to these data. For the medium-density stratum the negative binomial is a reasonably fair fit. The mean group density per quadrat is 2·91; the calculated value for k is 1·900 and on the null hypothesis,

Table 7.3

Frequency distribution of elephant group densities per 10 square kilometre quadrat, recorded during three aerial counts; medium-density stratum

Numbers of groups per quadrat	November (N) 1966 No.	February (F) 1967 No.	August 1967 No.	Combined average				N + F	
				(1)		(2)		(3)	
				No.	%	No.	%	No.	%
0	26	·17	48	91	19·6	10	6·5	43	13·9
1	23	21	34	78	16·8	23	14·8	44	14·2
2	26	26	21	73	15·7	39	25·2	52	16·8
3	24	19	18	61	13·1	28	18·1	43	13·9
4	16	16	12	44	9·5	27	17·4	32	10·3
5	11	20	10	41	8·8	16	10·3	31	10·0
6	12	13	5	30	6·5	5	3·2	25	8·1
7	10	10	1	21	4·5	7	4·5	20	6·5
8	´4	3	3	10	2·2	0	0·0	7	2·3
9	1	6	2	9	1·9	0	0·0	7	2·3
10	0	1	0	1	0·2	0	0·0	1	0·3
11	2	2	1	5	1·1	0	0·0	4	1·3
12	0	0	0	0	0·0	0	0·0	0	0·0
13	0	1	0	1	0·2	0	0·0	1	0·3
Total	155	155	155	465		155		310	

Notes. (1) Separate group distributions added (November, February, and August)
(2) Separate numbers of groups per quadrat summed and average per quadrat over the three counts calculated
(3) Separate group distributions added (November and February only)

Table 7.4

Frequency distributions of elephant group densities per 10 square kilometre quadrat recorded during three aerial counts; high-density stratum

Number of groups per quadrat	November 1966 No.	February 1967 No.	August 1967 No.	Combined average (1) No.	(1) %	(2) No.	(2) %
0	51	47	61	159	40·1	37	28·0
1	31	32	30	93	23·5	39	29·5
2	11	15	15	41	10·1	22	16·7
3	14	12	11	37	9·4	14	10·6
4	6	12	6	24	6·1	11	8·3
5	5	4	2	11	2·8	3	2·3
6	5	4	1	10	2·5	4	3·0
7	2	1	4	7	1·8	1	0·8
8	3	3	1	7	1·8	1	0·8
9	2	0	0	2	0·5	0	0·0
10	1	1	0	2	0·5	0	0·0
11	0	0	0	0	0·0	0	0·0
12	0	1	1	2	0·5	0	0·0
13	1	0	0	1	0·3	0	0·0
Total	132	132	132	396		132	

Notes. (1) Separate group frequency distributions added
(2) Separate numbers of groups per quadrat summed and average per quadrat over the three counts calculated

$p = 9-10$ per cent. For the high-density stratum the negative binomial is a very good fit. The mean group density per quadrat is $1·71$; the value obtained for k is $0·786$ and $p = 44$ per cent. According to Southwood (1966), values of k are generally in the region of 2 and fractional values of k lead into the logarithmic series.[†]

What can we say about the over-all use of the elephant range? Although it certainly would be preferable to have more than three sets of data to work with, the over-all distribution of groups throughout the elephant range over the three counts has been studied by comparing the combined data from the three counts. Thus, for each quadrat, the mean number of groups per count recorded in it during the three counts has been calculated and frequency distributions drawn up for the medium- and high-density strata separately (Tables 7.3 and 7.4, column (2)). These have been compared with the theoretical Poisson distributions corresponding to the respective means. For the medium-density stratum the Poisson distribution model is a very good fit (9 d.f.; $\chi^2 = 9·225$, $p = 42$ per cent), but the Poisson distribution does not fit the high density stratum data (3 d.f.; $\chi^2 = 18·283$, $p < 0·1$ per cent); even when three counts are averaged the high-density pattern is still highly clumped.

†We are indebted to Mr. K. Lakhani, Biometrics Section, The Nature Conservancy, London, for fitting the negative binomial models in Tables 7.5 and 7.6.

Table 7.5

Comparison of observed and fitted negative binomial frequency distributions of group densities in the two strata. 'Instantaneous' distribution summed ((1) in Tables 7.3 and 7.4)

Number of groups per quadrat	Medium-density stratum		High-density stratum	
	Observed	Negative binomial	Observed	Negative binomial
0	91	79·6	159	159·7
1	78	91·5	93	86·0
2	73	80·3	41	52·6
3	61	63·2	37	33·5
4	44	46·8	24	21·7
5	41	33·4	11	14·2
6	30	23·3	10	9·4
7	21	15·9	7	6·2
8	10	10·7	7	4·2
9	9	7·1	2	2·8
10	1	4·7	2	1·9
11	5	3·1	0	1·3
12	0	2·0	2	} 1·4
13	1	1·3	1	
≥14	0	2·3	0	1·2
Total	465	465·2	396	396·0

Notes. (1) Medium-density stratum: 12 d.f.; $\chi^2 = 18\cdot876$; $p = 9$–10 per cent; $k = 1\cdot900$; $k = $ dispersion parameter of negative binomial distribution.
(2) High-density stratum: 11 d.f.; $\chi^2 = 11\cdot002$; $p = 44$ per cent; $k = 0\cdot786$

Thus, in the medium-density stratum, over the combined period of the counts, the average spatial distribution of elephant groups was random. Perhaps with data from a larger number of counts, the distribution might tend to a more regular pattern of use. Even in the high-density stratum there is a tendency for the average distribution of groups to be less clumped compared with the distribution at any one time. Possibly if we had data from a sufficiently large number of counts in the high-density stratum it would also show a random, or even approach a regular, distribution. This is presumably the result of the social behaviour (which tends to produce local aggregations of groups) and over-all movements of the population within the range. Together these factors tend to randomize or regularize the use of the habitat within each stratum at a particular density.

We have also examined in the same way the distributions of single animals, the majority of which are males (Laws 1969b). The mean densities per 10 square kilometres over the three aerial counts were 0·71 and 0·25 in the medium- and high-density strata respectively, that is, 0·071 and 0·025 per square kilometre. When the frequency distributions of single animals for the three counts are examined separately they are found to be very similar within each stratum, but there is an obvious inter-stratum difference. Again there is evidence that, at any one

Table 7.6

*Comparison of observed and fitted negative binomial distributions of single
animal densities in the two strata. 'Instantaneous' distributions summed*

Unit frequency	Medium-density stratum		High-density stratum	
	Observed	Negative binomial	Observed	Negative binomial
0	273	271·6	325	324·8
1	111	112·7	50	51·4
2	40	47·0	16	13·7
3	28	19·6	3	4·1
4	10	8·2	1	
5	2	3·4	1	
6	0	1·4	0	2·0
7	1	} 1·0	0	
⩾8	0		0	
Total	465	464·9	396	396·0

Notes. (1) Medium-density stratum : 5d.f.; $x^2 = 7\cdot074$; $p = 22$ per cent; $k = 0\cdot991$
(2) High-density stratum : 2 d.f.; $x^2 = 0\cdot747$; $p = 70$ per cent; $k = 0\cdot425$

time, the spatial distribution of single animals is strongly clumped. In Table 7.6
the instantaneous frequency distributions for the three counts have been summed
to obtain a combined 'instantaneous' distribution. Negative binomial models have
been fitted to these data. For the medium-density stratum the negative binomial
is a good fit. The value obtained for k is 0·991 and on the null hypothesis
$p = 22$ per cent. For the high-density stratum the negative binomial is an extremely good fit; k is 0·425 and $p = 70$ per cent.

The 'averaged' distributions have been compared with the Poisson model, as
before. For the medium-density stratum this gives an extremely good fit
(2 d.f.; $x^2 = 1\cdot211, p = 54$ per cent) and for the high-density stratum it is a good
fit (1d.f.; $x^2 = 1\cdot525, p = 22$ per cent).

At any one time, then, the distribution of single animals was clumped, but
when averaged over the three counts it was random. If more counts were averaged
it might well approach a regular distribution of use.

7.2.   Group-size frequencies

In the course of the 'complete' aerial counts (see Plates 2.2, 5.1—5.4) in the
grassland part of the North Bunyoro elephant range, 2029 discrete elephant
groups or units were counted (including 439 units of single animals). They contained 24 405 elephants, giving a calculated mean group size of 12·03. For the
individual counts (November, February, and August) the mean group sizes were
10·7, 10·9, and 15·9 respectively. This suggests a possible build up in group size
in the early part of the mating season as independent material from Kenya and
Tanzania had also suggested (Laws 1969b). However, it could also be related to

the cropping of some 600 animals in the medium-density stratum between the second and third counts, because, as noted above disturbance may be a causative factor in the formation of larger groups. We think this is unlikely, because the medium-density area actually shows a smaller proportional increase in mean group size over the three counts (6·3, 6·1, and 7·9 respectively) than does the high-density area, whereas if disturbance were the primary cause its effect should be greatest in the medium-density zone.

When the mean herd sizes are calculated separately for the two density strata they average 6·6 and 22·5 for medium- and high-density areas respectively. It is of interest that the mean group size for the medium-density stratum is similar to the mean group size of 5·9 calculated for 1144 herds observed in the Queen Elizabeth National Park (Laws and Parker 1968). This was apparently at variance with the figures from other populations but now falls into place, for the average density of elephants in this park is between 1·9 and 2·3 per square kilometre, that is, similar to the Murchison, South medium-density zone.

The group-size-frequency distribution for the two strata combined when plotted graphically shows a hollow curve. But as the high density-stratum is known to be characterized by the presence of some very large herds, the group-size frequencies for the two density strata have been analysed separately.

As pointed out above the boundary between medium- and high-density strata is to a considerable extent arbitrary. In the spatially defined medium-density stratum there were, over the three counts, 11 groups containing more than 40 individuals. Ten of these were peripheral in distribution, at an average distance of only 3·3 kilometres (1·3 miles), range 0·5—8·0 kilometres (0·2—3·1 miles) from the stratum boundary. They average 54 per group (range 42—76) and have been included in the high-density stratum in the following analysis, on the premise that they are more representative of the high-density stratum. A distance of 8 kilometres is well within the daily range of elephant groups. (Their inclusion in the high-density stratum does not, however, affect the conclusion reached.)

Comparing the data for the two strata, it is found as expected that the frequency distributions are very significantly different. Because it has already been shown that large herds are characteristic of the peripheral area we have also compared the frequencies of group sizes up to 20 elephants. They are also very significantly different ($\chi^2 = 30·46, 3$ d.f.; $p < 0·001$ per cent), so the difference is not solely due to the very large herds.

The total numbers of elephant in each group-size class can be calculated for the two strata and in Figs 7.4 and 7.5, the frequency distributions of total numbers of elephant present in groups of different sizes have been plotted graphically. A polymodal pattern is apparent, such that in the medium-density zone, peaks occur at group sizes of 7, 12, 17, and 23 or, when smoothes, at 6, 11, 17, and 23. This suggests that the basic unit is about 6 and that the larger herds are aggregations of several family units and bull herds. This pattern is less clear in the high-density stratum but there are peaks at 5, 9, 15, and 20 or, when smoothed,

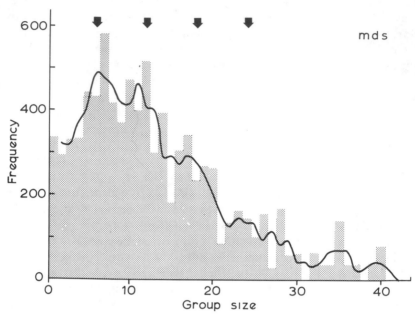

Fig. 7.4. Frequency distribution of elephants counted in the medium-density stratum in three aerial counts (1966–7) by group sizes. The frequencies have also been smoothed and successive modes are indicated.

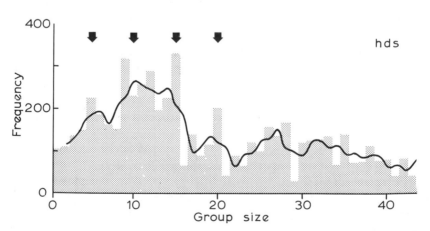

Fig. 7.5. Frequency distribution of elephants counted in the high-density stratum in three aerial counts (1966–7) by group sizes. The frequencies have also been smoothed and successive modes are indicated. Numbers in groups larger than 43 are not shown.

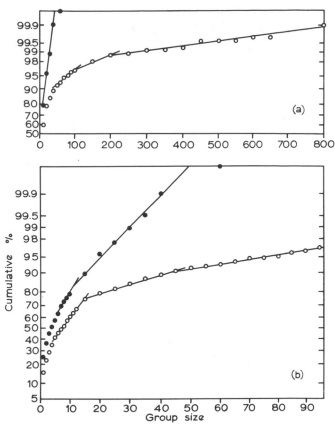

Fig. 7.6. Probability plot of cumulative group size frequency distributions for medium-(black circles) and high-density (open circles) strata: (a) full group size range shown, class interval 50; (b) shows only group sizes up to 95, class interval 5.

at 6, 10, 14, and 19, which suggests that the basic unit is about 5. In a similar study in the Tsavo ecological unit, Kenya (Laws 1969b), where bull herds were classified separately from mixed herds, it was shown that in the mixed herds there was a polymodal size frequency, with peaks at group sizes of 6, 12, and 18, although a possible seasonal change was also demonstrated, and these samples represented a number of different unit populations.

Some 45 per cent of all elephants recorded in the medium-density zone were in groups of 10 or fewer elephants, compared with 11 per cent in the high-density area; 82 per cent were in groups of 20 or less, compared with 23 per cent; and 100 per cent in groups of 60 or less, compared with 44 per cent in the high-density stratum. In the high-density stratum 44 per cent of all animals counted were in herds of over 100 animals.

The culmulative frequencies of successive group sizes have been plotted on probability graph paper for the two strata in Fig. 7.6. A normally distributed set of frequency data plotted in this way lie on a straight line. In the case of the medium-density stratum the data lie about a straight line for group sizes above 10–15, and the data as a whole can be regarded as a truncated normal distribution. The truncation is interpreted as due to the social structure (the basic unit averaging 5–6 animals), and modified by the superimposed male group frequencies. The data for the high-density stratum show a similar pattern up to a group size of 15, but then diverge markedly.

In Fig. 7.6(a) the total cumulative frequency ranges are shown and it can be seen that, whereas the data for the medium-density stratum approximate to a single straight line (from group size 10 upwards) to a group size of 40, the data for the high-density stratum show a series of inflections at group sizes of about 50, 100, and 200, suggesting that the largest groups may tend to form by aggregations of successively larger groups.

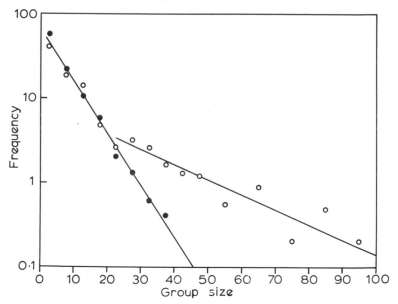

Fig. 7.7. Group size-frequency distribution shown on a logarithmic scale for medium-(black circles) and high-density (open circles) strata. Group sizes above 100 not included. The size of each sample was converted to 100 for direct comparison.

The data can also be described by a logarithmic series (Fig. 7.7), the successive frequencies closely approximating to a straight line in the medium-density stratum but showing an inflection in the high-density stratum at a group size of about 20, after which the data approximate to a second straight line of lesser slope, at least up to a group size of 100. This indicates, as did the probability plot, an increase in diversity of sizes of groups in the high-density stratum. Of these two mathematical descriptions the former would seem to have the greater biological significance.

These analyses confirm the reality of the differences in the structure of the populations in the two strata, originally defined on the basis of population density alone. The factor, or factors, causing the more pronounced aggregation to form large herds in the high-density stratum were earlier shown not to be related to specific environmental characters but probably to population density. Thus, associated with an 100 per cent increase in density (from 1·9 to 3·8 per square kilometre) there is a 241 per cent increase in average group size (from 6·6 to 22·5), and this is probably related in a simple way to increasing frequency of contacts at higher densities. Elephant by virtue of their nutritional requirements are relatively mobile animals. Thus, there is a high probability of intergroup contacts occurring purely by chance. Because they are also highly social animals it is likely that contacts result in more than transitory aggregation. Viewed in this way increased group size is an extension of the contagious distribution of discrete groups that has already been demonstrated.

Let us suppose that the absolute density of a hypothetical population is increased by a factor of two. If the density of groups is to remain the same, other things being equal, then the groups at the higher density will average twice the former size. But if the groups are larger they need to cover more ground for feeding; contacts should therefore tend to become more frequent, the average group size larger, and mobility therefore even greater, so that the average density of groups in the higher density area might be expected to be less than formerly.

This would appear to be borne out by the observation that the density of groups is in fact lower in the high-density stratum than in the medium-density stratum (0·17 per square kilometre compared with 0·29 per square kilometre). However, if the quadrats containing two or more groups of elephants (i.e. excluding zero records and single groups) are compared, then it is found that for the medium- and high-density strata the respective mean group densities are 4·31 and 4·06 per 10 square kilometres (0·43 and 0·41 per square kilometre). For both density strata the frequency distributions of numbers of 2 or more groups per quadrat were found not to differ significantly ($\chi^2 = 10·28$, 7 d.f.; $p = 17$ per cent). This agreement suggests that within the neighbourhood of concentrations or clumps in the over-all elephant distributions a certain level of group spacing obtains, irrespective of absolute population density. Thus, at least over the observed range of densities, if densities are higher then group sizes are disproportionately higher.

The conclusions about the two density strata are summarized in Table 7.7. The estimated density of 9·1 per square kilometre over 341 square kilometres (23·6 per square mile over 132 square miles) in the sub-strata with two or more groups per quadrat is very much higher than has been reported elsewhere. It represents a concentration of elephant biomass amounting to nearly 16 000 kg per square kilometre (nearly 90 000 lbs per square mile) additional to the biomass of other species, such as buffalo.

Table 7.7
Summary of conclusions on the two density strata

Parameter	Density strata	
	Medium	High
Mean group size	6·6	22·5
Mean elephants density per km^2	1·9	3·8
Mean group density per km^2	0·29	0·17
k for group distribution†	1·90	0·79
Mean group density in sub-strata with ⩾2 groups per quadrat	0·43	0·41
Mean elephant density per km^2 in above sub-strata	2·8	9·1
Area of strata (km^2)	912	341
Strata as percentage of total range	63·6	36·4

† k of negative binomial

7.3. Group structures

The frequency distributions and spatial distributions of group sizes and locations have been described and it remains to investigate the internal structure of the discrete groups as determined by analysis of animals killed in groups in the course of the cropping operations. The method of cropping has already been outlined and reasons given to support the assumption that the sample approximates to a random cross-section of the population (Chapter 6).

7.3.1. *Bull herds*

Of the total numbers cropped, 14·6 per cent were in bull herds. This is comparable to the proportion in several Kenya and Tanzania populations (Laws 1969b). In the operations in M.F.P.S., 117 bulls in 38 bull herds were cropped, the herds ranging in size from single animals to eleven (see Plates 2.7, 7.3). Their mean group size was 3·08. For 72 bull herds cropped and examined in M.F.P.N., the size ranged from one to nine, averaging 2·39 (unpublished data). Unfortunately bull herds were not identified and classified separately in the aerial counts in Uganda, but for 427 bull herds recorded in aerial counts in the Tsavo National Park, Kenya (Laws 1969b) the mean group size was 2·42 (range 1—14). This suggests that, allowing for the small size of the sample of groups cropped, it is representative.

The ages of animals in the bull herds, all of which were sexually mature (sperm present in the epididymal smears) are presented in detail in Figs 7.8 and 7.9. The mean age was 30·6 years. Fig. 7·8 indicates that there may be a wide range of ages in a bull herd (e.g. 20—49 years, group no. 29), but that often the age range is quite small, and sometimes bimodal, as if two groups of differing age ranges had joined up. Several groups had an old bull, many years older than the next oldest, recalling the stories common in the literature about the old bull and his much

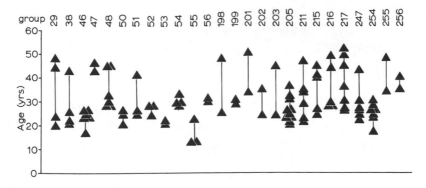

Fig. 7.8. Age distribution of bulls in 26 bull herds cropped in M.F.P.S.

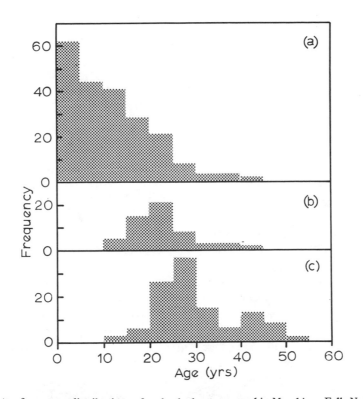

Fig. 7.9. Age-frequency distributions of male elephants cropped in Murchison Falls National Park, South: (a) total males in mixed herds; (b) sexually mature bulls in mixed herds; (c) in bull herds (sexually mature).

younger 'askaris'. The age distribution of solitary bulls was not significantly different from that of all bulls in bull herds; this is true of both Murchison Falls Park elephant populations.

7.3.2.   *Solitary females*

In the course of the operations six solitary cows were cropped and examined. They were all anoestrous and not lactating, with an average age of 55 years (range 52–59 years). Before being shot they were observed to be slow-moving, senile-looking and apparently in poor condition. We suppose that they had become detached from mixed herds, of which they had formerly been matriarchs, because they were unable to maintain their position or to keep up with the younger animals. It is likely that they had not much longer to live.

7.3.3.   *Family units*

In the cropping programme 59 mixed herds were taken, of mean size 11·6 (range 2–29). The animals in these 'family units' comprised 85 per cent of the total number cropped and, as mentioned above, this is the basic social unit in elephant populations (Plates 7.1 and 7.2). The family comprises adult females, immature females, immature males, and some sexually mature males, which are usually unrelated to other members of the group, as will be seen from a detailed consideration of the group structures.

Some relationships are clear from the most superficial observation (e.g. cows with suckling calves) and others become apparent on analysing the group structure in terms of age, sex, and reproductive status (Fig. 7.10). In addition to the 59 family units analysed in this way from the M.F.P.S. population, 129 were analysed from M.F.P.N., 25 from Tsavo National Park (T.N.P.), and 23 from Mkomasi Reserve (M.K.E.). It is hoped to present the detailed analyses in papers later, but a summary analysis of the information from the other populations is given here for comparison with M.F.P.S. (Table 7.8). Unfortunately, owing to the hunting technique employed there is no comparable information about the Budongo Forest elephants.

Buss and Johnson (1967) remark that 'although large bulls are generally attached to family units loosely and temporarily (Buss and Smith 1966) some large bulls are true family members'. As an example they quote a 13-year-old bull (their ageing criteria) collected from a family group of five, and as the only evidence of relationship, the fact that the matriarch of the group defended the body. Its body weight was only 2766 kg and it could well have been immature or pubertal. Only one bull described by them in a family unit was clearly fully mature (age about 40 years, body weight 4798 kg).

In the M.F.P.S. sample nearly half the family units had sexually mature males with them, and the proportion in M.F.P.N. was similar, but for T.N.P. and M.K.E. (Mkomasi Reserve) nearly three quarters of the family units contained adult males. This may be related to the earlier age at puberty in the latter populations

PLATE 7.1. Elephant family unit—alarmed matriarch nearest camera.

PLATE 7.2. Family unit on the defensive (photograph C. A. Spinage).

Table 7.8

Comparison of family group structures for four elephant populations sampled by cropping

Sample	No. of groups	Group size	No. adult males	No. adult females	Number immature	Ratio adult females: immatures	Ratio adult females: all others	Family units with attached bulls		
		All family units (averages)						No. of groups	%	Average no. of bulls
M.F.P.S.	59	11·61	0·98	4·75	5·88	1:1·24	1:1·44	27	45·8	2·15
M.F.P.N.	129	7·80	0·71	2·76	4·33	1:1·57	1:1·83	52	40·3	1·77
T.N.P.	25	11·28	1·12	3·72	6·44	1:1·73	1:2·03	18	72·0	1·56
M.K.E.	23	12·26	1·69	4·00	6·57	1:1·64	1:2·07	17	73·9	1·35

Notes. M.F.P.S.–Murchison Falls Park, South
M.F.P.N.–Murchison Falls Park, North
T.N.P.–Tsavo National Park, Kenya
M.K.E.–Mkomasi East Reserve, Tanzania

(Chapter 9). For the M.F.P.S. sample there were on average 2·15 adult males in each family unit containing them, which is not significantly different ($p > 5$ per cent) from the mean group size of the bull herds sampled (3·08), and is suggestive of a temporary aggregation of mixed groups and bull herds.

Family units which were associated with the larger bull herds would not be sampled because their size would be too large to meet the conditions suitable for cropping them. Thus, no family unit cropped in M.F.P.S. contained more than 6 adult males (in M.F.P.N. and M.K.E. there were no more than 5 and in T.N.P. no more than 4).

The possibility of a seasonal difference in the proportion of adult males in family units perhaps related to a male reproductive cycle was examined. The percentage of adult males in the total numbers within the family units sampled was calculated separately by months for M.F.P.S. and M.F.P.N. and found to be not significantly different over the year ($p > 5$ per cent). Even when the two samples were combined the monthly values were not significantly different. The results are presented in Table 7.9. The over-all mean percentage of mature bulls in the family units was $8·90 ± 1·38$ ($p = 5$ per cent), for the two Murchison Falls samples; for Tsavo the percentage was $9·93 ± 3·56$ and for Mkomasi, $13·80 ± 4·10$. These differences are not significant.

The age distribution of adult males in the family units was compared with the ages of adult males in bull herds (Fig. 7.9). Both distributions are skewed and the mean age of mature bulls with family units was 24·4 years, compared with a mean of 30·6 years for animals in bull herds. The difference is highly significant ($p < 0·1$ per cent). This suggests either that bulls tend to remain with their family units for some years after reaching sexual maturity, or that there is a tendency for the younger mature age groups of bulls to spend more time associated with the family units. Of the 58 mature bulls in the M.F.P.S. family units, half were found to be incompatible (on account of their ages) with close relationship to the other animals in the group (Fig. 7.10); their mean age was 25·8 years (range 16–45 years), significantly different from that of the bull herds ($p < 0·2$ per cent). The ages of the other 29 were compatible with close relationships within the mixed herds, though this is not to say that such relationships actually existed in all cases. Their mean age was 21·0 years (range 13–28 years), again significantly different from that of the bull herds.

This finding supports the suggestion that the younger bulls spend more time with their parental family units for two to three years after attaining sexual maturity than they do later. Since the mean age of 'incompatible' bulls in the family units is significantly different from the mean age of bulls in bull herds, the older bulls (aged more than 40 years) probably spend very little time with family units.

Tyler (1969) has evidence from repeated observations of known individual wild ponies that the process of separation is protracted, with the newly mature colts spending progressively longer periods away from their original family unit. Douglas-Hamilton (personal communication) also informs us that in the Lake

Table 7.9

Percentage of adult males in family units, by months

Month	M.F.P.N. total	Bulls	%	M.F.P.S. total	Bulls	%	Combined total	Bulls	%	S.E.
Jan.	141	7	5·0	–	–	–	141	7	5·0	1·84
Feb.	2	0	–	3	0	–	5	0	–	–
Mar.	23	2	8·7	137	15	10·9	160	17	10·6	2·43
Apr.	39	8	20·5	115	6	5·2	154	14	9·1	2·32
May	99	8	8·1	273	24	8·8	372	32	8·6	1·45
June	82	6	7·3	–	–	–	82	6	7·3	2·87
July	87	5	5·7	–	–	–	87	5	5·7	2·48
Aug.	207	26	12·6	–	–	–	207	26	12·6	2·31
Sept.	172	10	5·8	–	–	–	172	10	5·8	1·78
Oct.	39	4	10·3	–	–	–	39	4	10·3	4·87
Nov.	68	8	11·8	157	13	8·3	225	21	9·3	1·99
Dec.	47	8	17·0	–	–	–	47	8	17·0	5·48
Total	1006	92	9·1	685	58	8·5	1691	150	8·9	0·69

Note. S.E.–standard error

Manyara National Park populations, young pubertal males often establish contact with bachelor herds long before they finally leave the family unit. He believes that they leave because they are driven out by the older females and straightway join a bachelor group. They do not go through a protracted period as solitary animals. This agrees with our observations on the age frequency distribution of solitary animals that were cropped.

In Fig. 7.10 is illustrated the composition by age, sex, and reproductive status, of the 59 family units cropped in the M.F.P.S. These figures explain more clearly than any words the probable structure of the family units involved. It must be pointed out however, that they represent our presumptive interpretation of the composition of the groups in terms of familial relationships. In some cases we are no doubt mistaken over details, but we do not believe that the general conclusions we draw are affected by this and they have now been confirmed by Douglas-Hamilton (1972) by studies of individually recognized animals in a small population which occupies a small range.

In drawing up these 'kinship diagrams' we have drawn upon the records of occurrence of placental scars (Laws (1967a); also see Chapter 9, Plate 9.1). Unfortunately these were not distinguishable in pregnant uteri and no records are available for the initial sample (of 200 animals) mainly taken in August 1965 (Laws and Parker 1968) before the importance and persistence of placental scars was recognized. From these kinship diagrams it now seems clear that the scars do tend to disappear after about 30 years, as suggested by Laws (1967a, 1969a). Nonetheless, they have been helpful in interpreting relationships within groups. (e.g. a recent scar implies a suckling calf; a young female with one placental scar

×   foetus or embryo   ▽   suckling male calf   ▲   cycling

⧊   suckling female calf   ▽   sexually immature male   ●   pregnant

△   sexually immature female   ▽   pubertal male   ◆   lactating

△   pubertal female   ▼   sexually mature male   ■   anoestrous mature females

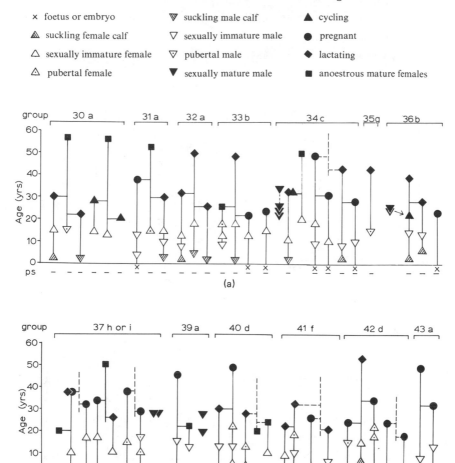

Fig. 7.10. Structure, by age and reproductive status, of 59 herds of mixed sex cropped in M.F.P.S. Presumed relationships are indicated by the lines; a broken line indicates a presumed relationship via a matriarch now dead; placental scar counts (ps) are given for non-pregnant mature females in all except the early groups, and a possible spacing of pregnancies, consistent with the number of scars is shown. The groups are classified (a)–(j) as described in the text and summarized in Table 7.10.

× foetus or embryo	▽ suckling male calf	▲ cycling
◭ suckling female calf	▽ sexually immature male	● pregnant
△ sexually immature female	▽ pubertal male	◆ lactating
△ pubertal female	▼ sexually mature male	■ anoestrous mature females

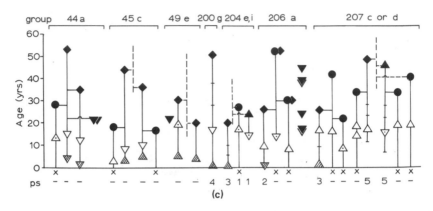

(c)

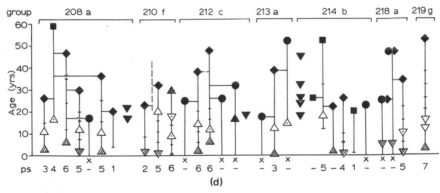

(d)

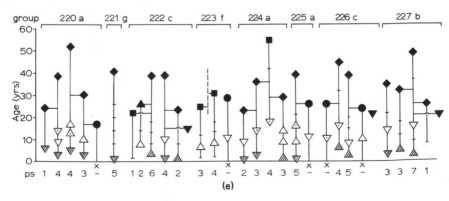

(e)

x foetus or embryo	▽ suckling male calf	▲ cycling
△ suckling female calf	▽ sexually immature male	● pregnant
△ sexually immature female	▽ pubertal male	◆ lactating
△ pubertal female	▼ sexually mature male	■ anoestrous mature females

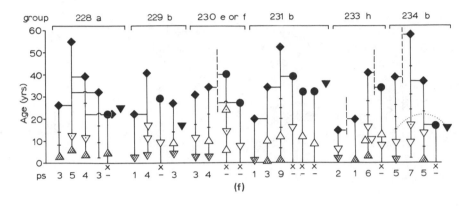

(f)

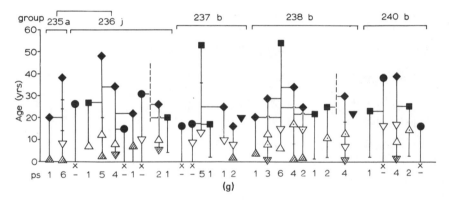

(g)

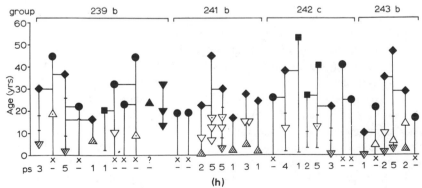

(h)

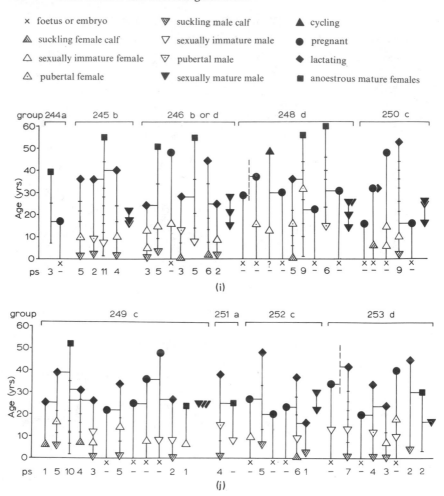

× foetus or embryo	▽ suckling male calf	▲ cycling
⬟ suckling female calf	▽ sexually immature male	● pregnant
△ sexually immature female	▽ pubertal male	◆ lactating
△ pubertal female	▼ sexually mature male	■ anoestrous mature females

(i)

(j)

in the uterus is unlikely to have more than one offspring). The estimated ages of individuals may be accurate only to within a few years.

With these reservations in mind, let us examine the presumptive group structures. The simplest structure is that of a single adult female accompanied by immature animals which are clearly her offspring; examples of these 'mother–offspring' groups are numbers 35, 200, 219, and 221. These groups average 2·75 animals in size, that is one adult female to 1·75 offspring. Considering the total family units sampled the average ratio is found to be 1:1·24 (Table 7.8). This ratio does not change with increasing group size, as shown when the group size (excluding associated mature males) is plotted against the number of mature females in the group for the 59 groups cropped. Similarly, when the number of subgroups estimated from the presumptive group structures in Fig. 7.10 is plotted against group size, the proportion does not change with increasing group size. These findings also hold good for the other populations sampled in this way. Allowing for the associated adult males, the ratio of females to all others for the M.F.P.S. groups is 1:1·44 (Table 7.8).

It would appear then, that the mother—offspring unit is the fundamental population unit, as might be expected, but we have shown that the polymodal group-size frequency in elephant populations is based on a unit of 5—6 elephants. This suggests that in M.F.P.S. an average of 2—3 mother—offspring units are usually combined, averaging 4·5—6·7 animals (4·9—7·3 with attached adult males). The diagrams in Fig. 7.10 suggest that the two or three mother—offspring groups in a larger family unit are often related as a matriarch and her immature offspring, together with one or more mature daughters and their offspring (Plates 7.1 and 7.2). Examples of small matriarchal groups are numbers 39, 43, 44, 206, 213, 218, 225, 235, and 251.

Group 244 is a special case in which a matriarch aged 39 years apparently had no immature offspring associated with her. It remains a possibility that in some of these groups the younger females may not always, or not usually, be related to the matriarch, but the pattern of the age structures is very suggestive. It seems reasonable to assume that an animal like the elephant, which is a member of a family unit for 10—20 years while immature, will develop strong social bonds with her mother and siblings.

Other group structures are best interpreted as associations of sibling or related females, the original matriarch having left the group or died. Examples of these 'sibling groups' are numbers, 45, 49, and 204, and subgroups of numbers 40, 41, 210, and 223. Douglas-Hamilton (1972) has good evidence from repeated observations of known elephants that ties between individuals may be strongest between calves of similar age although different mothers. In aggregated family units or extended families without a clear matriarch, the leaders therefore need not necessarily be sisters, but may be cousins.

As the group to be analysed becomes larger, so the possible relationships increase, but in general they all fit a basic pattern dictated by the aggregation of structures similar to those already described. Thus Groups 40 and 42 are interpreted as combinations of matriarchal and sibling groups, Group 41 as a sibling/mother—offspring group, and so on.

A presumptive classification of the family units, based on this type of interpretation, is given in Table 7.10. The most common types within this size range are those involving matriarchal type groups, whether alone or in combination with mother—offspring or sibling groups. These types comprise 73·8 per cent of all groups examined. Matriarchal groups alone or in combination with other matriarchal groups comprise 41·5 per cent of all groups analysed. Within the family units studied there is great variation in maternal—infant ties. This ranged from females which calved at intervals (as evidenced by placental scar counts) but whose offspring evidently left them at maturity (Groups 200, 219, 221) to matriarchs

Table 7.10

Presumptive classification of family units illustrated in Fig. 7.10

Class	Frequency	%	Mean age of oldest female (yrs)	Average size	Group numbers
(a) Matriarchal	16	24·6	46	6·0	31, 32, 39, 43, 44, 206, 213, 218, 225, 235, 244, 251
			55	13·0	Large groups 208, 220, 224, 228
(b) Matriarchal/ mother–offspring	15	23·1	49	13·2	33, 36, 214, 227, 229, 231, (234), 237, 238, 239, 240, 241, 243, 245, (246)
(c) Matriarchal/ matriarchal	11	16·9	49	12·8	30, 34, (45), (207), 212, 222, 226, 242, 249, 250, 252
(d) Matriarchal/sibling	6	9·2	52	16·2	40, 42, (207), (246), 248, 253
(e) Sibling	5	7·7	40	8·4	(45), 49, 204, (230), (234)
(f) Mother–offspring/ sibling	4	6·2	34	9·5	41, 210, 223, (230)
(g) Mother–offspring	4	6·2	47	2·8	35, 200, 219, 221
(h) Sibling/sibling	2	3·1	40	14·0	(37), 233
(i) Mother–offspring/ mother–offspring	1	1·5	(38)	15·0	(37)
(j) Matriarchal/sibling/ mother–offspring	1	1·5	(48)	18·0	236

which are possibly still accompanied by all their surviving mature female offspring and their associated groups (e.g. 208, 220, 222).

In the larger family units illustrated in Fig. 7.10, subgroups can be identified which are intermediate in size between the basic mother–offspring group and the large family unit. The individuals comprising these intermediate groups are presumed to be inter-related. Excluding the adult males associated with them, 127 of these subgroups have been identified within the 59 groups cropped, containing from 1 to 17 elephants, averaging 4·93. If we assume that adult bulls comprise 8·5 per cent of the animals in family units, then each of these sub-units is associated on average with 0·46 bulls, suggesting an average subgroup of 5·4 elephants, containing 2–3 adult females.

Thus the average subgroup of 5–6 animals presumably contains a matriarch and/or 1–2 adult daughters, and on average the family units cropped contained about two such subgroups and one adult male (average group size 11·6, Table 7.8).

We have therefore some confirmation, at this level, of the polymodal frequency distribution of group sizes mentioned earlier (Figs 7.4 and 7.5), and it seems reasonable to assume that these subgroups, averaging 5—6 elephants, are the largest stable population unit or the smallest discrete unit, depending on the viewpoint.

Douglas-Hamilton (1972) who has made extended observations of recognizable elephant groups in Lake Manyara National Park, Tanzania, has observed the re-peated recombination of individual family units. Such a repeatedly recombining group may be termed an 'extended family' and he has observed such recombi-nations of up to three family units. The mean family unit size in that population was 10·7.

Analysis of a further 177 family units from other populations sampled on these lines gives a similar picture and it is hoped to present and discuss the results in later papers. These results, based on accurate information on age and reproductive status are complementary to and of great value to studies of elephant behaviour based on field observation only.

The mean age of solitary senile females cropped was 55 years (range 52—9 years); that of the 'matriarchs' in the first four categories of family units in Table 7.10 averaged 49 years (range 38—60 years). The mean age of the oldest animals in the last six categories was 40 years (range 27—53 years). It is shown elsewhere in this book (Chapter 9) that age-specific fecundity reaches a peak between 30 and 40 years and then declines in older females, producing the nearest parallel to the human menopause that has yet been established for a wild population. The implication is that, as in man, the grandmother is an integral part of the group and has an important leadership and/or infant care function.

7.4.   Behaviour

7.4.1.   *Group behaviour*

During this study no attempt was made to conduct ethological research. How-ever one aspect of elephant behaviour deserves mention as around it evolved the whole system of cropping family units. This was the relationship between mem-bers of a family unit and its matriarch. We have not attempted to adhere to ethological terms or criteria in the simple description which follows.

Laws and Parker (1968, and also in this book) have described the structure of family units and present strong evidence for believing them to be composed in the main of a mother, her immature and mature offspring and the progeny of her mature 'dependents'. Elephant hunters have long recognized that such units have 'leaders', and in taking nearly 3000 elephants in cropping operations in Uganda, Kenya and Tanzania it has been outstandingly obvious to us that these leaders are invariably the groups' oldest females—the matriarchs.

In undisturbed situations involving a large family unit, cursory observation of group behaviour does not necessarily reveal the matriarch, although she is usually the largest female in the group. However, when alarmed or alert there is an immediate tendency to 'bunch' on the matriarch. If she has insufficient stimulus to flee, the group remain with her until the alarm has subsided. If the matriarch is sufficiently frightened she runs, the herd bunched with her. If she is aggressive or threatening the herd often follow her towards the source of alarm. Even when fleeing, if the matriarch is shot, it is usual for the whole unit to stop and cluster about her, often with much nudging and apparent efforts to lever the fallen beast upright. Similarly, on several occasions a matriarch has been seen to stop and endeavour to lift a fallen member of the unit.

As a result of this co-ordination about the matriarch, it was possible to bunch herds, shoot the matriarch first, and in the ensuing confusion, during which the herd continue to cluster about her body, destroy the remainder taking the largest individuals first (see Chapter 6, Plate 6.1). When the herds consisted of two or more aggregated family units, it was essential to take all matriarchs very quickly as, if one survived and fled, this usually caused a fallen leader's group to abandon her and make off with the new leader. So strong are the ties between the matriarch and her followers that on several occasions a younger animal has been up to 200 metres away from the main group when they were shot, yet despite the extreme disturbance of rifle fire, has run towards it in an endeavour to rejoin the unit.

This 'bunching' reaction applies consistently only with family units. Although bull groups do show it on occasion, it is more usual for adult males to react as

PLATE 7.3. Mature bull elephant.

individuals even when associated with family units. This made shooting of bull herds much more difficult and is the reason why the largest bull group taken numbered only 11 animals. The normal male reaction on being disturbed was flight, each individual for himself, in various directions. Large males in family units were invariably shot first along with the matriarch, because they provided a potential substitute leader when the matriarch was killed (see Plate 7.3).

We feel that the dependence of a family unit upon its matriarch even in the most extreme of situations (such as occasioned by cropping) illustrates the great importance of the acquisition of experience and learning made possible by the evolution of longevity. We consider that this situation represents an evolutionary development that is now probably essential for the stability of elephant communities.

The occurrence of the vast herds in phalanx formation has already been mentioned, and it has been shown that these are peripheral to elephant populations in conflict with man. Invariably such situations result in heavy mortality through 'control' shooting, and in populations declining through taking excessive numbers in these operations, the older age classes are the first to disappear. We suggest that the huge herds may be a gross manifestation of 'bunching' which, through lack of leadership has developed to an exceptional extent (see Plate 5.2). Further research into this aspect of behaviour has obvious interest and relevance to management.

The management implication of the overwhelmingly matriarchal structure of elephant populations is that selective culling of old or barren cows, as in the early years of the Luangwa Valley cropping scheme (Bainbridge 1967), is likely to be disadvantageous. It removes from the population the adult females with the lowest reproductive rate, which is unhelpful in the context of most elephant problems (though not necessarily under a sustained-yield regime). But what is more serious, for any form of management, is that it removes the leaders and, while the full consequences of this are unknown, the elimination of their accumulated experience must at least add appreciably to the disturbance factor. Moreover, the removal of matriarchs may well lead to the formation of larger groups, with consequent unfavourable effects on the habitats due to more intensive localized use. If for any reason selective cropping is to be practised it should not concentrate on the removal of the matriarchs.

7.4.2.   *Diurnal behaviour*

Some evidence relating to individual elephants which became well-known to the observers, shows that they moved very little in the course of several months in the Murchison Falls Park. Bull No. 1546 ('Krumpul') was easily distinguished by his immense size, and prior to his being shot had occupied the same restricted area in the vicinity of the Zoila River (less than 250 square kilometres, 100 square miles) for 18 months. Whenever he was looked for he was found in this area, at all seasons and on numerous occasions. Several recognizable family

PLATE 7.4. Small herd in a rare patch of shade, M.F.P.S.

units also showed long association with the same area. Similar observations of very localized residence of both bull herds and family units are known from the Queen Elizabeth National Park (Laws, unpublished) and Lake Manyara National Park (Douglas-Hamilton 1972).

No consistent records were kept of diurnal behaviour patterns. However, irregular observations throughout the two year cropping programme suggested that where no shade existed elephant fed continuously, at an apparently constant rate throughout the day. Where shade was available in the immediate vicinity, they made use of it (Plate 7.4) and rested for periods of several hours during the heat of the day (10.00–15.00 h).

No regular drinking period was observed and elephant were recorded at water during all observation times. This is in strong contrast to their behaviour in areas of restricted water availability. During the dry season in the arid areas of the Galana Game Ranching Scheme (Parker 1964) and Tsavo National Park, elephant adopt a regular routine of drinking at the Galana River during the night and returning to the more productive feeding areas—at least 15 kilometres (10 miles) inland—in the early morning. They walk many miles to do so and the movements are obligatory under these conditions if they are to survive.

In these arid areas elephant also make marked use of any shade available and spend several hours during the heat of the day resting and not feeding. These Kenya observations are also contrary to the findings of Buss (1961) who concluded that elephant had to eat continuously to avert death by starvation. The existence of virtually continuous feeding is crucial to the work Wing and Buss

(1970) undertook in the Kibale Forest, as without the regular and continuous ingestion they postulate, a regular defecation rate is unlikely.[†]

7.4.3. *Geographical segration*

In view of the spatial distribution of elephants that has been demonstrated by analysis of the aerial counts it seemed worthwhile to investigate the possibility of geographical segregation within the population in terms of sex and/or age.

Family units and bull herds cropped and examined were classified according to their nearest distance to the River Nile in a straight line, in Zones 0–2, 2–4 . . . more than 12 kilometres from the river. The average age in each of these zones was calculated, and also, in the case of family units the mean age of adult females in the groups (Table 7.11).

For both mixed herds and bull herds there is a trend of increasing mean age with distance from the river. The samples are quite large and when animals within 12 kilometres and more than 12 kilometres from the river are compared, those further from the river appear to be 3–6 years older on average, the bull herds showing the greatest difference. The mean age of matriarchs also showed an increasing, though less clear trend. The data were also analysed in terms of the family unit types listed in Table 7.10, but the differences between zones in the proportions of different types of family unit were not found to be significant.

The percentages of the sample that were in bull herds at varying distances from the river have also been calculated and show an increasing trend. There is a significant difference ($p < 5$ per cent) between the average percentage up to 12 kilometres from the river and more than 12 kilometres (respectively $8 \cdot 4 \pm 8 \cdot 56$ and $29 \cdot 4 \pm 10 \cdot 52$).

The habitat resources (amount of browse and woody growth) probably improve in terms of elephant requirements with increasing distance from the river. The animals in the subsample more than 12 kilometres from the river were mainly taken in the area west of Rabongo, a region where browse, mainly in the form of geophytic shrubs (e.g. *Lonchocarpus laxiflorus* and *Combretum* spp.) is more abundant. Here there are also scattered trees which afford shade and some relict patches of gallery forest. The six solitary senile cows were also taken within this locality. The zones nearer the river have very little shade or browse, even in the form of geophytes, and are heavily grazed by hippopotamus. Low elephant densities in the zone of hippo use have already been commented upon.

A similar analysis was carried out within the 12 kilometre zone from east to west, but showed no consistent age trend for either sex. No bull herds were

† In a study of elephant defaecation rates in the Tsavo National Park, Coe (1972) made some relevant observations. He found no significant divergence between the rates of defaecation by day or at night. There was some evidence of an apparent periodicity with a minor peak at mid-morning and a distinct peak in the afternoon, possibly correlated with the resumption of feeding after resting in the shade during the hotter part of the day.

Table 7.11

Relation of mean ages of animals in family units and bull herds, and proportion of cropped sample in bull herds, to distance from the River Nile

Distance from Nile (km)	Family units			Bull herds		% in bull herds	S. E.
	No. of animals	Mean age (years)	Mean age adult cows (years)	No. of animals	Mean age (years)		
0– 2	38	18·1	27·0	0	–	0·0	–
2– 4	105	17·8	30·8	4	20·2	3·7	–
4– 6	146	18·5	30·4	14	25·1	8·8	–
6– 8	76	19·4	31·2	10	25·8	13·7	–
8–10	91	17·6	34·3	5	30·4	7·1	–
10–12	40	22·5	36·4	9	30·8	18·4	–
0–12	496	18·6	31·6	42	26·6	8·4	4·28
>12	180	23·9	34·9	75	32·9	29·4	5·26
Total	676	20·0	32·6	117	30·6	14·8	1·26

Note. S. E.–standard error

taken within this zone in an area between 13 kilometres and 39 kilometres from the eastern boundary of the park. This is possibly the least favourable area for elephant in the National Park and supports relatively low densities (Figs 7.1 and 7.2).

The existence of areas favoured by large bulls (which are readily identified from the air or on the ground by their large tusks), is well known, particularly in the vicinity of the Zoila River in M.F.P.S. and the Tangi River in M.F.P.N. It is suggested that within the North Bunyoro elephant range there may also be a segregation of family units in terms of age, such that the home ranges of groups led by older animals are located in more favourable areas.

7.5.   Summary

The total area of the elephant range, including the forest is 3200 square kilometres, with an estimated over-all elephant density of 2·9 per square kilometre initially, reduced to 2·7 per square kilometre by the end of 1967 as a result of cropping and control shooting. The 1969 estimate, with 95 per cent confidence limits, was 3·47 ± 1·00 per square kilometre, which is in agreement (although excluding the forests). These values are higher than average densities previously reported for this and other elephant populations occupying ranges of similar extent.

Two density strata were defined, a central zone averaging 1·9 elephants per square kilometre and a peripheral zone averaging 3·8 per square kilometre. The instantaneous density distributions for both strata were clumped. Low densities along the Nile probably reflect competition with hippopotamus and the peripheral high densities are to some extent related to more favourable environmental conditions, though this is not considered to be the most significant factor involved.

The structure of the populations was studied at several levels. For medium- and high-density strata the average group densities were 0·29 and 0·17 per square kilometre respectively and the instantaneous frequency distributions of group densities are highly clumped in both strata, although over a period of time the shifting instantaneous distribution probably results in a random or even a regular pattern. The distribution of single animals followed similar patterns.

In the course of the aerial counts, 2029 discrete groups (including 439 single animals) were counted, with a mean group size of 12·0 animals. There is no evidence for seasonal differences in group size, but frequency distributions for the two density strata are significantly different. They suggest that the basic population unit contains 5 or 6 animals and that larger herds are aggregations of these small units.

Comparing the two density strata, there is a 241 per cent increase in mean group size (from 6·6 to 22·5) associated with a 100 per cent increase in average density (from 1·9 per square kilometre to 3·8 per square kilometre). This is probably related in a simple way to increasing frequency of contacts between herds, leading to progressively increasing aggregation tendencies at the higher densities. It is probably enhanced by disturbance and the shooting of matriarchs in control operations in the past.

Of the total numbers cropped in the National Park, 14·6 per cent were males in bull herds or solitary, and the mean bull herd size was 3·1. The age distribution of solitary males was not significantly different from that of bull herds. Some 85 per cent of all elephants cropped were in family units which comprise adult females, immature females and males, and some adult males, the latter usually loosely attached. Young mature males apparently spend more time with their parental family units in the immediately post-pubertal years than they do later.

The simplest family unit structure, averaging 2·75 individuals, includes a single adult female accompanied by immature animals which are clearly her offspring, and an average of 2–3 'mother–offspring' units are usually combined as a 'matriarchal' group of mother and a mature daughter with their calves. Some 74 per cent of all groups were matriarchal groups, but other types of group were encountered. The survival value of the leadership function of the matriarchs is clearly very important.

Geographical segregation of mixed herds and bull herds within the range was shown, and mean age and proportion of bulls found to increase with increasing distance from the River Nile. No comparable trend from east to west, that is along the river, could be demonstrated, although bull herds were absent from one area and another area was particularly favoured by large bulls.

8. Nutrition and growth

8.1. Nutrition

8.1.1. *Quantitative food intake*

Data on the weight of food in the stomach were obtained for samples from Murchison Falls Park, North, M.F.P.N. ($n = 198$), Murchison Falls Park, South, M.F.P.S. ($n = 185$), and Tsavo National Park, T.N.P. ($n = 261$). Owing to the fact that conditions during the Mkomasi operations were particularly unfavourable, no stomach fill data were obtained from those samples.

The stomachs were ligatured at the oesophagus and pylorus, to prevent escape of fluid and solids, and weighed on a tripod-mounted spring balance in a large container. They were then weighed a second time after the stomach contents had been carefully removed, and the weight of the container was subtracted to obtain the weight of the stomach full and empty. By subtraction the weight of the stomach fill was calculated. Air-dried samples indicated that the dry weight was approximately 0·25 times the wet weight.

In Fig. 8.1, the mean stomach fill values for successive 5-year age classes are compared for the two sexes for the M.F.P.S. samples. In calculating these means, six low values for each sex have been omitted, because it is considered that they were individuals that had lost some of the stomach contents through regurgitation after being shot. For some of them there was clear evidence for this assumption.

Buss (1961) concluded that there was 'similarity between the sexes in the maximum amounts eaten by these elephants', but Laws and Parker (1968) commented on the difference between the sexes, both in stomach fill at age and in relation to live weight. Fig. 8.1 indicates that the relation of stomach fill to age is curvilinear. Ford-Walford plots (Ford 1933; Walford 1946), based on the first seven or eight 5-year means give a good fit and suggest asymptotic stomach fill weights of 85 kg and 74 kg for males and females respectively. However, the later class means are not in close agreement with curves fitted in this way, and curves fitted by eye suggest mean stomach fill weights at 60 years of *ca* 110 kg and *ca* 80 kg for male and female respectively. At any one age however, there is a wide range of stomach fill weights about the mean (*ca* ± 25 − 30 per cent).

Individual stomach fill weights plotted against live weights for the M.F.P.S. samples show a large amount of scatter, but an approximately linear relationship between stomach fill and body weight.

The stomach fill weights as a percentage of live weight have also been calculated and are presented in Figs 8.2 and 8.3, for 85 males and 100 females examined. The results differ slightly from those presented by Laws and Parker (1968) in a preliminary paper. This is due to the fact that individual percentages of stomach fill have now been calculated and the live weight estimates (Laws,

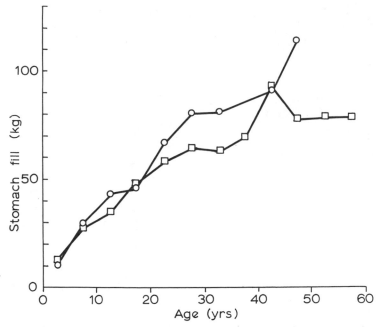

Fig. 8.1. Mean stomach fill at age, by 5-year classes, for elephants cropped in M.F.P.S. Circles—males; squares—females.

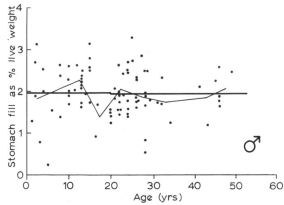

Fig. 8.2. Plot of percentage stomach fill against age for 85 male elephants cropped in M.F.P.S. Thin line—5-year means; thick lines—means for animals aged <20 years and >19 years.

Parker, and Archer 1967) have been improved by taking into account a larger sample of animals for which hind-leg weight and live weight were obtained (Appendix B). In the figures the average percentage stomach fill has been calculated for each sex in 5-year age classes. This suggests that the stomach fill in the male remains proportionally constant throughout the age group (average 1·97 per cent of live weight).

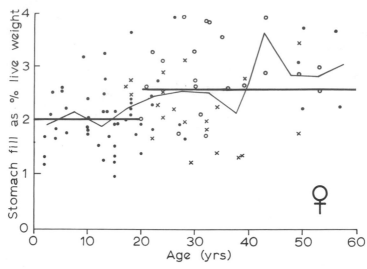

Fig. 8.3. Plot of percentage stomach fill against age for 100 female elephants cropped in M.F.P.S. Thin line–5-year means; thick lines–means for animals aged <20 years and >19 years. Black circles–immature or anoestrous females; open circles–lactating females; crosses–pregnant females.

In the female the average proportional stomach fill is 2·34 per cent but there is an increasing trend throughout the age series from about 2 per cent to about 3 per cent. The mean stomach fill for immature females was 2·03 per cent of live weight, for the mature females it was 2·59 per cent; and for the male the corresponding values were 1·98 per cent and 1·95 per cent. The proportional weights of stomach fill in immature females are not significantly different from all age groups of males ($p > 5$ per cent), and the difference between immature and mature females is found to be due to the significantly higher stomach fill of lactating females ($p < 5$ per cent). Thus, the stomach fill of immature females in the sample is 2·03 ± 0·16 per cent ($p = 5$ per cent); for anoestrus mature females it was 2·62 ± 0·72 per cent, for pregnant females it was 2·25 ± 0·27 per cent, and for lactating females it was 3·00 ± 0·25 per cent. The stomach fill percentages of all classes of female except lactating females and of males were not significantly different ($p > 5$ per cent).

A higher stomach fill in lactating females is known from studies on other species (e.g. Laws and Field 1965; Grimsdell 1969). Grimsdell's results provide an interesting comparison with the elephant. Lactating female buffalo had a 15 per cent higher food intake than mature non-lactating females, compared with a 14·5 per cent difference in elephant (this study). Pregnant female buffalo were twice as fat as lactating females, a reserve which is presumably mobilized for milk synthesis during lactation. Grimsdell suggests that in the evolution of breeding seasons there has been a selective compromise between the needs of the near-term female and the lactating female.

From the ecological point of view it is important to know, not merely the stomach fill at the time of sampling, but also the average daily intake and if possible the seasonal variations. If feeding is spread regularly over the 24 hours and the passage time is constant and known, the average rate of intake can be estimated from the average stomach fill of the sample. With the data presently available this presents difficulties, but an attempt has been made to obtain an approximate value which would certainly be modified to a greater or lesser extent if further experimental studies were undertaken. There is very little evidence on quantitative changes in seasonal rates of food intake. However, it is possible to compare the food intake of different elephant populations if certain assumptions are made, and even an approximate assessment is thought to be of value.

In Murchison Falls Park irregular observations suggested that elephant fed continuously throughout the day, but when shade was available they rested for several hours during the day. Buss (1961) gives evidence indicating that elephant fed throughout the 24-hour period but most frequently in the early morning. In the Queen Elizabeth Park Wyatt and Eltringham followed a marked female elephant continuously for three days and recorded activity at 4-minute intervals '. . . over 72 hours, the major activity was feeding (76%) with short periods of walking occurring throughout the day and night (9·1%). During each night the elephant rested for about 2–3 hours just before dawn' (Anon 1970).

Raiding of cultivated crops at night is common and well-known throughout the elephant range in Africa, the animals having learnt that it is safer than daylight raiding. We have numerous observations of elephant leaving the sanctuary of National Parks at dusk to feed in adjacent country or in shambas (smallholdings). Also, in night hippopotamus-cropping operations in Murchison Falls Park and in Queen Elizabeth Park, elephant were frequently seen feeding.

There is no reason to suppose that feeding is less intensive at night than during the day in Western Uganda. In drier areas, such as Tsavo, where a regular diurnal movement to water occurs in the dry season, it is unlikely that the rate of feeding is at all constant, although the reduced rate of feeding during the movement to and from water (in the vicinity of water, food is usually less abundant owing to the concentration of elephant use (Laws 1969b)) may be partly or wholly compensated for by the reduced rate of feeding during resting periods in the heat of the day. During the rains the pattern changes greatly and feeding is probably much more continuous.

In contrast to this dry-country pattern are the observations of Wing and Buss (1970) who observed elephant feeding nearly every hour of the 24 hours in the Kibale Forest, Uganda, and its vicinity. They noted that elephants closely followed changes in the thermal gradient within and between forest cover types and regulated their movements accordingly. On sunny days they were never observed feeding in open grassland between 10.30 and 15.30h. They were consistently observed moving into shaded areas and downhill into swamps (Plate 2·9) shortly after the morning sun became hot. During the night and early morning they fed usually at the forest edges, hillsides or on the catena tops, mostly in open cover types. However, these elephants were close to forest and its abundant shade.

Our sample was taken during the early and middle hours of the morning. When analysed by elephant groups (family units or bull herds), there was relatively little variation in the percentage stomach fill between groups and no significant differences could be demonstrated even when subclasses within groups were compared between groups (e.g. sexually immature animals). There was no evidence from our sample that time of day or social facilitation of feeding affected the recorded stomach fill weights. The evidence presented by Buss (1961) indicates that elephant fed most frequently in the early morning. The difference in the mean percentage stomach fill between his 45 elephants collected in the morning and 8 collected in the afternoon was significant ($p < 5$ per cent).

We conclude that diurnal behaviour is modified according to climate, season, and habitat type (particularly shade and water availability). In the greater part of the North Bunyoro elephant range there is no shade, and water is readily available. This is consistent with more or less continuous feeding, which is to be expected if the animals suffer nutritional stress—an assumption which the evidence of later sections supports.

There is very little information on the time of passage of food through the gut of the elephant. The only information on the African elephant of which we are aware is the observation of Bax and Sheldrick (1963) who reported that oranges fed to a tame semi-wild African elephant in the Tsavo National Park 'were excreted between 11 and 14 hours after feeding but some continued to appear in the faeces up to 19 hours later'. However, Benedict (1936) reported minimum passage times for a captive Indian elephant of 21–31 hours. His value for the passage time is thus about twice that reported by Bax and Sheldrick. The maximum excretion of stained food in the faeces occurs at 24 hours in the horse and pig, both of which are non-ruminants, but at 48 hours in the sheep (Lenkeit 1933) and 72 hours in the cow (Usuelli 1933). This is largely due to delay in the rumen, for when stained particles are introduced directly into the abomasum, 90 per cent are eliminated in the faeces in 24 hours (Phillipson 1963).

If the passage time in the elephant is as much as 24 hours, then the stomach fill at any one time would be equivalent to the daily intake (assuming virtually continuous feeding); if the passage time is 12 hours then the daily intake will be approximately twice the stomach fill. On these assumptions the daily intake of the North Bunyoro elephants sampled was about 2–4 per cent for all classes except for lactating females, for which it was about 3–6 per cent. But there are good reasons for accepting the lower passage time of 12 hours and therefore the upper estimates for daily food intake.

First, rapid passage is indicated by the fact that there was a significant difference in stomach fill between the elephants collected by Buss (1961) in morning and afternoon periods. The difference in the mean percentage stomach fill was 1·22 per cent, and the average difference in the mean time of collection of the two subsamples was about 8·5 hours. Thus, other factors being equal, the estimated throughput in 24 hours is 3·44 per cent of live weight (1·22 × (24/8·5)); allowing for the confidence limits of the stomach fill estimates, the estimated daily intake is between 3·13 per cent and 5·72 per cent of live weight.

Secondly, Petrides and Swank (1966) made an estimate of the daily consumption of food by a wild adult male elephant in the Queen Elizabeth National Park. This was based on a total weight of droppings, 49 kg (108 lb), produced by this animal in the field during 12 hours. Benedict (1936) showed that the defecation rate in captive elephants did not show a significant diurnal difference. He also established, for an Indian elephant, a ratio of 1·78:1 between the dry hay intake and the dry weight of faeces produced. Petrides and Swank made use of these findings to calculate that the intake of their observed elephant was 43 kg (94 lb) dry weight per day, that is 162 kg (356 lb) wet weight. They estimated the weight of this elephant, an adult male, at 4080 kg (9000 lb), so the estimated daily intake was about 4 per cent of live weight.

Thirdly, Wing and Buss (1970) estimated the average daily wet weight of droppings produced as 136 kg (300 lb). This was calculated from the observed average weight of 132 elephant droppings in the Queen Elizabeth National Park in the wet season (April—May 1964), and an average defecation rate of 17·0 droppings per 24 hours, based on 400 hours of observation.

This, however, was a heterogeneous sample from different seasons and possibly from more than one locality. Their results imply an estimated average daily intake of 242 kg (534 lb) per 24 hours, applying Benedict's (1936) ratio and assuming a similar wet: dry weight ratio for forage intake and faeces. If we assume an average elephant weighs about 1700 kg (3800 lb) (Laws 1966) then an estimate of 14 per cent for the daily wet weight intake is obtained. This is very much higher than the other estimates and is we believe, erroneous. It would imply a seemingly impossibly rapid throughput.

Their sample, however, was not a representative cross-section of a population and there are several obvious possible sources of error. The data on dropping weights relate to adult, sub-adult, and intermediate size classes only. Re-calculating on the basis of the adult dropping weights only (Wing and Buss 1970, Table 4), gives an estimated dropping weight of 176 kg (388 lb) per day and a daily intake of 313 kg (691 lb) applying Benedict's (1936) ratio. Assuming an average adult live weight of 3500 kg (7720 lb) (see Fig. 8.13) indicates a mean daily intake of 8·9 per cent of body weight. This is still probably rather high, since the highest observed percentage stomach fill (Buss 1961) suggests, with a passage time of 12 hours, a mean daily intake of only 6·8 per cent of body weight.

Taking this varied evidence into account, we conclude that a passage time of about 12 hours is reasonable, and applying this to the observed stomach fill weights gives an estimated daily intake for the M.F.P.S. elephants sampled in November 1965 of 4 per cent for immatures, mature males, and non-lactating mature females; and of 6 per cent for lactating females. The over all estimate on this basis for all classes is 4·4 per cent of live weight. As the sample was taken at the end of the rains (November) it probably represents an optimal seasonal intake.

A comparison of the M.F.P.S. sample with those from M.F.P.N. and T.N.P. should establish the relationships of the three populations in respect of this parameter. The mean stomach-fill weights at age for the other two samples will be presented in a later publication but the conclusions may usefully be summarized here.

The M.F.P.S. females have consistently lower stomach fill at age than the M.F.P.N. females, but consistently higher values than the T.N.P. females. As regards the male, M.F.P.N. stomach fills are again considerably higher than those in the M.F.P.S. sample, but there is no consistent difference between M.F.P.S. and T.N.P.

The M.F.P.N. sample was taken mainly in August-September (a few in March-May and November), which should be comparable with the M.F.P.S. sample. It was taken on average slightly later in the day, which, in view of the evidence presented earlier should tend to give lower stomach-fill weights.

In Fig. 8.4 the stomach-fill weights for the different samples are presented as histograms showing stomach fill frequencies, as a percentage of live weight for each of the sexes separately. In each case the male stomach fill is lower on average than the female stomach fill. The mean values and confidence limits are presented in Table 8.1.

Table 8.1

Mean stomach fill percentages for four elephant samples; 95 per cent confidence intervals are shown

Samples	Male	Female
T.N.P. August 1966	1·84 ± 0·12	2·00 ± 0·11
M.F.P.S. November 1965	1·98 ± 0·12	2·34 ± 0·15
M.F.P.N. August 1965	2·51 ± 0·22	2·93 ± 0·21
Buss (1961), 1958–9	3·14 ± 0·55	3·40 ± 0·40

Considering the present Western Uganda samples first, the M.F.P.S. stomach fills are lowest and this is in accord with the progress of habitat change over the range of these elephants. The M.F.P.N. elephants have a higher stomach fill, and this sample was taken in the Chobe area of the Murchison Falls National Park, where the habitat changes are least advanced. The small sample from the environs of Budongo Forest (Buss 1961) was selected and does not represent a random sample of all age classes. It was also collected over a period of several seasons. Nevertheless, it has been shown that age does not affect the percentage

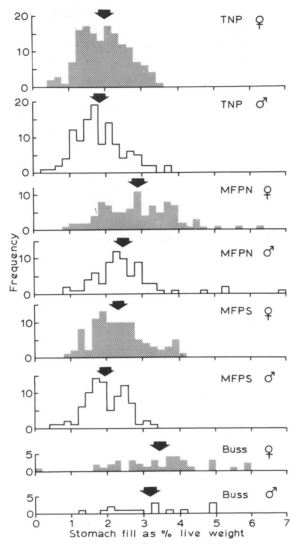

Fig. 8.4. Histograms showing frequency distribution of percentage stomach fill by sex, for four samples of elephants. The mean percentage values are indicated.

stomach fill of the male elephant (and this is confirmed by the other samples). The average male stomach fill in the Buss sample is significantly higher than the mean for the M.F.P.S. sample. This could be due to the fact that the habitat from which it was drawn was more favourable to elephant than that occupied by the other populations, being in the periphery of the elephant range; that it was collected mainly in the wooded country between Masindi and the Park boundary (Buss (1961), Figure 1); or that it was collected 6–7 years earlier than the

M.F.P.S. sample, that is at an earlier stage in the process of habitat deterioration. It is not significantly different from the M.F.P.N. sample which also represents a population associated with an earlier stage in habitat change.

We suggest that the stomach-fill weights of the T.N.P. sample are not directly comparable with those of the Uganda samples. The elephant in this sample were collected in the early morning as they returned from drinking in the Galana River, having spent at least several hours in the area of poor forage near the river. It is likely that the low stomach-fill percentage reflects their different diurnal pattern and that maximum feeding activity occurs in this population, at this season, later in the day. Also, it was sampled in the dry season, whereas the Murchison Falls Park samples were taken in the wet season. The proportion of browse in the stomachs was higher than in the Uganda populations sampled (Laws and Parker 1968) and this may be accompanied by reduced bulk of food, but not necessarily by a reduction in total energy and/or protein in the diet.

The evidence presented above suggests that the M.F.P.S. elephants may have a reduced food intake compared with the M.F.P.N. animals and that this could be a causative factor in the observed differences in population parameters, especially those related to reproduction (reduced fecundity, deferred sexual maturity, a larger post-reproductive section of the population, and retarded onset of oestrus during the breeding season). However, the quality of the food is more important than its bulk and we shall now consider this aspect of feeding.

8.1.2.   *Qualitative food intake*

8.1.2.1.   *Forest.* Wing and Buss (1970, p. 60) observed that 13 droppings examined in the Budongo Forest 'contained an average of approximately 60% herbaceous material and 40% woody material'. We are not yet able to add to this statement, although samples of stomach contents of elephant shot in the forest are being analysed by Dr. M. D. Gwynne, East African Agriculture and Forestry Research Organization.

During the study of elephant damage in the Budongo Forest, described in Chapter 11, it was found that the main damage was to young regeneration. Wing and Buss (1970) also found in their study in the Kibale Forest that 'A very striking preference by elephants for the smaller size classes is apparent. Nearly 75 per cent of all woody stems utilized by elephants are less than 1 inch d.b.h. and 97·54 per cent are less than 4 inches d.b.h.'. Of all woody stems in the elephant diet 80·3 per cent were from species that seldom exceed 1·5 ft (46 cm) d.b.h., according to these workers. Damage in both studies was found to consist of the breaking of leading shoots, which were rarely found. This suggests that these shoots were broken off and eaten, and in this event a consideration of the amount of damage to each species should indicate whether or not the elephants have any preference in their selection of trees for food.

During our damage study (Chapter 11) it was noticeable that not all the desirable species in any plot were damaged and that in many cases where two adjacent trees of the same species and size occurred, one would show damage and the other not. It was evident that the number of trees broken was related to the numbers of elephants passing through an area and the amount of time they spent in a particular area. There was a tendency for elephants to spend longer in those areas which had a concentration of particular species. Thus, where *Cordia millenii* and *Morus lactea* were found together elephants would spend more time in that area than others.

It was equally evident that selection depended on other unknown factors, probably including availability of other preferred species; thus *Antiaris toxicaria* was greatly subject to damage in Budongo Compartment N 7, yet in Compartments W 18 and N 9 the damage to this species was much less.

The investigation showed that all species were liable to damage, but some less than others. In the total area sampled certain species were heavily damaged, some suffered a moderate amount of damage and others were only slightly damaged; thus:

Damage high	Damage moderate	Damage slight
Morus lactea	*Khaya anthotheca*	*Guarea cedrata*
Cordia millenii	*Chrysophyllum albidum*	*Holoptelia grandis*
Trichilia spp.	*Maesopsis eminii*	*Olea welwitschii*
Albizia spp.		*Schrebera arborea*

It follows that the species in the first group are probably highly preferred foods, whereas the species in the third group are not.

It is of considerable interest that the two most prolific desirable timber-producing species in Budongo (*Khaya anthotheca* and *Chrysophyllum albidum*) suffer only a moderate amount of damage. This suggests that these species occur in sufficient numbers to more than satisfy the feeding demands of the elephant population. If, however, the numbers of elephant were to increase, either generally or locally, then the amount of damage to these species would probably also increase. It also seems probable that elephants are partly responsible for the large numbers of these species that occur, because it was noted from inspection of their droppings that large quantities of fruit, particularly *Chrysophyllum albidum*, are consumed, pass through the stomach, and germinate in the droppings.

It was noted during the enumeration of damage (Chapter 11) that damage to the boles of trees (removal of bark) is relatively slight. This contrasts with the observation of the older trees in the forest, or in grassland, where bark damage is heavy (see Chapter 11, Plate 11.1) and would support the suggestion that in areas where there is a plentiful supply of herbaceous material, namely the young regeneration areas, elephant do not need to take bark from adult trees. It suggests that bark removal is in response to a nutritional requirement and that the elephant needs a substantial proportion of woody or fibrous material in its diet. If this is correct, then the exclusion of elephants from the young regeneration areas would probably result in an increase in the incidence of bark removal elsewhere in the forest, thus reversing the process later shown to have occurred since the mid-1950s.

8.1.2.2. Grassland and woodland. As Buss (1961) and Laws and Parker (1968) have demonstrated, grass comprises 80—90 per cent of the stomach fill in this habitat type in North Bunyoro. Wing and Buss (1970) report 94 per cent grass in elephant droppings examined in the Queen Elizabeth Park, Uganda, in April/ May. Buss (1961) remarked: 'the exact proportions of grasslands and forest which comprise the optimum range for the African elephant have not yet been determined. However, the importance of grass as a food suggests that maintenance of relatively large areas of grassland in the Murchison Falls National Park region may be highly significant to the high population of elephants which the area currently supports.'

His reasoning appears to be that, because there are large numbers of elephants and they have large amounts of grass in their stomachs, grass is essential for high-density populations. However, we have presented evidence to show that high densities are the result of the reduction in the area of the elephant range due to human activities, and the elephant population is in fact declining (see Chapter 10). Laws and Parker (1968) suggested 'that reduction of available browse, leading to dependence on grass, particularly in the dry season, is a contributory factor to the decline. Viewed in this way grassland does not produce high populations of elephant, but is induced by their action and is then inadequate to support continuing high densities.'

The forest studies have clearly indicated that when abundant young woody growth is available it is preferred to older trees. Laws (1969b) suggested that this was true throughout the elephant range in Africa. In the North Bunyoro woodland and grassland there is little or no regeneration and the mature trees have been attacked by elephant. It is not known what order of species preference the elephants exercised in the pristine woodland. No species are currently completely free from damage, but the heaviest barking damage occurs to *Terminalia glaucescens* and *Combretum binderanum.* Further details of the habitat changes, which suggest inferences about food preferences, are given in Chapter 11.

We agree with Beuchner and Dawkins (1961) that in the grassland, wooded grassland, and woodland

selection of bark as food is seasonal in the case of the deciduous *T. glaucescens*, which is leafless during the dry season from early January to early March, and feeding on bark is concentrated during the period of regrowth of the foliage when the bark will peel. Possibly the taste of the sap satisfies the elephant's palate or perhaps the bark and sap contribute important nutrients to the diet. Whatever the reason, elephants debark *T. glaucescens* trees to the extent that, combined with burning the habit contributes to the mortality of the trees . . . [and] . . . the most severely damaged trees appeared to be ones for which elephants had developed a predilection. Once removal of the bark was sufficiently advanced, the animals repeatedly sought out the same tree rather than attack less damaged trees.

The selection is relative for, as these authors point out, in Pandera woodland (M.F.P.N.), 'the composition was changing rapidly in favour of *T. glaucescens* in part because elephants preferred the bark of *P. africana*'.

Field (1971) has recently studied the feeding habits of elephants in Western Uganda by direct observation. He compared the food taken in two study areas in the Queen Elizabeth National Park. One was predominantly long grass, the other a short grass-thicket mosaic. Grass was the main item taken, browse varying according to availability; there were large seasonal fluctuations in the type of food, with more browse taken in the dry season. In the long-grass area, where there was very little browse, the herbs taken varied inversely with the grasses and were highest during the rains, when they are most abundantly available. Thus the ranges of seasonal fluctuations were: long-grass area, 45–93 per cent grass, 1–12 per cent browse, 2–49 per cent herbs; short grass/thicket, 31–74 per cent grass and sedges, 8–45 per cent browse 9–42 per cent herbs. A similar short-term study during the single dry season (January) in the Kidepo Valley, north-east Uganda, found only 32 per cent grass and 40 per cent tree material (fruit, bark, branches) (Field, personal communication). Two herds were observed consuming abundant *Balanites aegyptiaca* fruits.

Thus, it appears that in woodland and bushland, much lower proportions of grass (*ca* 30–50 per cent) are taken if woody growth and herbs are available than those recorded in the North Bunyoro study (80–90 per cent).

8.1.3. *Chemical composition of stomach contents*

Our colleague McCullagh (1969a) investigated the instantaneous growth rates of elephants in the North Bunyoro and West Acholi populations. He found that young animals go through a period of growth restriction during the dry season and that even mature animals suffer a period of reduced connective tissue metabolism at this time.

He therefore studied the possibility that this was caused by a shortage of food, specifically by reduced protein intake during the dry season (McCullagh 1969b) and it is of interest briefly to summarize his results. Samples from the oesophageal region of the stomach were analysed from 148 elephants in four roughly equal-sized groups, collected in November/December 1966, January, March, and May, 1967. The first two samples were taken from the M.F.P.N. population, the latter two from the M.F.P.S.

The average composition (dry weight) of the food ingested for all four samples was 8·4 per cent protein, 1·5 per cent lipid, 43·5 per cent carbohydrate, 35·7 per cent fibre, and 11·0 per cent ash. The average energy content was 243 kcal per 100 g. Comparisons between the four samples indicated that energy, protein, fibre, and ash vary with rainfall, the relative change in protein content being the most pronounced. Fat and carbohydrate were not significantly different. The fat was characterized by a high palmitic acid content (43–6 per cent of total fatty acids), which interestingly compares with its uniquely high concentration in elephant depot fat (40—5 per cent (Duncan and Garton 1968)).

The protein level was only $5 \cdot 2 \pm 1 \cdot 1$ per cent in the dry season (January) compared with $12 \cdot 5 \pm 3 \cdot 4$ per cent in the May sample. The latter value compares with a wet season (May) value of $12 \cdot 5$ per cent obtained by Dougall and Sheldrick (1964) for a single day's diet of a Tsavo National Park elephant. The diet for the latter animal included many herbaceous, leguminous and woody plants; grass amounted to only about 10 per cent of intake, expressed on a time basis. Field (1968) presents the results of monthly analyses for crude protein of seven species of grasses collected in the Queen Elizabeth Park, also in Western Uganda. The leaf crude protein level varied between 6 per cent and 11 per cent with peaks in the rains; stem crude protein varied between 3 per cent and 6 per cent with little fluctuation. Bredon and Horrell (1961, Fig. 1) show a decline in average crude protein content of several grass species from *ca* 15 per cent at the beginning of the rains to *ca* 5 per cent over the rest of the year.

McCullagh (1969b) assumed that 75 per cent of the crude protein is digestible, so that during the dry season, the Murchison Falls Park elephants obtained only 4 kg digestible protein per 100 kg food. This is low compared with recommended levels for domestic animals, but may be misleading as the elephant is a non-ruminant with a short passage time and a vast throughput of cellulose (see below). Mean daily wet-season food consumption was estimated at about $4 \cdot 8$ per cent (male) or $5 \cdot 6$ per cent (female) of body weight (Laws and Parker 1968). Thus, for a young growing elephant of 1000 kg the mean daily wet-season intake was estimated at 48 kg (wet weight).

Making some rather large assumptions, McCullagh (1969b) calculated that this would provide some $0 \cdot 26$ kg digestible protein in the dry season and $0 \cdot 60$ kg in the wet season. He estimated daily maintenance requirements at $0 \cdot 3$ kg for an elephant of this size. As McCullagh points out, some of the assumptions are over optimistic (e.g. that elephant digestion of protein is as efficient as a ruminant's and that digestibility does not vary with the seasonally changing protein: fibre ratio). Also further studies on the North Bunyoro elephants suggest that daily food consumption is somewhat lower than the values on which McCullagh based his calculations. For growth to occur, a level of protein intake which is above maintenance requirements is necessary and it seems very possible that in the dry season the protein intake is insufficient for maintenance and that the elephants must draw on their reserves.

Subsamples taken in January and March (dry and wet seasons) were compared for mineral content. Phosphorus and sodium were constant, but amounts of other minerals were significantly different in the samples from the two months, the January sample showing more calcium and less potassium and silicates. McCullagh sought to confirm that this did not reflect a higher proportion of browse in the samples, by comparing predominantly grass samples, and this gave a similar result. However, this is a very critical point in the argument and in the absence of detailed analysis of the food by species or families, the possibility of differential plant composition cannot be ruled out.

Dougall, Drysdale, and Glover (1964) found, for Kenya browse and pasture that 'the average calcium (Ca) content of the grasses is only one-third of that of the legumes and one-fourth of that of the leguminous and non-leguminous browse respectively' and 'on average silica (SiO_2) constitutes over 45 per cent of the total ash of the grasses but only some 10 per cent of that of the legumes and some 6 per cent of that of the leguminous browse' and a similar proportion of that of non-leguminous browse.

Potassium attains on average a reasonably high level throughout the vegetation. The different mineral compositions of wet- and dry-season samples is similar to that to be expected from a higher proportion of grass in the South bank elephant diet, compared with the North bank. A detailed examination of stomach samples collected by us from several elephant populations is being carried out by Dr. M. D. Gwynne, East African Agriculture and Forestry Research Organization. It can be expected to clarify this point.

McCullagh (1969b) calculates that the basic calcium requirement of a growing 1000 kg elephant is 8–9 g of calcium per day, and it obtains in its diet 13 g in the wet season (south bank) and 38 g in the dry season (north bank)—assuming the dry-season bulk intake to be the same as in the wet season. Unfortunately there is no information on the gross daily intake of food in the dry season.

These estimates also assume a similar skeleton-bodyweight ratio and a similar calcium metabolism to man. The tusks of a 1000 kg male elephant (aged about 5–6 years) grow at the rate of about 0·7 kg a year on average, that is about 2 g per day. The calcium content of elephant ivory is about 45 per cent (Bishop 1964) so the tusks alone account for about 1 g calcium per day at this age. In a 30 year old male elephant of 4500 kg bodyweight about 3 g calcium per day are required for tusk growth alone (Laws, unpublished).

It is possible that there is an excess of calcium in the diet in the dry season and a deficiency in the wet season, but it is also a possibility that the south bank elephants obtain even less calcium in the dry season, and the north bank animals even more in the wet-season. A certain amount of calcium may be taken in by drinking, passing rapidly through the stomach to the intestine so that it would not be represented in stomach content analysis, and the elephant may make good a possible calcium deficiency by drinking calcium-rich water in the wet season.

8.1.4. *Nutritional factors involved in the de-barking of trees by elephants*

The suggested wet-season deficiency of calcium would not necessarily conflict with indirect evidence from elephant behaviour indicating that nutritional deficiencies may be experienced mainly in the dry season or at the beginning of the rains, for the wet-season sample analysed by McCullagh (1969b) was taken at the beginning of the rains. This is the season when de-barking of trees is most noticeable in Murchison.

Bredon and Horrell (1961) have shown that for several grass species collected in Uganda there is a high protein content (12—19 per cent) at the beginning of March and a low fibre content (20—29 per cent). The main decline in protein content occurs during the first months of the growing season and then fluctuates only slightly for the rest of the year. Conversely the fibre content shows a complementary increase. Thus, in March, the protein: fibre ratio may be suboptimal for the elephants' digestive process and de-barking of trees a response to the shortage of fibre in the diet.

In their penetrating study of selection of vegetation by grazers, Gwynne and Bell (1969) and Bell (1969, 1970) discuss the difference in cellulose (fibre) content of the diet of certain ruminants and non-ruminants and conclude that the horse and zebra are specialized for a diet of high cellulose content. 'In view of the general agreement that the particular function of the rumen is to break down cellulose, it is surprising that the animal the diet of which consistently contains the most cellulose is not a ruminant', and they point out differences in the feeding mechanisms of horses and ruminants. 'There is some evidence that the cellulose is broken down more readily in the caecum of the horse than in the stomach of the ruminant and that the horse habitually relies more on cellulose than on soluble carbohydrates as an energy source than do ruminants' (Alexander 1952).

The elephant, also a non-ruminant, feeds by plucking entire plants or large bundles of vegetation, which also results in a diet of high fibre content, particularly in the dry season. The colon and caecum of the elephant are large and probably act as fermentation chambers.

It was also noted in the Tsavo studies that in some areas 'the first response of the elephant population to rain was a movement on to grassed areas, digging for roots and pushing over trees (possibly for the roots)' (Laws.1969b). It seems possible then, that in order to exploit the high protein content of young growing grasses, elephants need to augment the cellulose content of their feed by taking woody material. Although a limited number of bark analyses (Tables 8.2 and 8.3) do not indicate any correlation between fibre content and extent of elephant damage, the average fibre content for the nine samples (40 per cent) is very nearly double Bredon and Horrell's (1961) value for grasses at the beginning of the rains (*ca* 25 per cent). For *Terminalia* it is nearly 50 per cent. The stomach samples analysed by McCullagh (1969b) showed 41·0 ± 6·0 per cent fibre in two dry season months and 37·9 ± 1·4 per cent and 32·6 ± 3·5 per cent fibre at the beginning of the rains (March) but included woody material.

We are indebted to R. H. V. Bell (*in litt.*) for the following comment on the question of why high protein—low fibre grass might be unfavourable.

(1)There might be a relationship between rate of breakdown of ingesta and rate of throughput (as in ruminants) so that easily digestible stuff is going through too fast and giving a low *absolute* rate of assimilation.

(2) In ruminants there is a relationship between water availability and metabolic rate [Taylor and Lyman 1967] so that high water content diet (i.e. high protein content in grass) can have an adverse effect on condition because of higher maintenance requirements.

Taylor, Spinage, and Lyman (1969) in their study of water relations in the waterbuck, showed that it ate less food when its water intake was restricted. 'This was a steady-state condition, and could be explained only by a decreased metabolism or a more complete digestion of its food. The decrease in food intake was entirely due to a more complete digestion of the food and, as a result, less dry feces were produced.' According to Foster and Coe (1968) much of the mortality of Nairobi Park associated with the drought of 1961–2 occurred after the beginning of the rains, and Spinage (1970) concluded that this was the time of greatest stress in the waterbuck. This problem deserves further investigation.

Our colleague, Dr. C. R. Field, undertook a minor investigation of the bark content of nine tree species characteristic of the southern part of the Murchison Falls National Park. He collected samples of bark and noted the extent of elephant damage to the individual tree, expressed as a barking index: (scar height + width)/2. The barking-index ranking conforms in general to our field observations on tree damage. Buss (1961) noted the higher incidence of elephant damage to *Terminalia* (see Chapter 11, Plate 11.1) than to *Balanites*. The samples were analysed for us by Mr. C. N. Karne, East African Agriculture and Forestry Research Organization, and the results are presented in Tables 8.2 and 8.3.

Table 8.2

Analyses of bark samples from trees de-barked by elephants, expressed as percentage of dry matter

Species	Barking index	Crude protein	Crude fat	Carbohydrate
Chlorophora excelsa	4·00	4·62	1·37	27·28
Terminalia glaucescens	2·85	1·75	0·54	49·87
Tamarindus indica	n.r.	3·59	0·78	29·95
Combretum sp.aff. *microlepidotum*	2·35	2·67	0·41	37·32
Kigelia aethiopicum	2·23	4·53	0·50	58·58
Euphorbia candelabrum	1·88	5·76	4·59	43·41
Trichilia roka	1·75	4·64	1·85	61·43
Crataeva adansonii	0·98	12·00	0·88	21·89
Balanites sp. (?) *aegyptiaca*	rubbed only	4·04	0·78	32·53

Note: n.r. = not recorded

There is no evident correlation between protein, fat, or carbohydrate content and degree of de-barking. With the exception of *Balanites* there is a significant correlation between barking index and calcium content, but it should be pointed out that factors other than chemical composition may be involved in determining the incidence of de-barking in a particular species, for example the mechanical properties of the bark, which can facilitate or hinder de-barking. In the present samples there is an inverse correlation between calcium and potassium and between calcium and phosphorus, and a direct correlation between calcium and sodium content. The relatively high manganese content in the sample of *Combretum* bark is notable and Dougall *et al.* (1964) discuss the high mineral content of some plants, mentioning specifically manganese, iron, boron, and copper. Clearly there is insufficient data from which to reach firm conclusions, but enough to show that further investigations should be worthwhile, as they may provide an explanation for species-selective elephant barking of mature trees.

Table 8.3

Analyses of mineral content of bark samples from trees de-barked by elephants, expressed as percentage of dry matter, except for Fe and Mn which are in p.p.m.

Species	Barking index	Ca	P	Mg	K	Na	Fe	Mn	Ca:P
Chlorophora excelsa	4·00	5·74	0·033	0·21	1·68	0·24	59	32	176·6
Terminalia glaucescens	2·85	6·75	0·020	0·07	0·90	0·41	62·	20	346·2
Tamarindus indica	n.r.	5·81	0·053	1·05	1·61	0·37	80	12	110·6
Combretum sp.aff. *microlapidotum*	2·35	2·62	0·036	0·38	2·30	0·05	212	356	72·8
Kigelia aethiopicum	2·23	1·62	0·101	0·13	2·73	0·09	198	12	16·1
Euphorbia candelabrum	1·88	0·70	0·054	1·05	6·80	0·03	120	30	13·0
Trichilia roka	1·75	2·56	0·111	0·74	4·95	0·14	56	22	23·1
Crataeva adansonii	0·98	1·23	0·066	0·25	8·80	0·02	176	44	18·6
Balanites sp. (?) *aegyptiaca*	rubbed only	4·76	0·029	0·75	2·10	0·38	204	32	164·1

Note: n.r. = not recorded

McCullagh (1969b) compared 'woody' and 'grass' stomach samples from both Murchison elephant populations and found the former to be higher in calcium as expected. Laws and Parker (1968), using a subjective method of examination found about 14·5 per cent bark and about 1·5 per cent browse in 60 M.F.P.N. stomachs examined in August 1965; in 53 M.F.P.S. stomachs examined in November 1965, there was approximately 0·9 per cent bark and 3·7 per cent browse. North bank animals may perhaps be less prone to calcium deficiency because the habitat contains more woodland, and it is unfortunate that concurrent samples were not available from the two populations. It is suggested elsewhere in this book that skeletal growth does not differ between the two populations but that the net seasonal increment in weight may be less in the South bank population.

This book gives no conclusive direct evidence to explain the de-barking and destruction of trees by elephant. In the Murchison Falls Park it seems probable that it is a direct nutritional effect of increasing density of elephant and seasonal over-use of the woodland resources to supplement diet, but we have thrown little light on the reasons for preferential damage of certain species. It may or may not be significant that *Chlorophora* and *Terminalia*, trees bearing bark with a high calcium content, are preferentially damaged by elephant, and that stomach content analyses suggest that in M.F.P.S., elephants may suffer a calcium deficiency, seasonally, if not over the year.

McCullagh (1969b) has pointed out the danger of assuming that the de-barking behaviour is initiated in response to the direct effect of a fall in the level of calcium circulating in the blood. It is not, however, necessary to postulate such a direct effect and one must be careful to distinguish between ultimate and proximate ecological factors, the proximate factor in this case probably being climatic. However, it is now suggested that, to maintain a suitable protein: fibre ratio at the beginning of the rains it is necessary for the elephants to supplement their diet by taking in bark and other fibrous material. This may not require pronounced selectivity since the fibre content of the bark may be relatively constant in relation to effort expended in de-barking. The preferential de-barking of certain species may therefore be related to the relative mineral content of the bark, and this subject merits fuller investigation.

8.2. Condition

It was desirable that population parameters should be related if possible to the condition of the animals in the various populations studied. This would establish whether or not the ranked series of reproductive patterns (Laws 1969a) were closely correlated with condition and by implication with nutritional status and habitat change. To this end limited field observations were made and serum samples collected from the cropped animals for subsequent analysis. The results of serum analyses were presented and discussed by McCullagh (1970). Two samples (M.F.P.S. and T.N.P.) were compared in respect of total lipids, total cholesterol, free cholesterol, phospholipids, triglyceride, and free fatty acid. There were highly significant differences ($p < 1$ per cent) in total cholesterol and free fatty acid levels which were higher in the T.N.P. sample. These appear to correlate with differences in levels of atherosclerosis, which was more severe in T.N.P. animals than in M.F.P.S. animals. There was however, some support for the suggestion that circulating lipid levels varied seasonally, being higher in the dry season (when the T.N.P. sample was collected). McCullagh gives reasons for concluding that 'there is no simple relationship between atherosclerosis and serum cholesterol in the elephant'. The M.F.P.N. and M.F.P.S. samples were not significantly different in terms of total cholesterol and total phospholipids; other lipids were not determined in the M.F.P.N. sample.

Two other indices of condition are considered here. Unfortunately, the overriding effect of inevitable seasonal differences in the time of sampling complicates interpretation of the results which cannot be directly compared. As a result only qualitative conclusions are possible. Nevertheless, it is evident that, where growth or reproductive rates are lower they are correlated with poorer condition as measured by our criteria.

8.2.1.   *Kidney-fat indices*

This method has been used widely in wildlife research, particularly on deer, and the advantages and disadvantages have been discussed (Riney 1955; Ransom 1965). Laws (1964) and Grimsdell (1969) employed a similar method for the study of condition in hippopotamus (*H.amphibius*) and buffalo (*Syncerus caffer*) in Uganda, expressing omental fat as a percentage of body weight.

In the initial elephant samples collected, including about 200 from M.F.P.N., 200 from M.F.P.S., and 300 from T.N.P., kidney fat deposits were measured as an index of condition (Appendix B). Removing the fat from the large elephant kidney is time consuming and pressure of other work unfortunately led to its being abandoned in later operations. It is worth describing the results because they indicate differences in fatness between populations and between classes of animals within those populations. They are relevant to an assessment of the status of the M.F.P.S. population.

For each individual a kidney-fat index (weight of kidney fat/kidney weight), for the two kidneys combined was calculated, and the results expressed to three decimal places; high values represent large kidney-fat deposits. The direct influence of body size or kidney size is eliminated by taking the index in this way.

Indices varied from 0·060 to 1·400 in T.N.P. males, from 0·090 to 1·000 in T.N.P. females, from 0·025 to 0·670 in M.F.P. males, and from 0·030 to 0·930 in M.F.P. females. The mean indices for 5-year age classes by sex and population (M.F.P.S., M.F.P.N., and T.N.P.) are compared in Fig. 8.5.

The Tsavo sample was taken in August 1966, towards the end of the dry season, and the Murchison Falls samples in August (M.F.P.N.) and November (M.F.P.S.), in the second half of the rains. Other factors being equal, then, it would be expected that the animals in the Murchison Falls Park samples would be fatter than those in the T.N.P. samples. The overwhelming field impression was that the T.N.P. animals were in fact much fatter than those examined in Murchison Falls Park. This was confirmed by the subsequent analysis (Fig. 8.5), the T.N.P. sample being fatter at all ages than the Murchison Falls Park samples and M.F.P.S. animals in general fatter than those from M.F.P.N.

In the Murchison Falls Park samples, at least from the second 5-year class on, there is little age-specific difference in kidney-fat index, whereas in T.N.P. the average kidney fat indices show a progressive decrease with age. From the second 5-year class onwards the average T.N.P. indices are higher in the females than in the male, but in Murchison Falls Park the kidney-fat indices are similar in the two sexes. However, if the classes of mature females in the M.F.P.S. sample are

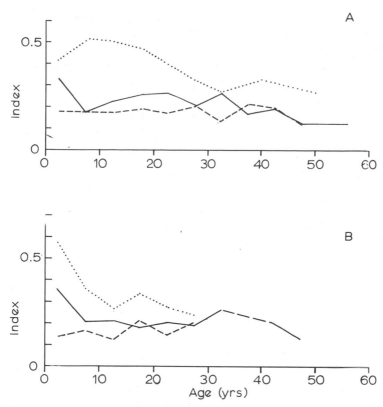

Fig. 8.5. Comparison of kidney-fat indices for three populations sampled: (A) female, (B) male; dotted line–Tsavo; continuous line–M.F.P.S; broken line–M.F.P.N.

compared, the mean kidney-fat indices are for cycling, pregnant, and pregnant/ lactating, $0·280 ± 0·062$; lactating anoestrous, $0·155 ± 0·046$; and for anoestrous females $0·200 ± 0·092$ ($p = 5\%$). Thus, the pregnant females are in significantly better condition, as measured by this index, than lactating females.

Although it is difficult to draw firm conclusions from such small samples, restricted in time, it is evident that the difference between the Kenya and Uganda samples is greatest in the younger age groups. Presumably the difference would be even greater if the Tsavo sample had been taken during the rains or earlier in the dry season, when its nutritional status should have been better. The indication that M.F.P.S. animals were slightly fatter than M.F.P.N. animals might be reversed if samples from the same month were available for comparison. The present M.F.P.S. sample was collected three months later in the rainy season than that from M.F.P.N. The high kidney-fat indices of young Tsavo animals imply that nutrition may not be limiting for them at a time when growth is maximal and that there is an excess of energy which can be stored as fat. In contrast, the relatively low kidney fat indices for Murchison Falls Park animals may indicate that food is limiting, especially in the young age groups and is in accord with the suggestion that higher calf mortality rates obtain in Murchison Falls Park (Chapter 10).

It is unfortunate that kidney-fat data were not obtained from the Mkomasi (M.K.E. and M.K.C.) populations, because these elephant populations prove to be the most productive that have yet been studied, and the examination of the shoulder height—body weight relationship shows that they were in better condition than the other three populations. However, field conditions during these operations were particularly unfavourable.

8.2.2.   *Shoulder height—body weight relationship*

The relationship between shoulder height and body weight gives an indication of relative condition; the methods of measuring height and weight are described in Appendix B. Samples are available from four populations, M.F.P.S., M.F.P.N., T.N.P., and M.K.E. The first three samples were the same animals as those from which kidney fat indices were obtained; the M.K.E. sample was collected in March 1968 at the beginning of the rains. The T.N.P. and M.K.E. elephants are at a lower population density than the Murchison Falls elephants and the M.K.E. habitat is considered to be more favourable to elephant than that with which the T.N.P. animals are associated (Laws 1969b). Thus, on these grounds of all the samples the M.K.E. elephants would be expected to be in the optimal physical condition, if allowance could be made for seasonal differences.

The relationship between height and weight calculated for the Murchison Falls samples gave the following equations for the prediction of weight w from shoulder height h; where r is the correlation coefficient:

M.F.P.S. females	$w = 0 \cdot 001267 \ h^{2 \cdot 631}$,	$r = 0 \cdot 968$
M.F.P.S. males	$w = 0 \cdot 000507 \ h^{2 \cdot 803}$,	$r = 0 \cdot 989$
M.F.P.N. females	$w = 0 \cdot 000258 \ h^{2 \cdot 917}$,	$r = 0 \cdot 981$
M.F.P.N. males	$w = 0 \cdot 000306 \ h^{2 \cdot 890}$,	$r = 0 \cdot 990$

For comparative purposes a simple cube relationship is assumed and plots of shoulder height against the cube root of body weight for M.F.P.S. are presented in Fig. 8.6. The plots are similar for M.F.P.S., M.F.P.N., and T.N.P., but the mean weights of the M.F.P.S. sample are lighter at all shoulder heights than the M.K.E. sample. At a shoulder height of 200 cm the M.K.E. males weighed 133 kg (or 9·3 per cent) heavier on average than M.F.P.S. males (1561 kg cf. 1428 kg); at 300 cm they were 550 kg (12·4 per cent) heavier than M.F.P.S. animals (5000 kg cf. 4450 kg). At 200 cm shoulder height the difference was the same in the females as for males; at 250 cm the females were 344 kg (or 13·3 per cent) heavier in Mkomasi than in Murchison Falls Park (2924 kg cf. 2686 kg).

The M.F.P.S. sample was taken mainly in November; that is towards the end of the rains, whereas the T.N.P. sample·was taken in August 1966 during the second half of the dry season, and the M.K.E. sample was taken in March 1968

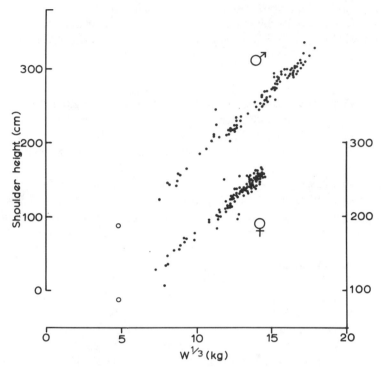

Fig. 8.6. Plots of shoulder height against cube root of live weight for male and female elephants cropped in M.F.P.S.

at the beginning of the rains. Other factors remaining equal, then, the T.N.P. sample, during the dry season, and the M.K.E. sample, after the dry season, should be in progressively poorer condition than that from M.F.P.S., because nutritional status improves with the progressive improvement in quantity and quality of vegetation during the rains. As the M.F.P.S. sample was taken towards the end of the rains, the inescapable inference is that the condition of the M.F.P.S. elephants is even poorer in the dry season, and the difference in condition between these populations much greater than direct comparison of the three samples would suggest. However, even assuming that the seasonal factor has no weight, the M.K.E. elephants were 9–13 per cent heavier at given shoulder heights than the M.F.P.S. animals.

This strongly suggests that M.F.P.S. elephants are well below the optimal physical condition for the species, with consequences for growth, reproduction and population dynamics that will be seen in subsequent sections.

8.3. Growth

Laws and Parker (1968) presented growth data based on size at age for the initial samples of elephant cropped in the Murchison Falls National Park and provisional growth equations were calculated. Further information on growth is now available, both for the M.F.P.S. population and for elephants shot in the Budongo Central Forest Reserve (B.C.F.R.), and some evidence of seasonal fluctuations in growth rates has become available.

8.3.1.　*Shoulder height*

8.3.1.1.　*Murchison Falls Park, South.* Shoulder height or height at withers (Appendix B) is a very good dimension for describing linear growth of elephants and has a much smaller variance at age than body weight, because it is not subject to the rapid seasonal fluctuations which clearly characterize body weight It can also be used to estimate the ages of wild elephants in the field if heights can be measured by a photographic method (Douglas-Hamilton 1972).

In Figs 8.7 and 8.8 the shoulder height measurements of 335 male and 458 female elephants from M.F.P.S. are plotted against age. The scatter is surprisingly small, giving confirmation of the consistency of the ageing. The two sexes would appear to show similar growth up to about 20 years, after which the male appears to grow much faster than the female, so that the maximum heights attained are very different. This was first reported by Laws (1969b).

The difference between the sexes is even clearer if the mean shoulder heights at age are plotted (Fig. 8.9) when it is seen that the sexes do diverge from about four years of age onwards, but that from about 20 years onwards there appears to be a marked acceleration in the male growth rate which is responsible for the definitive mature sexual disparity in size of the species. The parameters of the von Bertalanffy (1938) growth equation have been calculated for both sexes, based on the mean shoulder height h at age t for both sexes from birth to 20 years (Beverton and Holt 1957). The equations obtained are:

male $\qquad h_t = 265\ [1 - \exp(-0{\cdot}114\ (t + 3{\cdot}95))]$ cm
female $\qquad h_t = 252\ [1 - \exp(-0{\cdot}099\ (t + 6{\cdot}00))]$ cm

These equations give a very good fit to the data from age 2 years upwards in the female and from $1-20$ years in the male. But in the male the mean shoulder heights at ages above 20 years, according to this equation, are very much lower than the observed values, strongly supporting the suggestion that there is a secondary acceleration of growth in the male at these higher ages.

A second growth equation has been fitted to the male shoulder heights at ages $21-30$ onwards, and gives a very close fit to the data for ages above 20 years. This equation is:

$$h_t = 307\ [1 - \exp(-0{\cdot}166\ (t - 10{\cdot}48))]\ \text{cm}.$$

The present growth equation for the female is similar to that reported by Laws and Parker (1968), based on a much smaller combined sample from M.F.P.S. and M.F.P.N., but the male growth curve is very different. This difference is largely due to the apparent secondary growth spurt not having been recognized previously in the smaller sample and to the data from two populations having

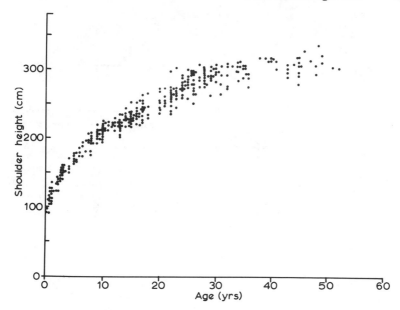

Fig. 8.7. Plot of shoulder height against age for 335 male elephants cropped in M.F.P.S.

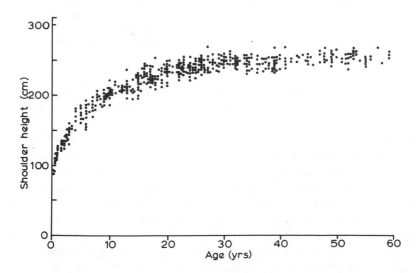

Fig. 8.8. Plot of shoulder height against age for 458 female elephants cropped in M.F.P.S.

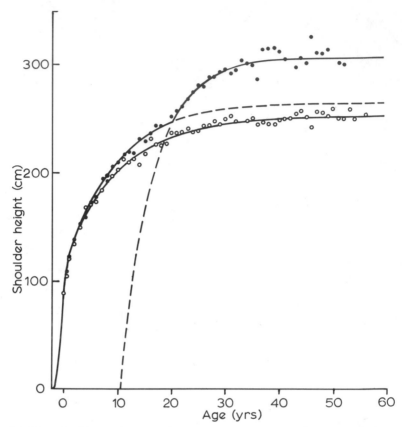

Fig. 8.9. Mean shoulder heights at age for M.F.P.S. males (black circles) and females (open circles). The fitted von Bertalanffy growth equations are drawn and foetal growth shown (see text).

been combined to enlarge the earlier sample. The average potential male shoulder height at 60 years is 55 centimetres (nearly 2 feet) (or 21·8 per cent) higher than in the female.

The similarity of the present growth curves for the sexes based on ages 1–20 years is very interesting. As Laws (1969a) suggested, it appears that in the Indian elephant (*Elephas maximus*) and the African forest elephant (*Loxodonta a. cyclotis*), the secondary growth spurt in the male may be lacking or insignificant. If true this may point to important differences in the social organization of the Indian and forest elephants as compared with the African bush elephant (*L.a. africana*). In the next chapter the implications of this post-pubertal growth spurt and delayed 'sociological maturity' are discussed and compared with other species, such as some highly polygynous pinnipeds. But now let us compare growth of the M.F.P.S. elephants with those frequenting the Budongo Forest.

8.3.1.2. *Budongo Forest elephants.* It was not possible to obtain reliable shoulder height (or body weight) records of Budongo Forest elephants. This is due to the fact that elephant were shot by Game Guards working alone or in pairs, who were not able to roll the heavy carcase on to its side and manipulate the fore-leg so that it locked into shape. The shoulder height records they obtained were very variable and a preliminary analysis showed that they could not be used to study growth.

However, it is possible to compare growth of the elephant sampled in the Murchison Falls Park with those sampled in the Budongo Forest Reserve (B.C.F.R.), by analysing length data from the lower jaws of animals shot (Laws 1969b). The lower jaw measurements were taken with calipers from the rostrum at the symphysis, the most anterior point of the jaw, in a direct line to the bulge on the posterior margin of the mandible.

In practice it is possible to measure this quite accurately, as the small amount of scatter in Fig. 8.10 confirms. In this figure the lengths of the lower jaws are plotted against shoulder height for male and female elephants in the M.F.P.S. sample. There is no significant difference between the sexes in the slope of the regression line, nor with those for two other populations that have been studied in this way (M.F.P.N. and T.N.P.). Thus jaw-length-at-age data can be converted to shoulder-height-at-age, or compared in the same way as shoulder-height data. Differences in jaw length will indicate differences in shoulder height (and hence body weight).

The size of M.F.P.S. and B.C.F.R. elephant is compared in this way in Figs 8.11 and 8.12, where jaw length is plotted against age. To date, some 2700 lower jaws, representing thirteen different populations, have been aged and measured. 'When the samples for the other populations are plotted it is found that, with the exception of the Budongo Forest sample, the age records fall almost completely within the [average] range of scatter, indicating that there is little, if any, difference in mandible growth (and therefore shoulder height) between the various East African populations.' (Laws 1969b).

The normal range of scatter for these populations is indicated in Figs 8.11 and 8.12 (broken lines). It can be seen that the male jaws show a spurt of growth similar to that shown by shoulder height growth, and there is a clear difference between the sexes. Fig. 8.12 shows clearly that the jaw lengths at age for B.C.F.R. elephants of both sexes are in general lower than those recorded for other populations, including the M.F.P.S. elephants.

The absence of large old males from the B.C.F.R. population and the presence of a number of very small old males is the most conspicuous difference; fully adult females fall approximately within the M.F.P.S. scatter, but the records for a large proportion of females up to 30 years of age fall well below the normal' bush elephant (*Loxodonta a. africana*) scatter, and the young males fall within the normal female scatter in contrast to the M.F.P.S. sample.

It is possible that large old males have been removed by selective control

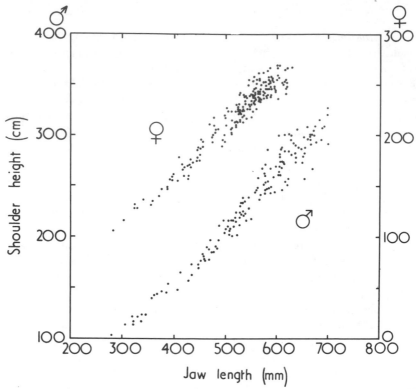

Fig. 8.10. Plots of shoulder height against jaw (mandible) length for M.F.P.S. and M.F.P.N. elephants.

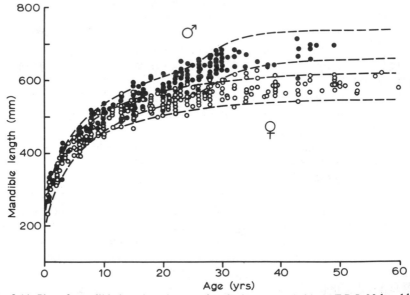

Fig. 8.11. Plot of mandible length against age for elephants sampled in M.F.P.S. Males—black circles; females—open circles. The broken lines define the normal range of scatter.

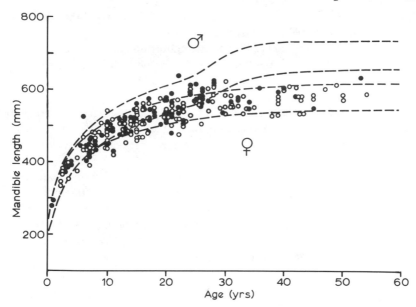

Fig. 8.12. Plot of mandible length against age for elephants shot on control in the Budongo Forest and its vicinity. Males—black circles; females—open circles. The broken lines define the scatter shown in Fig. 8.11.

shooting and sport hunting over a period, or that fully mature bulls do not frequent the forest; but it is not possible to explain in this way the relatively large number of adult males above 30 years of age that fall within the female mandible length range. Conceivably some of these records have been wrongly identified by the Game Guards as to sex, but it seems unlikely that all were. In any case there is clearly a marked difference between the two samples in the jaw lengths at age, for animals under 30 years of age. Conversely, the single very small 43-year-old male from M.F.P.S. (Fig. 8.11) could well be a forest elephant that had strayed into the grassland.

In none of the other eleven samples were there fully mature males within the mature female mandible length scatter. Among the (unsexed) found jaws within the Murchison Falls Park, including some animals probably shot in the vicinity of the forest, were several individuals which were very small for their age. The other samples did not include such anomalous individuals, among many hundreds.

In the course of examining and measuring the B.C.F.R. jaws for age determination it was very evident to us (R.M.L. and I.S.C.P.) that there were a number of clearly anomalous jaws. These were much less massive and carried smaller teeth for their age than the normal elephant jaws in the many hundreds we had previously examined from several localities in East Africa, and our immediate impression, which we have since seen no need to revise, was that they must be forest elephants (*Loxodonta a. cyclotis*). For the morphological reasons given above it seems clear that the B.C.F.R. elephants do include a different stock from those in the M.F.P.S., and Laws (1968c, 1969b) suggested that the differences could be accounted for by hybridization and/or intermingling between a relict stock of forest elephants and the surrounding population of bush elephants.

The Budongo Forest was continuous in the past with the Bugoma and Semliki Forests, the latter also continuous with the Ituri Forest and the other Eastern Congo forests (Moreau 1966) and known still to contain populations of forest elephants. Moreover, we have shown that there is probably a resident population of about 300 elephants in the Budongo Forest. These are separate from the M.F.P.S. population and could well belong to the subspecies, *Loxodonta a. cyclotis*.

It is of course also possible that we have here merely a phenotypic difference in growth of forest-living elephants, rather than a subspecific difference, but the important point is that the size difference indicates that the stocks are separate. We think it will be important to conduct taxonomic studies, or systematic observations in the future, with a view to confirming or rejecting the suggestion that Budongo contains a small relict population of *cyclotis*.

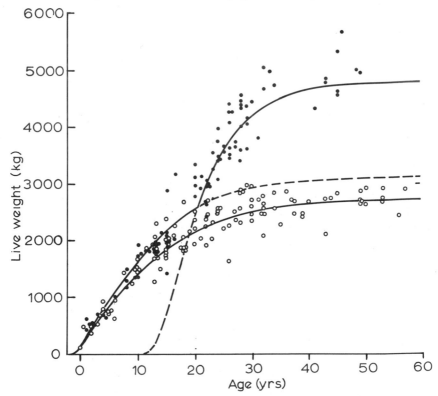

Fig. 8.13. Plot of individual live weights against age for M.F.P.S. males (black circles) and females (open circles). The von Bertalanffy growth equations are drawn and foetal growth shown (see text).

8.3.2. *Body weight*

Body weight-growth curves were presented by Laws and Parker (1968) in their preliminary report, and are revised in this paper, taking account of the adult male growth spurt, and some additional weight records that have been obtained. The weight-growth curves relate to the M.F.P.S. population sampled, but unfortunately there are no data for the B.C.F.R. sample.

Live weights were obtained for 95 male and 112 female elephants examined in M.F.P.S., making use of the relation between dissected hind-leg weight and live weight (Laws *et al.* 1967). The advantages of this approach were discussed in that paper. However, a further 16 weight records were obtained from Mkomasi relating hind-leg weight to live weight (making 54 in all), and confirming that there is no significant difference in this relationship between the four populations that have now been sampled in this way. A re-appraisal of the expanded data indicates that both sexes follow approximately the upper regression of Laws *et al.* (1967, Fig. 4) and that there is no significant difference in this respect between mature males and females. The relation for animals less than a year (i.e. live weight less than 250 kg) diverges from the published regression, the leg weights over this range being slightly higher than shown.

The body-weight data are plotted in Fig. 8.13 for the sexes separately. In view of the relatively small size of the sample, mean growth curves have been fitted by estimating the values of W_∞ in the von Bertalanffy (1938) growth equation from the H_∞ values already calculated from the much larger sample of shoulder height and $w^{1/3}$, and W_∞ is easily calculated from H_∞. H_∞ and W_∞ are the asymptotic shoulder height and body weight respectively. Where w_t is body weight at age t, the growth equations thus obtained are:

male	(1–20 years)	$w_t = 3112 \ [1 - \exp(-0.114 \ (t + 3.95))]^3 \text{kg}$
male	(> 20 years)	$w_t = 4742 \ [1 - \exp(-0.166 \ (t - 10.48))]^3 \text{kg}$
female	(> 2 years)	$w_t = 2744 \ [1 - \exp(-0.099 \ (t + 6.00))]^3 \text{kg}$

The parameters in the revised female growth equation are very similar to those presented by Laws and Parker (1968), W_∞ being in fact identical, but the male parameters are very different.[†] Thus the male W_∞ is seen to be much less than was originally estimated. These calculated mean growth curves are indicated in Fig. 8.13. Extrapolation of the primary male growth curve gives a relatively small difference between the sexes, increasing to a hypothetical maximum difference of 367 kg at 60 years, the male being 13·4 per cent heavier than the female on this basis. But

† Hanks (1972) examined the use of the von Bertalanffy growth equation for elephants, using a computer to carry out iterative calculations of the coefficients that minimize the squares of the deviations about the fit. He concluded that the computer-calculated curves give the best fit to the data and that for the elephant the equation serves as a purely empirical representation of the weight-at-age data and that there is little biological significance in the parameters it contains. For the purpose of the present study, and acknowledging the other approximations involved, the present equations derived by the three-stage desk calculation are thought to be adequate.

the superposition of a secondary growth spurt in the male results in a vastly greater actual difference in size between the sexes, the average male being potentially 2006 kg, or 73·3 per cent heavier than the female at 60 years.

Hanks (1969a) drew attention to the difference in weight of pregnant and non-pregnant female elephants in Zambia. Other things being equal, a population with a higher pregnancy rate will show an appreciably higher female growth rate and W_∞ than one with a lower pregnancy rate. He does not consider the possibility of growth rate differences between populations and particularly seasonal differences in body weight within a population. Some 45 per cent of females over 18 years old in this sample were pregnant and the mean weight difference between pregnant and non-pregnant females in this sample is about 250–300 kg. Even large variations in the proportion pregnant will have a relatively small effect, compared with the seasonal representation in the samples compared. (At mid-term (330 days) the increased weight of the reproductive tract alone is about 60 kg (Laws, unpublished data).) We have not therefore thought it necessary here to calculate separate growth equations for pregnant and non-pregnant females.

The condition of M.F.P.S. elephants was considered above to be poor in relation to some other populations studied, although the sample was collected in a favourable season of the year. The Mkomasi sample showed the best weight-height relationship, and it is instructive to apply the shoulder height-body weight relationship calculated for the Mkomasi sample to estimate optimum body weight-growth curves for M.F.P.S. This should give an indication of the extent to which growth may have been suppressed in the M.F.P.S. population by the environmental and population density conditions that have developed. It is assumed that the shoulder height growth of the M.F.P.S. elephants has not altered, although comparison with the Mkomasi and Tsavo samples indicates that early growth in M.F.P.S. may formerly have been more precocious, although similar asymptotic heights were attained. This was reported by Laws and Parker (1968) and Laws (1969b).

On this basis optimal W_∞ values have been calculated (male $W_\infty = 5314$ kg; female $W_\infty = 2986$ kg) and inserted in the growth equations presented above. The resulting growth curves were compared with the current growth curves. The difference in mean body weights at age is considerable, being proportionately the same as the difference in the W_∞ values, the current W_∞ being 572 kg, or 10·8 per cent less than the estimated optimum value for the male, and 242 kg, or 8·1 per cent less for the female. It is possible that seasonal changes within a population may be of similar magnitude, and that in M.F.P.S. the dry-season and early wet-season body weights may be much lower than the values given.

8.3.3. *Biochemical aspects of growth*

Earlier work on the Murchison Falls Park elephants (Laws and Parker 1968) suggested that the M.F.P.S. population differed from the M.F.P.N. population in having a lower rate of reproduction, higher population density, and a habitat (formerly wooded) which had changed further in the direction of grassland than that north of the Nile. It seemed probable that the differences were related to nutritional status. Further studies partly described by Laws (1969a) and in this book confirm that these differences exist. However, neither the earlier work nor the present work indicates any significant difference in body size between the two populations.

A biochemical investigation of material from the two populations was therefore carried out and the initial results have been published (McCullagh 1969a). These relate to the urinary excretion of hydroxyproline, an amino acid derived from the breakdown of collagen, the excretion of which is related to the rate of collagen metabolism, and hence also the rate of growth. Urine samples of elephants from the two populations were collected and analysed, and the results expressed as the ratio of hydroxyproline to creatinine, indicating the excretion of hydroxyproline per unit body weight.

The ratio of hydroxyproline to creatinine in the urine of young animals was high and decreased progressively with age, closely following the fall in the rate of growth (Fig. 8.14). This ratio can therefore be used as an index of the instantaneous growth rate at the time of collection. For practical reasons it was not possible to sample the two populations concurrently and the samples

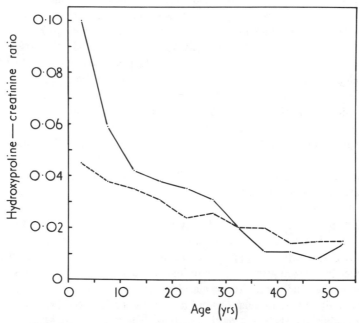

Fig. 8.14. Hydroxyproline–creatinine ratios for 5-year classes of male (unbroken line) and female (broken line) elephants examined in M.F.P.S. Data from K. G. McCullagh (personal communication).

were taken predominantly in the dry season (M.F.P.N.) and wet season (M.F.P.S.), the latter sample for each age group showing higher values. There was a significant correlation between the monthly hydroxyproline—creatinine ratios for all ages and the monthly rainfall values.

McCullagh's work showed the effect of the dry season on the elephant growth pattern, all age groups going through a period of slow or restricted growth at this time. Probably most animals cease to grow during this period and some or all may lose weight as has been established for some species of deer (Bandy (1965) quoted by Wood and Cowan (1968)). In the elephant this is presumably related to seasonally different nutritional conditions, both due to a primary effect of climate on the quantity and quality of the herbage, and to widespread burning in the dry season which reduces the gross amount of forage available. The qualitative seasonal variations in the food intake of elephant have also been investigated (McCullagh 1969b).

The seasonal variation in growth occurs in both sexes; the curves for the sexes combined, reflecting seasonal changes in hydroxyproline excretion, show variations of ± 36—7 per cent in both young and old age groups (McCullagh 1969a). Males grow at a faster rate than females as shown by the cross-sectional data (Figs 8.9 and 8.13), and males show a higher hydroxyproline-creatinine ratio during the wet season, amounting in animals under 15 years old to 30—35 per cent higher than the female ratio. No significant sex difference between the ratios was observed in the dry season and the seasonal variation in growth is therefore much greater in the male than in the female.

Unfortunately at the time McCullagh's work was carried out, the possible existence of a secondary growth spurt in the male was unsuspected. In fact the growth velocity apparently increases by some 300 per cent between 18 and 24 years of age, even when calculated from the cross-sectional data. Males in their early twenties should show a relatively higher than expected wet season hydroxyproline-creatinine ratio than younger or older age groups, reflecting the increased growth velocity. The biochemical results do show this (McCullagh (1970) and Fig. 8.14).

The seasonal variations made it impossible to compare the instantaneous growth rates of the two populations by means of our samples, or to be certain of their relative nutritive status over the year. McCullagh concluded that seasonal variations were sufficient to obliterate any primary differences between the populations and that if such a difference exists it is unlikely to be of any great magnitude. This conclusion supports the results of the cross-sectional studies of dimensional and weight growth, but still leaves a further possibility unresolved.

In view of the small variability of mandible lengths at age for a number of environmentally diverse populations in East Africa (Laws 1969b, and unpublished) it seems possible that skeletal growth, and hence shoulder height, which has been shown to be correlated with jaw length, shows relatively slight variability between populations, whereas body weight is variable not only seasonally, but in relation to habitat conditions. Thus, a sample of 300 elephants from M.K.E. examined in March 1968 at the beginning of the rains was significantly heavier at all ages than a sample M.F.P.S. elephants (taken at the end of the rains), but not markedly different in shoulder height.

The two Murchison Falls samples from which the weight-growth curves were constructed were collected in the wet season, August–September and November for M.F.P.N. and M.F.P.S. populations respectively. From the results of McCullagh's (1969a) investigations these are periods when the instantaneous growth rates can be considered to be near maximal. However, the South bank animals should have had an extra two months' growth. In view of the seasonal growth pattern, if growth velocities were similar between the populations, South bank elephants would be expected to be heavier at comparable ages than the North bank animals. Those sampled are not.

Thus, it is unlikely that skeletal growth rates are different between these two populations, but it is possible that there are differences in seasonal body weight at age. These would be more pronounced in unfavourable years, when it is postulated that the habitat is relatively more favourable in nutritional terms on the north bank of the Nile. Other differences between the populations are real, but in the absence of concurrent samples from the two populations the question of the postulated difference in seasonally attained body weights must remain open.

8.4.   Summary

The nutrition of these elephants has been investigated in several ways. The mean stomach fill, expressed as a percentage of live weight, does not vary with age in the male and was not significantly different in immature and non-lactating mature females (average 2 per cent). There is a significantly higher stomach fill (3 per cent) in lactating females. An assumed passage time of 12 hours indicates a mean daily food intake of about 4 per cent of live weight for all classes except lactating females, for which it averaged 6 per cent. Comparisons with other populations, allowing for seasonal and habitat differences suggest that M.F.P.S. elephants now have a lower food intake than either M.F.P.N. animals or a sample collected at the periphery of the M.F.P.S. range ten years ago.

Superficial observation of stomach samples collected in forest indicated that woody material was more abundant than in grassland samples and vegetation studies demonstrate a clear preference of elephant for leading shoots of the smaller size classes of tree regeneration. Certain tree species are highly preferred.

In the grassland or wooded grassland range, grass comprises 80–90 per cent of the diet, but this reflects availability rather than a dietary preference. Higher proportions of browse are taken if available and de-barking is probably a response to a nutritional need. It occurs at the beginning of the wet season, when the protein: fibre ratio of other food may be particularly unfavourable for elephant digestive processes and the de-barking of trees a response to shortage of fibre in the diet. There is also a correlation between calcium content and degree of barking, and M.F.P.S. animals may be more prone to calcium deficiency than others.

Chemical analyses of stomach samples indicated that the protein level was much lower in the dry season (January) than in the wet season (May), and it seems likely that the dry-season protein intake is insufficient so that elephants draw on their reserves. The dry-season samples showed significantly more calcium, and less potassium and silicate, while phosphorus and sodium were constant. Interpretation is difficult, but it seems clear that calcium deficiencies may be experienced by both populations in differing degree.

The physical condition of elephants in several populations has been compared to establish whether population parameters were correlated with nutrition and condition. In terms of kidney-fat index, pregnant females were found to be in better condition than lactating females, but significant differences could not be demonstrated between other classes. When the samples for the two Murchison Falls populations were compared no significant differences were found, but because they were sampled in different months this result is not inconsistent with the hypothesis that the M.F.P.S. population is in poorer condition than the M.F.P.N. population. Comparison with Tsavo elephants suggests that nutrition was currently less limiting for them than for M.F.P.S. animals.

The relation between shoulder height and body weight has also been compared for four populations. Allowing for seasonal differences, the ranking follows the expected order, with the more fertile and rapid-growing populations showing the best height—weight ratio.

These results indicate that the M.F.P.S. elephants are well below the optimal physical condition for the species, with important consequences for growth, reproduction, and population dynamics.

Extensive data on height at age have been used to calculate growth equations for the M.F.P.S. elephant population. The mean potential male shoulder height at 60 years of age is 55 centimetres (or 21·8 per cent) higher than in the female, and the discrepancy is apparently largely due to a post-pubertal growth spurt in the male.

Unfortunately adequate height records are not available for the B.C.F.R. population, but mandible length shows a close linear correlation with shoulder height for several elephant populations from diverse environments in East Africa and so skeletal growth of the forest elephants can be compared with the M.F.P.S. elephants. This comparison indicates that there is a separate resident population in the forest, which may belong to the subspecies *L.a. cyclotis* or represent hybridization of *africana* × *cyclotis*.

Body weight data are available for the M.F.P.S. population and weight-growth equations have been derived. The postulated secondary post-pubertal acceleration in growth results in the male being potentially over 2000 kg (or 73·3 per cent) heavier than the female at 60 years of age. Taking the relatively poor condition of M.F.P.S. animals into account it was calculated that asymptotic male and female weights are probably at least 572 kg (or 10·8 per cent) and 242 kg (or 8·1 per cent), respectively, lighter than the optimum values.

The results of a biochemical study of instantaneous growth rates involving the estimation of hydroxyproline—creatinine ratios in urine are summarized. The growth rate was highest during the rains, seasonal variation being ± 36 per cent for the sexes combined, and one-third greater in the male than in the female. These biochemical results also show the expected increase in growth velocity at the time of the supposed male growth spurt. Skeletal growth rates of the M.F.P.N. and M.F.P.S. populations are identical, but weight-growth rates may differ.

9. Reproduction

9.1. Age at the attainment of sexual maturity

An important parameter of any animal population is the age at which individuals start to reproduce. Cole (1954), in his review of the population consequences of life-history phenomena, remarks: 'one of the most striking points revealed by this study is the fact that the age at which reproduction begins is one of the most significant characteristics of a species . . .'. Puberty has been variously defined in genetic, physiological, behavioural, or ecological terms (Sadleir 1969). In the male it is often defined as the age at which viable sperm are first released, or when viable sperm are released in quantity adequate for successful fertilization. In the female puberty is usually taken to be the age at first oestrus, estimates of this depending on follicular development (i.e. attainment of a certain minimum follicle size), or presence of corpora lutea or corpora albicantia in the ovaries denoting an ovulation.

Laws and Parker (1968) and Laws (1969a) gave preliminary observations on the attainment of puberty, as defined by the production of sperm in quantity, and age at first ovulation. They showed that for five elephant populations studied in East Africa the mean ages at puberty were 11, 12½, 14, 18, and 20 years in the female, and that males attain puberty one or two years later than the female. The results for M.F.P.S. were based on the examination of an initial sample of 200 elephants examined in November 1965. From this, estimates of the mean age of puberty of 19·5 years (range 18−21 years) and 18 years (range 11−22 years) for male and female respectively were obtained.

Further studies have now been carried out on the larger samples available which lead to modification of these values, although they do not affect the general conclusions. It is intended to publish the comprehensive results of the investigations on elephant reproduction later, but in view of the importance of the parameter in question the more relevant results for M.F.P.S. are given here and compared with the summary findings from other populations.

9.1.1. *The male*

The results of our investigations into the age at attainment of sexual maturity for M.F.P.S. elephants are illustrated in Fig. 9.1. The male tract has recently been described by Short, Mann, and Hay (1967). Smears from the wolffian duct were examined in the field, using a high power microscope (Zeiss GFL with built-in illumination). The animal was recorded as immature if the smear showed no sperm; pubertal, if very few sperm and much cellular debris, the sperm usually showing motility when fluid from the seminal vesicles was added; and mature if it showed a dense mass of sperm, almost all of which became motile on addition of seminal fluid (Laws and Parker 1968). These criteria were later checked

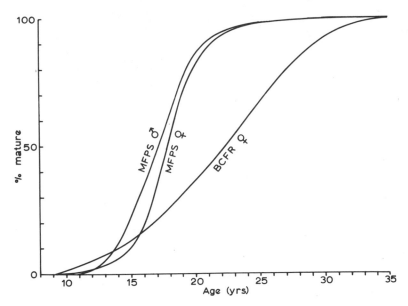

Fig. 9.1. Attainment of sexual maturity in M.F.P.S. males and females and Budongo Forest females (see text).

against histological criteria. Later collections when the senior author was not present in the field consisted of smears fixed in alcohol, dried, and subsequently examined by him.

In some months the field criteria are difficult to apply in some individuals because the distinction between pubertal and mature classes is less clear. In these cases the weights of testes and accessory glands (seminal vesicles, prostate, and bulbo-urethral glands) have been taken into account in reaching a decision. The testis cycle is being studied histologically and preliminary results indicate that there may be a seasonal cycle in tubule diameter and stages of spermatogenesis (Laws 1969a).

The age-frequency distribution of the pubertal group approximates to a normal curve. The mean age of this group was $14 \cdot 43 \pm 0 \cdot 76$ years ($p = 5$ per cent); the median was $14 \cdot 12$ years.

The method used to estimate the mean age at sexual maturity and to calculate confidence intervals is described in Appendix C. We are indebted to Mr. K. Lakhani, Biometrics Section, The Nature Conservancy, London, for suggesting the method and for carrying out most of the computations for us. The results are shown in Figs 9.1 and 9.2 and Table 9.1. They indicate that the mean ages at which male elephants reach sexual maturity may differ between populations over a range of 5–6 years. The M.F.P.N. and T.N.P. males appear not to be significantly different on the present evidence, although the M.F.P.S. and T.N.P. males are different and T.N.P. and M.K.E. males are significantly different. In M.F.P.S. the mean age at

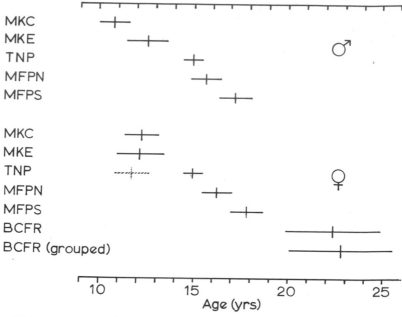

Fig. 9.2. Mean ages at attainment of sexual maturity in six elephant populations sampled. Crude approximate 95 per cent confidence limits are indicated (see text).

Table 9.1

Summary of data on attainment of sexual maturity in six elephant populations, mean ages and crude, approximate confidence intervals for the means ($p = 5$ per cent).

Sample	Male	Female
M.K.C.	10·77 ± 0·78	12·24 ± 0·91
M.K.E.	12·51 ± 1·10	12·18 ± 1·26
T.N.P.	14·94 ± 0·52	11·73 ± 0·93
M.F.P.N.	15·63 ± 0·82	16·28 ± 0·80
M.F.P.S.	17·20 ± 0·86	17·82 ± 0·86
B.C.F.R.		22·38 ± 2·52
B.C.F.R. (grouped)		22·80 ± 2·76

sexual maturity was estimated to be 17·20 ± 0·86 years. Puberty, defined as the first production of sperm, was 2–3 years earlier than sexual maturity as here defined. Note that the standard errors for age at puberty and sexual maturity are very similar.

From an ecological point of view we consider that the latter parameter has more validity for application in studies of population dynamics than the mean age at puberty, although there are no doubt important behavioural changes associated with hormonal changes at puberty, several years before successful mating is possible. Inspection of the group structures (see Chapter 7, Figs 7.8 and 7.10) also strongly suggests that the higher estimate is more realistic.

We have also examined the progress of attainment of what may be called 'sociological maturity'. Earlier we presented evidence suggesting that there is an acceleration of growth in the male during the third decade of life. This is similar to the adolescent spurt in man (Tanner 1962) but more nearly comparable to the post-pubertal growth spurt in some polygynous pinnipeds (Laws 1953; Scheffer and Wilke 1953), and toothed whales (Nishiwaki, Ohsumi, and Hibiya 1958; Sergeant 1962). Bryden (1972) has recently given a comprehensive review of growth and development in marine mammals which shows that several other species also undergo a male growth spurt.

Tanner (1962) remarks of the northern fur seal (*Callorhinus ursinus*): 'the appearance of the secondary sexual characters occurs at a time when the male begins to fight with others on the breeding grounds, but primary reproductive maturity has now been delayed so long, perhaps so that in a disastrous year for seals the younger ones are biologically (though not as a rule sociologically) capable of impregnating females'. Laws (1956, 1960) has shown that in South Georgia, where the stock of elephant seals (*Mirounga leonina*) was heavily exploited, the average age of the harem bulls had so decreased by 1951 that on many beaches young mature males of 4 years of age, which normally would have little chance to breed before 7 years of age (10 years at Macquarie Island (Carrick and Ingham 1962)) were holding harems.

In the elephant, the threshold of sociological maturity has been arbitrarily assumed to be equivalent to a shoulder height of 280 centimetres (Fig 8.9). Most fully mature animals are at least as large as this; animals below this size are assumed to be sociologically immature and the numbers immature and mature according to this criterion were tabulated by age classes. The average age at the attainment of sociological maturity is about 26 years for both M.F.P.S. and M.F.P.N. Owing to the small size of the samples from T.N.P. and M.K. they contain very few fully mature males and it has not been possible in their case to estimate values for the age of attainment of sociological maturity. There was no material representing B.C.F.R. males.

It may be relevant that 65 per cent of sexually mature bulls in the M.F.P.S. mixed herds were less than 26 years old, whereas only 29 per cent of sexually mature bulls in bull herds were less than 26 years old ($d = 4 \cdot 289, p < 0 \cdot 1$ per cent). The different age structures were also noted in Chapter 7.

9.1.2.   *The female*

A similar investigation was carried out on the female material. The fixed ovaries of all females in the samples were weighed and sliced on a rotary meat slicing machine; the slices were 2–3 millimetres thick. All identifiable corpora lutea and corpora albicantia were recorded and their mean diameters (mean of two diameters at right angles) were measured with calipers. The size of the largest follicle was recorded for each ovary and for subsamples of each population the numbers of follicles 5–10 millimetres and > 10 millimetres in diameter were recorded. Notes were also made of the general features of the ovaries, types of corpora lutea, and corpora albicantia etc.

In the subsequent analysis the criterion of immaturity adopted was the absence of corpora lutea or corpora albicantia and a maximum follicle size of < 6·0 millimetres. In fact there is a cycle of follicular activity in young calves, some of which have maximum follicle sizes of 6·0 millimetres, but in practice these can be eliminated from the pubertal group without affecting the conclusions. The detailed observations on the female reproductive cycle will be presented in a later publication.

The criterion adopted for 'puberty' was the presence of at least one Graafian follicle in the ovaries ⩾ 6·0 millimetres in diameter, but no corpora lutea or corpora albicantia. Alternative analyses based on a follicle size of 7·0 millimetres or 7·5 millimetres yielded similar results to those described here, but gave mean ages at puberty up to half a year higher. Sexually mature females were defined by the presence of at least one corpus luteum or corpus albicans in the ovaries, indicating that at least one ovulation had occurred.

The frequency distributions of sexually immature, pubertal, and sexually mature females were tabulated as before for M.F.P.S. and B.C.F.R. samples. For the sample of M.F.P.S. females there are 326 records in the range of overlap (3–35 years), for B.C.F.R. only 89 (3–40 years).

The mean age of the pubertal group was $14·42 \pm 1·17$ years ($p = 5$ per cent) and the median was 14·12 years, as for the male. The variance of this distribution was greater than for the male pubertal group, but the mean is almost identical.

The estimate of the mean age at sexual maturity in the female calculated as before (Appendix C) gave a value of $17·82 \pm 0·86$ years for the M.F.P.S. population. Thus puberty in the female, if defined as the enlargement of the Graafian follicles, was evidently 3–4 years earlier than sexual maturity (the first ovulation), as in the male. The standard errors are again similar for puberty and sexual maturity.

A similar estimate for B.C.F.R. females gave a value for the mean age at sexual maturity of $22·38 \pm 2·52$ years. Here the age range is wide (9–34 years) and the values are small and show large fluctuations. When the data are grouped, a reasonably smooth pattern emerges and the estimated mean is $22·80 \pm 2·76$ years, remarkably close to the results from the ungrouped data.

Comparisons with other populations are summarized in Table 9.1 and Fig. 9.2, the estimate in each case having been made by the method described in Appendix C, and the mean ages at sexual maturity are seen to differ between populations.

The mean age at birth of the first calf should be 2–3 years later than the mean age at sexual maturity (the gestation period is 22 months, some of the first ovulations would not lead to conception, and there would be some foetal deaths).

Comparing the sexes (Table 9.1 and Fig. 9.2) it now can be seen that the earlier conclusion that males attain maturity one or two years later than the female (Laws and Parker 1968) was erroneous. In fact, for each sample except T.N.P. (see below) the mean ages at sexual maturity are not significantly different between the sexes. For M.F.P.S. the mean ages at puberty in males and females are not significantly different. This evidence indicates that in a population for which the age at puberty or sexual maturity is established for only one sex, it can be assumed with confidence that this parameter will be the same in the other sex. Thus, in the case of the B.C.F.R. sample, for which no male sperm smears or testis samples are available, we can justifiably extrapolate to the male from the results of examination of the ovaries. Conversely, since the examination of sperm smears is a simple, rapid, and economic field operation, the estimated age at puberty of the males in a population to be sampled could confidently be used as an estimate of the same parameter of the female population. This finding is therefore important in relation to management research.

The T.N.P. samples are an exception, but the data are very sparse over the relevant age range, because these age groups were virtually absent from the samples. In the critical age groups 12–14 years there were only two males and no females. For this reason the T.N.P. estimates, particularly for the female, might be unreliable and it seems better to assume that the female age at maturity is the same as for the male, that is 14–15 years. This is given emphasis in Fig. 9.2. (Alternatively, combining the male and female samples gives an estimate of $12 \cdot 86 \pm 0 \cdot 54$ years.)

Although it is possible that the deferment of reproduction could be a genetic or geographical effect, it seems much more reasonable to assume that it is an environmental effect resulting from habitat change, change in population density, or both. As Laws and Parker (1968) pointed out, there is some evidence of an historical change in this parameter in the M.F.P.S. population. The material Perry (1953) collected in Western Uganda in 1947–50 suggested an age at puberty of 12–13 years, although the sample was very small. The very much higher mean age at sexual maturity in the B.C.F.R. population deserves further comment. The sample comes partly from the peripheral high-density stratum of the North Bunyoro elephant range (Chapter 7), although the habitat resources are presumably better for elephant in or near the Budongo Forest, where the sample was taken. But is has been shown that the growth rate of this group of elephants was slower and the asymptotic sizes less than in the M.F.P.S. group—and puberty is closely related to body size. Only $23 \cdot 7$ per cent of mature females were pregnant, suggesting a mean calving interval of $7 \cdot 7$ years. The age structure of this population also indicates a substantial reduction in recruitment (below and Chapter 10) and it has been subjected to very considerable disturbance by control shooting.

9.2.   The calving rate

Recruitment to the population is also influenced by variations in the calving rate of mature females. We may distinguish two types of variations—secular variation of the mean rate for the whole mature female population, and individual age-specific changes in fecundity. We have material which throws light on both aspects of the problem.

9.2.1.   *Mean calving interval*

From the distribution of adult females between two classes, pregnant and non-pregnant, the time-specific or current mean calving interval at the time of sampling can be estimated, assuming a gestation of 22 months and that the sample is representative of the adult female population. In this way Perry (1953) obtained a figure of nearly four years for the mean calving interval in the population he was studying. In more recent work a wide range of calving intervals has been inferred.

In the sample taken from M.F.P.S. in 1967 there are 285 sexually mature females of which 93 were pregnant (32·6 ± 5 per cent). The average interval from calving to conception calculated in this way is 43·4 months and adding 22 months for the subsequent gestation period gives an estimate of 5·6 years ($p = 5$ per cent, 4·8–6·8 years) for the mean calving interval. On a smaller sample from 1965 Laws and Parker (1968) obtained an estimate of 4·6 years. Buss and Smith (1966) obtained an estimate of 8·6 years for the mean calving interval of M.F.P.S. elephant collected in 1958–64.

For the M.F.P.N. sample there are 347 mature females of which only 70 were pregnant (20·2 ± 4·2 per cent). The current mean calving interval (1966) can be estimated in the same way giving an average interval from calving to conception of 87·1 months and a mean calving interval of 109·1 months or 9·1 years ($p = 5$ per cent, 7·5–11·5 years). On a smaller sample from M.F.P.N. collected in 1965, Laws and Parker (1968) obtained an estimate of 4·5 years.

The B.C.F.R. sample was much smaller, owing to the nature of the operations. 59 pairs of mature ovaries were collected and 14 of these (23·7 ± 10·1 per cent) had apparently active corpora lutea and are deemed to have been pregnant. (The sample was collected by Game Scouts and records of pregnancy are incomplete. The estimated average interval from calving to conception is 70·7 months, giving a mean calving interval of 92·7 months or 7·7 years ($p = 5$ per cent, 5·4–13·5 years).

Results of the analyses of six elephant populations in respect of this parameter are presented in Table 9.2. The most productive population, M.K.E. had 63·33 ± 9·95 per cent pregnant, giving an estimated mean calving interval of 2·9 years ($p = 5$ per cent, 2·6–3·4 years).

These data only partially support the hypothesis that as habitat resources decrease and population density increases, so fecundity declines. The data in Table 9.2 are ranked by populations in order of increasing population density

Table 9.2

Summary of proportions of adult females pregnant and calculated mean calving intervals, for six elephant populations

Population	Year	% pregnant	Calving interval (years)	
			Mean	Confidence limits ($p = 5$ per cent)
M.K.E.	1968	63·33 ± 9·95	2·9	2·6 – 3·4
M.K.C.	1969	43·33 ± 10·24	4·2	3·1 – 5·0
T.N.P.	1966	26·88 ± 9·02	6·8	5·1 – 10·3
M.F.P.N.	1966	20·17 ± 4·22	9·1	7·5 – 11·5
M.F.P.S.	1967	32·63 ± 5·44	5·6	4·8 – 6·8
B.C.F.R.	1966	23·70 ± 10·11	7·7	5·4 – 13·5

and habitat deterioration. The relative fecundities estimated from the first four samples agree fairly well with expectation, but M.F.P.S. (in particular) and B.C.F.R. are apparently more productive than M.F.P.N. although the reverse would be expected. It seems likely that this can be attributed to short-term fluctuations in the pregnancy rates of the populations sampled, as shown by the age frequency distribution of foetuses and animals in the first few age groups, where there can be no doubt about the ages allocated (Laws and Parker (1968), Fig. 5; and unpublished data). This could explain the difference in the percentage pregnant (or 'instantaneous mean calving interval') between M.F.P.S. (sampled mainly in 1967) and M.F.P.N. (sampled mainly in 1966).

As Laws (1969a) suggested, it may be better to present the data as 'percentage pregnant' which can be adjusted by reference to recruitment curves if these are known. The values for mean calving intervals that we have been discussing are time-specific and are greatly influenced by short-term fluctuations in the pregnancy rate. Only if the percentage pregnant were constant at 50 per cent would a constant mean calving interval (3·7 years) be estimated. This is highly unlikely in any circumstances and fluctuations about any mean can be expected. Such short-term changes would of course be enhanced by environmental fluctuations.

The 63 per cent pregnancy rate shown by M.K.E. elephants in 1968 could not be maintained, because when the pregnant females enter lactational anoestrus, only the remaining 37 per cent are available to become pregnant in the near future. Even if they all became pregnant as the others gave birth and went into anoestrus, the calculated time-specific or instantaneous mean calving interval during the next year or so would be almost five years.

Hypothetically, once such an alternation became established in a constant optimal environment, with a very fertile population, the alternation would tend to be reinforced by the long-term nature of the elephant reproductive cycle. Thus, the true mean calving interval could actually be constant, at about 3·7 years, but apparent mean calving intervals, calculated at intervals from the proportions pregnant could vary (in M.K.E.) from say 3 years to 5 years. In another similar hypothetical case, where the percentage pregnant alternated between, say, 80 per cent and 20 per cent, the corresponding mean calving intervals, calculated from these proportions, would be 2·3 and 9·1 years. The situation is of course more complex than this because environmental conditions fluctuate and can enhance or damp down such oscillations.

Laws and Parker (1968) and Laws (1969a) showed that there are large annual variations in reproductive success and that there is in several elephant populations, a cycle in recruitment with a length of 6—8 years, probably related to environmental conditions. Laws (1969a, Fig. 3) suggested that the M.F.P.N. had recently passed such a peak so that the pregnancy rate might be lower than that for M.F.P.S. Also, if there is a higher calf mortality in M.F.P.S., the calving interval may be shortened because of a reduction in the period of lactational anoestrus. The estimated mean calving intervals given above are in accord with this interpretation. The period when Buss and Smith (1966) collected their material was also associated with a lower level of recruitment (Laws 1969a, Fig. 3).

There are also large individual variations in the calving intervals. The shortest recorded appears to be about 2¾ years (Laws 1969a) and Douglas-Hamilton (1972) has recorded another short calving interval of just 3 years. Conversely, as the placental scar counts indicate (Laws 1967a), some cows may go 13 years between producing calves.

Enough has been said to indicate how unreliable are estimates of average long-term pregnancy rates or calving intervals based on single samples taken over a short period. Nevertheless there does seem to be a general agreement between the condition or status of a population in relation to its habitat and population density, the age at sexual maturity (which is presumably not so dependent on short term environmental cycles), and the pregnancy rate or time-specific mean calving interval (Laws 1969a). What we need to know in assessing the status of an elephant population is the calving interval, averaged over a longer period and its long-term trend. A series of samples over a period of years would give information on this, and would be available for M.F.P.S. if the proposals for reduction cropping and sustained cropping made in Chapter 12 are adopted. For other populations it does not appear to be a feasible proposition at present. Another indication might be provided by examination of counts of placental scars in relation to maternal age.

9.2.2. *Placental scars*

The occurrence and persistence of placental scars (Plate 9.1) in elephant uteri was reported by Laws (1967a). He showed that there was a progressive accumulation of placental scars with age in a sample of 44 non-pregnant females collected in the Tsavo National Park. When several anomalous females were eliminated from the sample he obtained an equation for the regression of age t on number of placental scars s: $t = 4 \cdot 02s + 12 \cdot 92$ years, giving an estimate of about 4 years

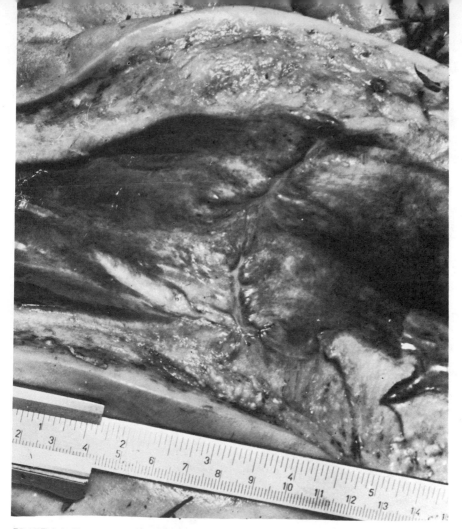

PLATE 9.1. Exposed uterine mucosa showing placental scar.

for the mean calving interval and suggesting that the first pregnancy began at 13–14 years. It was also suggested that some old animals gave under-counts due to disappearance of scars. A preliminary discussion of samples from the two Murchison Falls populations was presented by Laws (1969a).

In fact, the regression of placental scars on age is appropriate if we seek to estimate the calving interval; an unbiased estimate would be the reciprocal of the regression of scars on age. But, as the discussion below shows, a direct estimate is not possible if either calving interval or age at sexual maturity, or both have been changing, because such changes would influence the slope of the regression.

In Fig. 9.3 the number of placental scars accumulated is plotted against age for 144 non-pregnant females from M.F.P.S. The general relation between age and accumulation of scars is clear, though there are some anomalous females similar to the animals described by Laws (1967a). In calculating mean ages at successive scar numbers, six animals have been omitted (bottom right-hand corner

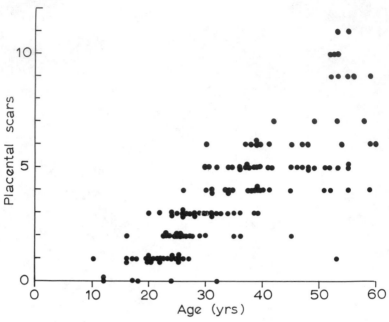

Fig. 9.3. Plot of placental scar counts against age for female elephants examined in M.F.P.S.

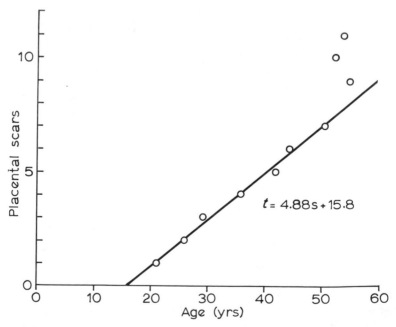

$t = 4.88s + 15.8$

Fig. 9.4. Mean ages at successive placental scar numbers for M.F.P.S. females.

of Fig. 9.3). In Fig. 9.4 the mean values have been plotted and the regression: $t = 4 \cdot 88s + 15 \cdot 8$ drawn. When $s = 1$, $t = 20 \cdot 7$ and the first conception is estimated to occur at about 17—19 years, assuming the one-scar class to average about 0—2 years *post partum*. This is in good agreement with the estimate of $17 \cdot 82 \pm 0 \cdot 86$ years for the present mean age at sexual maturity (Table 9.1).

However, Laws (1967a) pointed out that the mean calving interval was unlikely to have remained constant and that the relationship could be expected to be curvilinear. Similarly any retardation of the age at puberty would affect the number of scars at age. This effect is independent of the fact that scars probably fade with age, which also complicates interpretation (Laws 1969a).

In Fig. 9.5 a simple hypothetical model demonstrates the effect of (a) increasing mean calving interval from 3 years to 9 years, while keeping the mean age at sexual maturity constant; and (b) increasing the mean age at sexual maturity from 10 years to 17·5 years. In constructing it the mean calving interval was increased progressively in steps of one year from a period representing newly mature animals in the 1920s. It was in 1925 that intensive control shooting operations began in North Bunyoro, with the aim of restricting the elephant range (Chapter 1). Before 1925 the reproductive rate was possibly near maximal because the elephant population had been expanding to occupy the area vacated by man as a result of the sleeping sickness evacuations. For the same reason a progressive retardation in the average age at puberty is assumed to date from this

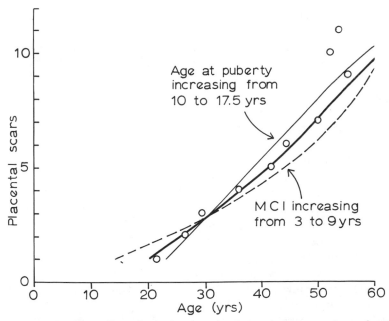

Fig. 9.5. Diagram to show effect of postulated secular changes in mean age at sexual maturity and mean calving interval (mci). A resultant curve has been drawn.

time. Animals aged 55 years in 1966–7 would have been 14–15 years old in 1925.

The resultant of the two hypothetical curves, representing progressive changes in the mean calving interval and deferment of puberty, agrees quite closely with the mean age at successive placental scar numbers shown by our sample. This supports the general proposition of a reduction in natality due to increased mean calving interval and deferred maturity over the four decades.

In fact it is most improbable that the changes would have been so regular. Thus, the pregnancy rate and therefore the mean calving interval evidently have fluctuated about the general trend contributing to the varying recruitment that we hold to be correlated with climatic cycles and by inference with nutritional status (Laws 1969b). In the same way the mean age at sexual maturity has possibly fluctuated within rather narrow limits in response to such environmental cycles.

A point should also be made here that the mean calving interval is a *mean.* There is a wide range of individual performance during the lifetime, indicated by the scatter of the points for any one age group, and in which two factors are presumably involved, namely, variation in the age at first conception and variation in the rate of calving thereafter. But also there is age-specific variation in the rate of reproduction, with maximum fecundity as we shall see below in middle age and virtual cessation of reproductive activity in the last decade of the life cycle for M.F.P.S. females.

9.2.3.   *Age-specific fecundity*

Variation in reproductive activity with age has been studied by tabulating the frequency of pregnant; recently pregnant or cycling; lactating; or inactive (neither pregnant, recently pregnant, cycling, nor lactating) females by five-year age groups. The criteria for the different classes of activity were as follows: pregnant—visible embryo or foetus present in the uterus; cycling or recently pregnant—at least one fresh corpus luteum present, although no embryo detected, or diameter of largest corpus albicans $\geq$ 10 millimetres (mean of two diameters, at right angles in section); lactating—milk could be expressed manually from the nipples; inactive—none of the above criteria apply. In practice the 'recently pregnant' usually had a recent or very recent placental scar (Laws 1967a) in the uterus; there were very few presumed 'cycling' animals in the samples. The mean corpus albicans diameter of 10 millimetres probably corresponds to a postpartum age of about 4 months (Laws 1969a).

Of the females in the cropped sample from M.F.P.S. $62 \cdot 3 \pm 5 \cdot 9$ per cent ($p = 5$ per cent) were sexually mature. The proportion of adult females showing evidence of recent reproductive activity was $54 \cdot 0 \pm 5 \cdot 9$ per cent, the proportion that were actually pregnant was $32 \cdot 6 \pm 5 \cdot 4$ per cent; and the proportion of all females that were pregnant was $20 \cdot 3 \pm 3 \cdot 8$ per cent. Some $34 \cdot 1 \pm 4 \cdot 5$ per cent of all females in the sample were lactating; and $54 \cdot 7 \pm 5 \cdot 9$ per cent of mature females.

The different age classes, however, departed from these average values in a regular way. In Fig. 9.6A the percentage of each five-year group that was pregnant or recently active is shown. After reaching maturity the proportion pregnant increases to a maximum of 43·2 per cent in the 31—35 year age group, but there is subsequently a decline to 8·3 per cent in the 51—55 year age group and to zero in the 56—60 year age group. The inclusion of recently active animals gives a more consistent picture of age-specific activity, and suggests that maximum reproductive activity is confined to the 21—45 year age groups, with more than 50 per cent of females showing recent activity. Peak fecundity is apparently attained in the 30—40 year age groups reaching 60 per cent. From 45 years onwards there is a progressive decrease in fecundity to 37 per cent at 46—50 years, 25 per cent at 51—5 years and to zero in the oldest group.

The proportion of females that were lactating shows a similar increase after the attainment of maturity, to maximum values in the 25—50 year groups, with a peak at 35—40 years, when 77 per cent were lactating (Fig. 9.6B). There is a

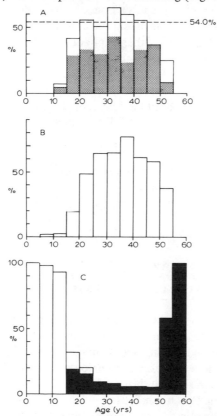

Fig. 9.6. Age-specific reproductive activity in M.F.P.S. females sampled (by 5-year classes). A. Shaded histogram—pregnant females; white histogram—recently pregnant females. 54 per cent of sexually mature females show recent activity. B. Lactating females. C. Females not pregnant, cycling, or lactating. White histogram—sexually immature; black—sexually mature.

progressive decline from 50 years onwards, to 37·5 per cent in the 51—5 year group and to zero in the 56—60 year group.

Some 27 per cent of pregnant females were concurrently lactating (Laws 1969a), but a residue of 17·2 ± 4·5 per cent of all mature females in the sample was reproductively inactive. Fig. 5.6C shows the age distribution of inactive females. After the high value of the immature years and an inactive group totaling 19 per cent in the early mature years there is a progressive decrease to values of 5—6 per cent over the 36—50 year age groups. This is followed by a very abrupt increase to 58·3 per cent in the 51—5 year age group, and all eight females in the oldest group were sexually inactive according to these criteria.

Thus, the maximum reproductive potential is reached in this population between 30 years and 40 years of age and there is a marked decline in activity from 50 years onwards, reminiscent of the menopause of human females. 'A phenomenon which, so far, has been found definitely only in man is the menopause, or cessation of ovarian function, at a fairly definite time of life. This is a very gradual process . . . . The modal age at menopause has been given as 49 years.' (Asdell 1965, p. 169). Other elephant populations that have now been studied in this way show a similar pattern with peak activity at 25—45 years (M.F.P.N.), 20—40 years (T.N.P.), and 10—45 years (M.K.). It is planned to present detailed analyses of these samples in later publications, but for the present the average proportions in the four reproductive classes are presented in Table 9.3, for comparison with the M.F.P.S. sample.

Table 9.3

Proportion of adult females in four classes of reproductive activity or inactivity (confidence intervals, $p = 5$ per cent)

	M.F.P.S.	M.F.P.N.	T.N.P.	M.K.E.
Percentage pregnant	32·6 ± 5·4	20·2 ± 4·2	26·9 ± 9·0	63·3 ± 10·0
Percentage active or recently active	54·0 ± 5·9	49·9 ± 5·4	73·1 ± 9·2	89·1 ± 6·5
Percentage lactating	54·7 ± 5·9	42·3 ± 4·4	81·7 ± 8·0	76·1 ± 8·9
Percentage inactive	17·2 ± 4·5	12·5 ± 4·0	4·3 ± 4·2	0·0

Over the series, there is a decreasing proportion in the inactive group, from 17·2 per cent in the M.F.P.S. sample to 4·3 per cent in Tsavo and to zero in Mkomasi. The proportion lactating is very much higher in Tsavo and Mkomasi than in the Uganda samples, and the proportion pregnant twice as great in Mkomasi as in the Murchison Falls National Park. The conclusion we draw is that the adult females in the Murchison Falls populations are significantly less active reproductively than those in the other populations, and that M.F.P.S. has a significantly greater proportion lactating and/or pregnant than M.F.P.N., though when recent activity was taken into account, there was no significant difference.

Laws (1969a) also suggested that some calves in M.F.P.S. continue suckling up to 8 years old, compared with a maximum duration of 4—5 years in T.N.P. However, comparisons are complicated by the fact that the sampling was not coincident; thus, most of the M.F.P.N. sample was collected in 1966, while the M.F.P.S. sample was taken largely in 1967. From other evidence the M.F.P.N. population would be expected to show a higher reproductive rate than the M.F.P.S. population, and this reversal may be caused by annual fluctuations in activity described by Laws (1969a) and discussed above. Also, in M.F.P.S. a longer-term cyclic effect described below has possibly been augmented by the heavy control shooting in North Bunyoro since 1958, which reached a peak in 1963 (see Chapter 10, Fig. 10.1). This may well have had a significant effect in alleviating the postulated nutritional and density-induced stresses.

Placental scars were classified in the course of the field operations as 'very recent', 'recent' (Plate 9.1), 'moderately old', and 'old'. (See Laws (1967a) for descriptions.) The age-specific distribution of these age classes of scars should give an additional indication of recent reproductive activity. The two extremes were plotted as histograms by 5-year classes, namely the percentage of animals in each age class for which the youngest placental scar was 'very recent' and those in which the youngest was classed as 'old'.

In order to enlarge the sample available additional data from M.F.P.N. were pooled with the M.F.P.S. data ($n = 220$). Allowing for the small sample size, this shows, after the early mature years, when 'very recent' scars outnumber 'old' scars, relatively stable proportions of 'very recent' (*ca* 10 per cent) and 'old' (*ca* 50 per cent) scars. There is possibly a slight increase in the proportion of 'very recent' scars between 35—45 years and a corresponding decrease in 'old' scars, but this was not significant. After 50 years there is a sharp increase in the percentage in which the youngest scar is classed as 'old', and no 'very recent' scars were recorded in animals in the last decade of the life cycle. The pattern is very similar to that shown by Fig. 9.6.

9.3.   The seasonal pattern of conception and births

Earlier authors concluded that there was no seasonal pattern to elephant repro-duction in Western Uganda (Perry 1953; Buss and Smith 1966) but, as Laws (1969a) pointed out, seasonality if present could well have been obscured in the analysis by the heterogeneity of their material. Laws and Parker (1968) and Laws (1969a) showed that there were well-marked seasonal patterns, which were different in each of the four populations studied by them. Recently Hanks (1969b) has demonstrated a well-marked short single mating season in a Zambian elephant population. These results are summarized in Fig. 9.7. Let us look at the probable ultimate and proximate factors (in the terms of Baker (1938)) that are involved.

In the analysis based on the findings of Huggett and Widdas (1951), it is assumed that the gestation period averages 660 days, the mean birth weight is 120 kg and t_0 (the intercept where the linear part of the foetal growth curve

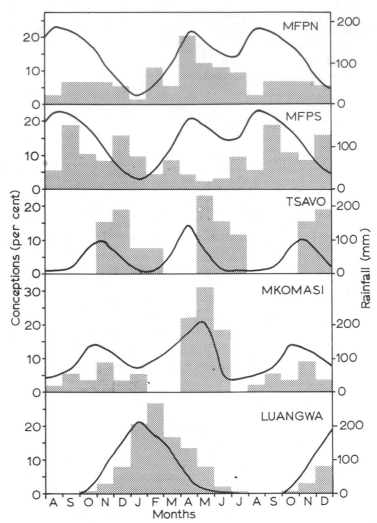

Fig. 9.7. Estimated monthly frequencies of conceptions (histograms) for five elephant populations. Mean monthly rainfall records (smoothed) are also shown. (Based on Laws 1969a
and unpublished; Hanks 1969a).

intercepts the time axis) is 66 days. The foetal growth equation is then $w^{1/3}$
$= 0.0083 (t-66)$ kg (Laws and Parker 1968), where w is the foetal weight and t
the foetal age. In the present discussion, data from 95 embryos or foetuses
recorded in the M.F.P.S. and 73 from the M.F.P.N. cropping operations are
considered (Plates 9.2 and 9.3).

Laws (1969a) concluded that the peak of M.F.P.S. conceptions was
retarded by about 5 months compared with MFPN so that the MFPN conception
peak is associated with the first half of the rains, while the MFPS conception

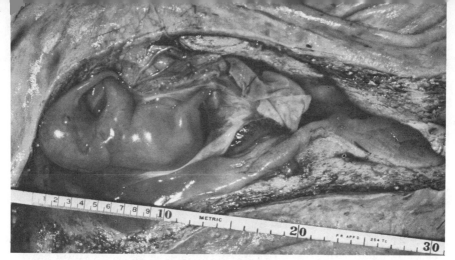

PLATE 9.2. Small foetus *in utero*

PLATE 9.3. Near-term female elephant twins; weight 81·7 kg and 98·1 kg (photograph A. Root).

peak is related to the second half of the rains, [that] the MFPN sample represents the normal seasonal pattern for this region, and that breeding is retarded in the MFPS population. The most probable causative factor is nutritional deficiency on the South bank (due to a more exclusively grass diet), but there may also be some, at present unstudied, density-dependent social effect.

This difference has important implications for the status and relation of the M.F.P.S. population to its habitat, and merits further discussion in this paper, which is concerned primarily with the interactions between an elephant population and its environment. Presumably the seasonal pattern of elephant breeding in M.F.P.N., T.N.P., M.K.E., and Luangwa Valley elephants (Fig. 9.7) has evolved as an adaption to ensure that births are concentrated in the months most favourable for the subsequent survival of the calf. (The histograms in Fig. 9.7 should be advanced by two months to show birth frequencies.) The most likely ultimate factors are seasonal availability of food and water.

In Fig. 9.8 the monthly distribution of births as estimated from the M.F.P.N. and M.F.P.S. samples are shown as histograms and the long-term average monthly

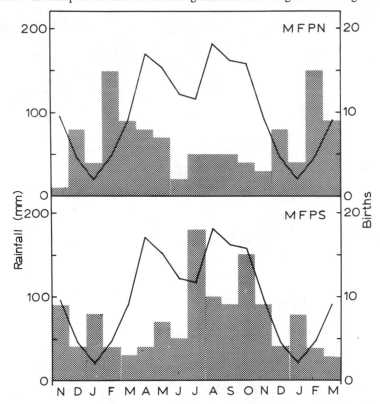

Fig. 9.8. Estimated monthly frequencies of births in recent years for the two Murchison Falls Park elephant populations. The mean monthly rainfall for catchment area 7c is shown for comparison.

rainfall for 21 stations in the Uganda drainage area 7c (Victoria Nile) (East African Meteorological Department, 1968) is shown for comparison. This illustrates the different patterns of births in the two populations, the M.F.P.N. peak of births in February being associated with increasing rainfall, but preceding the first rainfall peak in April by two months. This general pattern is also true of the T.N.P., M.K.E., and Luangwa Valley elephant populations, and is considered to represent the normal relationship between rainfall and elephant births. In the Luangwa Valley and Tsavo, however, the birth peak precedes the rainfall peak by only one month.

In the drier areas of Kenya, Tanzania, and Zambia, exemplified by the populations studied, there is a diurnal movement of elephant family units in the dry season, which involves nocturnal drinking at the rivers or water-holes and return to the more productive feeding grounds, perhaps 16 kilometres (10 miles) from the rivers, in the early morning. Owing to seasonal concentration of elephants along the rivers, the vegetation in the vicinity of permanent water is over-used and the available food severely reduced in quality and quantity. In the wet season, surface water exists away from the rivers and permanent water-holes, and the elephant population as a whole shifts away from the permanent water supplies to the more productive habitat in the hinterland.

In Tsavo this involved a displacement of some 15–30 kilometres (10–20 miles) (Laws 1969b). In these areas a mechanism ensuring that births occur during the rains would mean that the calf is born when the obligatory 15 kilometre (10 mile) trek to and from water is not necessary, because water is abundant in the interior and the population can remain in areas where nutritional conditions are most favourable. Calves born in the second half of the dry season, when smaller water-holes have dried up, would presumably be less capable of making the long diurnal trek to and from water and would not be expected to survive. The mother, if confined by her ties to the calf to the vicinity of the rivers or large water-holes, would experience severe nutritional stress which could be expected to affect her milk supply and hence the survival of the calf.

This factor may also be expected to operate in the case of the Murchison Falls populations, since even a small dry-season restriction in the availability of water would lead to enhanced movement and could affect calf survival. In most species showing seasonal births the ultimate factors are nutritional, ensuring maximal survival of the young, either by a direct effect (cover, water etc.), or as in the ewe (Hafez 1953), ensuring that the lactation period is tied to the optimal nutritional period.

But an alternative ultimate factor may be involved in Murchison Falls Park, and this is the availability of adequate nutrition at the period when the calf begins to supplement the milk diet by taking food independently. In a captive Indian elephant (*Elephas maximus*) the first teeth were cut at six weeks and all four were in wear at 8½ weeks, when the animal was taking food into its mouth. At 4–5 months it was chewing solids (Maberry 1963). An observation by

Bolwig (1965) together with other evidence, suggests that the African elephant may be precocious in this respect. In the Murchison Falls area the pattern of births should result in adequate food supplies being available at the time when the calf begins to supplement the milk diet.

The proximate factors influence conceptions nearly two years before the births occur. In Figs 9.9 and 9.10 the relative incidence of conceptions over a 3–4 year period in M.F.P.N. and M.F.P.S. is presented in the form of histograms. The absolute numbers are not comparable from year to year because of

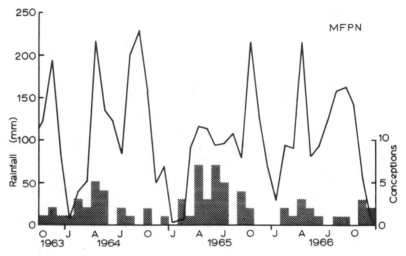

Fig. 9.9. Estimated monthly frequencies of conceptions in M.F.P.N. (1963–6). The monthly rainfall for catchment area 7c is also shown.

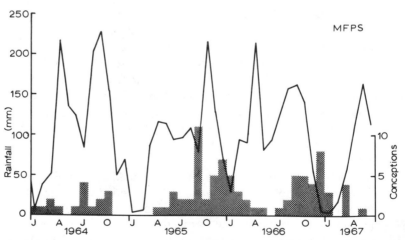

Fig. 9.10. Estimated monthly frequencies of conceptions in M.F.P.S. (1964–7). The monthly rainfall for catchment area 7c is also shown.

the variation in sampling periods. However, the data show that the average pattern represented by the histograms in Fig. 9.8 (retarded by two months to allow for the 22 months gestation period being not quite a multiple of whole years) was repeated from year to year. The monthly rainfall in Uganda drainage area 7c is shown for comparison. In each year the main conception period in M.F.P.N. is clearly associated with the first half of the rains, whereas in M.F.P.S. the majority of conceptions are associated with the end of the rains. Relative to the M.F.P.N. pattern, the M.F.P.S. conceptions are retarded by approximately 5–6 months in each of these years.

M.F.P.N. is considered to represent the normal pattern because a similar relation between rainfall and conception frequency holds for the Kenya, Tanzania, and Zambia populations for which data are available (Fig. 9.7). In each case the rise in the monthly frequency of conceptions closely follows the start of the rains. Why then is the M.F.P.S. population retarded in this way?

The evidence strongly suggests that the main proximate factor in the Murchison Falls Park is not rainfall directly, but its indirect effect on the habitat, or a combination of the two. In M.F.P.S., it is suggested, nutrition is limiting in the dry season and first half of the rains, so that female fertility is suppressed, and the proximate trigger is retarded by 5–6 months. Field (1968) states that nutritional conditions (qualitative and quantitative) for grazing animals are optimal during the latter half of the wet seasons and still high during the first month of the dry season in the Queen Elizabeth Park.

We suggest that, during the dry season, owing to the virtual absence of browse in the M.F.P.S. elephant range, the prevalence of serious widespread grass fires and the high population density, the nutritional status of the cows is severely depressed and several months of feeding are subsequently necessary to wipe out the energy or protein deficit caused by the dry season. The onset of oestrus is therefore delayed. On the North bank however, the lower population density, the greater amount of browse available, and the less widespread annual burning do not cause such severe nutritional stress and the improvement in the nutritional resources of the habitat associated with the rains leads to a more immediate reproductive response.

The level of nutrition in cattle affects the interval from calving to the first oestrus, as well as the conception rate (Bredon 1964; Tassell 1967, Grimsdell 1969). McCullagh's (1969b) findings discussed earlier were inconclusive and do not conflict with the hypothesis advanced above, but it still needs to be tested.

Shield (1965) has reported on a similar breeding season difference between two populations of the quokka (*Setonix brachyura*) in Western Australia. These populations were separated by only 80 kilometres (50 miles) and climatic differences could again be ruled out. In the less dense mainland population, breeding was continuous throughout the year, but it was restricted to six months in the dense island population, which showed a distinct seasonal peak. The observations pointed to a nutritional factor being responsible for the anoestrus period and

Sharman (1955) showed experimentally that a two year period was required before the anoestrus period was eliminated by enhanced nutrition. Shield (1965) suggested that in this species, population fertility was uninfluenced in the long term by good and bad seasons, but that 'Malthusian adjustments were dictated by the severity of the current season'.

It is not yet possible, however, to rule out completely the possibility that, in the case of the Murchison elephants, a *behavioural* effect of the higher population density on the South bank is involved.

Whatever the causative factors may be, the result of retarding the season of conception in elephant populations inevitably retards the birth season, so that it presumably no longer occurs at the most favourable time of year. As a result it is suggested that the incidence of early calf mortality may be increased and there is some evidence for this (Chapter 10). Here then is another possible density-dependent effect on recruitment to the M.F.P.S. population, operating probably through nutrition. It is very drastic and biologically wasteful, and lends further support to the view that the situation of the M.F.P.S. elephants in relation to their habitat is very serious.

9.4.   Summary

The mean ages at puberty and sexual maturity have been re-examined for the larger samples now available and slightly modify earlier conclusions. Estimates of the mean age at first production of sperm (14·4 years) and at attainment of sexual maturity (17·2 years) are presented for M.F.P.S. The mean ages in four populations are shown to be different. The reproductive consequences of the male growth spurt have been examined and the mean age at 'sociological maturity' estimated at 26 years. There was no significant difference between M.F.P.S. and M.F.P.N. in this characteristic.

A similar investigation of the attainment of sexual maturity in the female indicates that the mean age at first ovulation in the M.F.P.S. population is 17·8 years, and comparisons with other populations have been made. These results do not alter previous conclusions on density-dependent or habitat-dependent regulatory changes in the reproductive pattern.

In the sample of mature females from M.F.P.S., 32·6 per cent were pregnant and the mean calving interval was estimated at 5·6 years. This compares with a pregnancy rate of 20·2 per cent for M.F.P.N., suggesting a calving interval of 9·1 years. On other grounds M.F.P.N. is expected to have a higher pregnancy rate than M.F.P.S., but the samples were collected over different periods of time and the M.F.P.N. sample was collected at a less favourable period (when pregnancy rates should have been lower) than the M.F.P.S. sample. Placental scar counts provided further indication of pregnancy rates over longer periods.

In the M.F.P.S. sample, 62·3 per cent of females were sexually mature, of which 32·6 per cent were pregnant and 54·7 per cent were lactating. Within these classes there was an age-specific pattern in reproductive activity. Fecundity was highest in the 31–40 year age group, declining in the 51–55 year group, and falling to zero in the 56–60 year group. This decline in activity is similar to the menopause, a phenomenon so far reported only in the human female. It is apparent that the 'menopause' in elephants is density- or habitat-dependent, and in the series of populations sampled there was an increasing proportion of inactive adult females, from none in Mkomasi to 17·2 per cent in the M.F.P.S. sample. It was concluded that the M.F.P.S. population is much less active reproductively than other populations examined, which correlates with the extent of habitat change.

The most important ultimate factors influencing the annual reproductive cycle are probably seasonal availability of food and water. Rainfall, by its influence on vegetation, can also be invoked as a proximate environmental factor and the peak conception period in the populations studied, with the exception of M.F.P.S., corresponded each year to the rainfall peak. The M.F.P.N. frequencies of births were associated with increased seasonal rainfall, but the peak of births preceded the first rainfall peak in April by one or two months, and a similar pattern obtained for several other elephant populations. This is probably an adaptation ensuring that the calf is born at the optimum time of year. Over the study period of 3–4 years, however, the peak calving season in M.F.P.S. was retarded each year by about 5–6 months compared with M.F.P.N. Since the two populations are geographically very close, the seasonal climatic conditions they experience are the same, and the most conspicuous difference in their environments is the greater degree of habitat change towards grassland in the M.F.P.S.

We suggest that nutrition is now limiting in M.F.P.S. in the dry season and first half of the rains so that the operating of the proximate 'trigger' is delayed for 5–6 months. The retardation of the birth season in M.F.P.S. presumably means that it no longer occurs at the most favourable time of year and suggests that the incidence of early calf mortality may have increased. There are independent indications of this.

These studies lend further support to the view that the situation of M.F.P.S. elephants in relation to their habitat is most unfavourable.

10. Population dynamics

The age and sex structure and population dynamics of the M.F.P.S. and B.C.F.R. populations have been compared with other populations. It can be shown that recruitment has been declining both absolutely and relatively since about 1945, in spite of the annual toll taken by control shooting and sport hunting under licence (Laws and Parker 1968; Laws 1969b). This decline is equivalent to a population crash, but owing to the longevity of elephants it is spread out over many years, because the factors implicated (reduced natality and calf mortality) initially affect only the size of the younger age groups and adult mortality appears to vary within fairly narrow limits in the populations studied. If continued, this decline could lead to the virtual extinction of elephants in the range of the M.F.P.S. within 30 years or at the best, their stabilization at very low densities. The decline will continue if the present condition of the habitat in relation to elephant densities remains constant or deteriorates, as it will in the absence of further management action (Chapter 11). Other animal species will be at least as seriously affected as elephants (Chapter 4).

In this chapter we first propose to document the direct influence of human actions, notably control shooting, on the elephant populations, and then to examine the present age and sex structure, with a view to setting up models to describe probable past and present population structures, dynamics, and energetics, and to predict future changes. The consequences of these changes for the habitats in the elephant range will be discussed.

10.1. Control shooting and sport hunting in Bunyoro

The history of control shooting operations was discussed at some length in Chapter 1, and sport hunting as a form of land use in the Controlled Hunting Areas was dealt with in Chapter 3. The numbers of elephant shot on control by Game and Forest Departments and by licensed hunters in Bunyoro from 1925 to 1968 are presented in Appendix D.

Excluding the war years 1940–5, for which there are no records, a total of over 16 000 elephants were shot in Bunyoro during this period. Approximately 20 per cent of these were taken by licence holders. In 1925–39 and 1946–9 some 6047 are recorded, an average of 318 a year, and also the exact number recorded for 1950, which is the first point in the graph in Fig. 10.1. Numbers shot increased sharply after 1957. From 1961–8 the numbers shot annually on control only in Bunyoro averaged about 600 elephants, roughly twice as many as before 1958. The Game Department were unable to supply separate figures for the various districts within Bunyoro, but the majority—perhaps three quarters—of those recorded were probably shot in the vicinity of the Murchison Falls Park and the Budongo Forest. The graph (Fig. 10.1) can confidently be

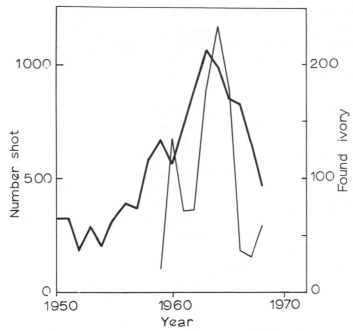

Fig. 10.1. Number of elephants shot on control and by licensed hunters in Bunyoro, 1950–68 (thick line) and elephant deaths (represented by found ivory) in M.F.P.S. below the escarpment (thin line).

taken to represent the relative incidence of control shooting in this locality. Probably then, an average of about 450 a year was taken in the vicinity of the M.F.P.S. and Budongo between 1961 and 1968. This includes the lower incidence of control shooting in the forest, which reached a peak in 1966–7 and averaged 167 a year in this eight year period.

10.1.1. *Operations in and around the Budongo Forest*

Methods for the control of elephants in the forest have so far largely been confined to shooting. A Game Guard was first posted to the forest in 1943, his duties mainly the protection of working parties and working areas in the forest; in 1957 a plan to control elephant in the forest was implemented and the kill increased. Since 1944, over 2000 elephants have been shot in the Budongo Forest and its immediate vicinity, the majority inside the forest. Until 1966 shooting was carried out only in the forest, particularly in the young regeneration areas, the aim being to chase elephants out of these areas. No attempt was made to prevent them entering. It was initially considered successful; but in view of the continued suppression of emergent tree species, probably only resulted in enhanced movement of elephants within the regeneration areas.

Since 1966 the shooting programme has concentrated on keeping elephants out of the forest, but at first sight appears not to have led to any decrease in the numbers of elephants entering the forest. The numbers of elephants annually shot in the forest and its vicinity from 1961 to 1967 increased by some 500 per cent. This has perhaps been partly due to an increase in the numbers of elephants entering the forest probably because of continued restriction of range, deterioration of the habitat outside the forest, and improvement of the forest habitat as a result of management; but also to an improvement in the supervision of the shooting. However, in 1967–8 there was a substantial decrease in the number shot, which was maintained up to November 1968, the last month for which figures are available.

The shooting was carried out by Game Guards who, until 1966, came under the control of the Game Department. Before 1966 there was little communication between the Forest and Game Departments and there was no systematic approach to the shooting. In mid 1966 the Game Guards came directly under the control of the Forest Department, which resulted in a considerable improvement in efficiency, with fewer elephants reaching the young regeneration areas.

During the period January–March 1966, a concentrated effort was made to keep the elephants out of the forest. Shooting was confined mainly to the area between the River Waisoke and Lukohe Hill (Sector 12, Fig. 5.6) as the dropping counts showed that this was the most frequently used route of entry to the forest. The method was to intercept elephants in the grassland and to turn them away from the forest back towards the Park, and this appeared to work well in the early stages. For example, on 6 January a herd was encountered near Lukohe Hill; three animals were shot and the herd split up; about 16 animals crossed into the forest and 30 turned back towards the Park. During the following night, however there was a movement of elephants into the forest, passing close to where the three had been shot earlier. Again, on 13 January, a large herd was contacted in the grassland near the Sonso River; six animals were shot and the remainder retreated towards the escarpment.

After the initial success, however, the operation failed. Very few elephants were seen in the grassland during the daylight hours and movements now seemed to be confined to the late hours of darkness, with elephants entering the forest before dawn. It is tempting to assume that they modified their behaviour in response to the shooting.

During the remainder of the dry-season reports indicated a build up of elephants in the forest. In March two large herds were encountered between the River Waisoke and Lukohe Hill during daylight hours. The Guards failed to turn these herds back towards the Park as the first few shots resulted in a precipitate rush towards the forest. At the end of March and after the first rains, elephants were observed feeding in the grasslands near the forest edge. Any shooting resulted in an immediate movement back into the forest, and at this time there was no movement away from the forest. It was concluded that it is not possible to prevent elephant entering the forest by shooting, because most of the movements were at night.

It is also possible that the shooting during 1966 resulted in a shift in the route used. Comparison of the earlier dropping counts and the track counts carried out between December 1966 and April 1967 indicates a decrease in the amount of movement between the Park and forest through the area between the River Waisoke and Lukohe Hill. The main movement is now across the eastern boundary of Budongo. Evidence presented in Chapter 5 suggested that the Butiaba Flats population of some 1500 animals, which formerly moved towards the forest from the west (Buechner *et al.* 1963), had been virtually wiped out by 1967.

It has not been possible directly to relate the numbers of elephants shot to the number of elephants in the forest. However, the numbers shot (Fig. 10.2)

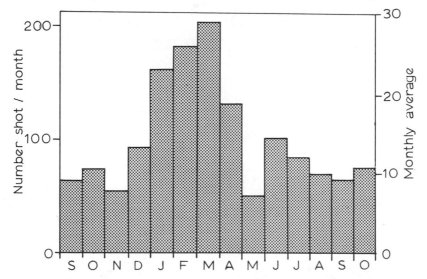

Fig. 10.2. Monthly numbers of elephants shot on control in Budongo Forest and its vicinity (1961–8).

follow a similar pattern to that shown by the numbers of droppings (Fig. 5.8) with peaks in the dry seasons. During the past eight years the largest numbers of elephant were shot in the period January–April.

Less detailed information is available from Game Department records on the incidence of control shooting around the forest. The numbers have been higher than those shot within, or in the immediate vicinity of the forest, in pursuance of the policy described in Chapter 1.

10.1.2. *Inefficiency of control shooting*

In Chapter 5 attention was drawn to the mass deaths of elephant in the vicinity of the Weiga swamp. The data on elephant deaths are presented in Figs 10.1 and 10.3, for comparison with the control shooting records (Fig. 10.2). The first recorded deaths from presumptive 'disease' in 1958 were related to an intensification of the control shooting programme around the forest and the peak in numbers of deaths from 'disease' was closely correlated with the peak in numbers shot on control in Bunyoro (Appendix D). (No data were forthcoming from Game Department records for the first half of 1962 and the 1121 plotted in 1963 (Fig. 10.1) represent animals shot in the period from May 1962 to December 1963. The true peak of this curve of control shooting should therefore be in 1964.) Subsequent to 1964 there has been a decline in control shooting and in deaths in the Weiga-Wairingo-Izizi area, as represented by found ivory.

Equally suggestive is the seasonal incidence of the deaths, mainly in January to April, when control shooting is at its height. Deaths of elephant represented by the monthly returns of found ivory in the south-western corner of the Park are presented in Fig. 10.3. if Figs 10.2 and 10.3 are compared, a very close

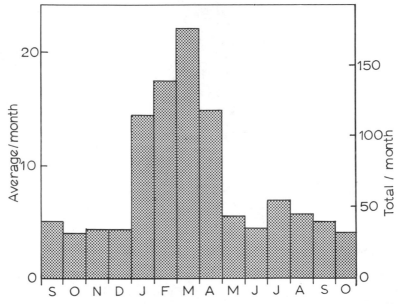

Fig. 10.3. Numbers of elephants dying per month along the Weiga River valley, within M.F.P.S. (1961–8).

correlation is evident between the seasonal incidence of control shooting and the recent deaths of elephant below the escarpment. This markedly seasonal pattern is not primarily due to burning in the dry season making carcasses more visible, because these areas are in medium-height *Hyparrhenia* grassland (Fig. 2.1) and are regularly patrolled by Park Rangers. The great majority of carcasses are noted within a week or so of death, vultures and other scavengers drawing attention to them. The geographical distribution of the deaths is also indicative; 87 per cent of deaths in the south-western part of the Park occurred along the Weiga, Wairingo, and Izizi Rivers, just within the sanctuary of the Park, below the escarpment and close to the location of control shooting around the forest.

On average, during the period 1961—8, 109 deaths were recorded annually by found ivory returns. Comparing the Weiga-Wairingo-Izizi area with the Sambiya-Joliya area it was assumed that an average of about 100 deaths a year may be due to inefficient control shooting. The figures now presented suggest that up to 450 elephants were shot and killed annually in North Bunyoro, and a further 100 shot and mortally wounded, that is a mortal wounding mortality rate of about 18 per cent of the total being killed. The average annual number shot in the forest or its close vicinity was 167, suggesting a maximum mortal wounding rate of *ca* 37 per cent in the forest operations. (Animals shot in the forest are more likely to be wounded than elephants shot in the grasslands.) These are animals, mortally wounded, but able to travel 8—16 kilometres (5—10 miles) and survive for a few hours, days, or even weeks before dying. Probably a substantial number in addition is wounded but recovers.

On this evidence it seems reasonable to assume that of elephant killed in the control operations, a substantial number is not recorded in the Game Department records. This applies from the start of the records in 1925, when the proportion dying slowly of wounds was evidently higher (See Chapter 1). In recent years perhaps 20—30 per cent of elephants shot on control were mortally wounded but died lingering deaths, while an unknown proportion was shot but survived. This is an inevitable but distressing consequence of the method of piecemeal control shooting, employing Game Guards working as individuals and therefore with little supervision. It has continued over the past 40—50 years, as the accounts in Chapter 1 show. As well as being inefficient, wasteful, and uneconomic, the method is grossly inhumane and, if control shooting is necessary, it should obviously be replaced by rational, efficient, and humane sustained-yield cropping by a trained team on the lines of the reduction cropping carried out within the Park.

10.1.3.   *Effect of control shooting on potential population size*

In Appendix D are shown the numbers of elephants shot annually on control in Bunyoro, 1925—68, by the Game and Forest Departments and by licensed hunters. There are no records for 1940—5, nor were we able to obtain information about 1962. For the first half of that year (see above) we have assumed a take of 500, which is in line with the totals for adjacent years. In 1965 a further 185 were cropped in the National Park, M.F.P.S. For reasons which will become apparent in discussing population models below, the post-war period 1946—66 is of particular relevance and in these years some 10 476 elephants are recorded as having been shot in Bunyoro.

Under natural conditions populations usually stabilize, or fluctuate about a level in approximate balance with the environmental resources. Hunting or control shooting disturbs this equilibrium, reducing numbers, and compensating mechanisms come into play, including reduced natural mortality, faster growth, increased fecundity, and earlier puberty, because the limiting factors are relaxed and usually more food is available. But, as we have seen, for the elephant, despite intensive hunting and, as we shall demonstrate, a decrease in numbers, the compensating mechanisms have operated in the other direction. There has been a decrease in the birth rate, increased natural mortality (at least of young animals), slower growth, and later puberty. The constraints on numbers have not been relaxed, but increased, presumably because there has been a progressive reduction of the elephant range. This indicates that control shooting has been a secondary factor in the decline, although there can be little doubt that without it habitat destruction would have been more rapid and the compensating mechanism perhaps faster acting.

However, it is desirable to obtain an estimate of the real reduction in population that this offtake represents. For present purposes we assume a stable population in 1946 in Bunyoro, from which 221 were taken (Appendix D). These would have suffered an estimated annual natural mortality rate of about 6·4 per cent so that if there had been no control shooting only 207 would have been expected to survive to 1947. Similarly 266 were shot in 1947, making an adjusted cumulative real reduction of 473, of which at 6·4 per cent natural mortality, 443 would have survived to 1948. In 1948, 217 were shot making a potential cumulative real reduction of 660 and so on. In this way it was calculated that the 10 476 actually shot represent when natural mortality is taken into account, a cumulative potential net reduction of the original population (from this cause alone) of 7076. Natural mortality has probably not remained constant in recent years and its arbitrary increase in the calculations to 10 per cent a year from 1960 onwards reduces the estimate from 7076 to 6182.

However, the recorded figures of elephant deaths may be as much as 15 per cent low on average, because some animals probably escape unwounded and later die unrecorded, as mentioned previously. This would suggest a maximum estimate of about 8300 for the potential reduction in the original (1946) population size due to shooting. If we assume that about 75 per cent were taken in North Bunyoro, then a rough estimate for the reduction in the population due to this factor alone is 5500 to 6200. A value of about 6000 seems reasonable. However, it is clearly no more than a *very* rough estimate.

Because there are no reliable population estimates prior to 1966, it is difficult to apply these figures, and we make this crude allowance for shooting mortality in our subsequent analysis. This is an obvious disadvantage of such a short-term study.

There are a few points that can usefully be made before going on to discuss age structures and construct population models. First, we consider that, for the most part, the over-all effect of control shooting and licensed hunting is random with respect to age, a tendency to take smaller and younger animals in control shooting operations probably being balanced by a positive selection of larger animals in sport hunting for trophies. The average weight of trophy ivory in Uganda showed a highly significant decline over the period 1925–58 (Brooks

and Buss 1962). However, these authors demonstrated an increase in both number of tusks and average weight of ivory between the two periods 1946—51
and 1952—7, the proportion of tusks over 22 kg (49 lb) in weight increasing
from 29·0 per cent to 33·5 per cent in Bunyoro. Unfortunately a similar analysis
has not yet been carried out for the subsequent years. It is here assumed that
population reduction as a result of shooting in the period since 1946 has not been
selective with respect to age, or at least not significantly so in relation to our
analysis.

Secondly, control shooting and sport hunting have been peripheral to the
north Bunyoro population, and the elephant in the central area (which is where
sampling took place) were probably not directly affected by it. We have already
discussed the movements and distribution of the population (Chapter 5) in some
detail, and concluded that the elephant in the central area were resident within
that area and did not move into the peripheral areas. Despite this, an aerial
photographic analysis showed that the age structure of the existing peripheral
populations did not appear to be significantly different from that of the central
population (Laws 1969b). This tends to support the view that control shooting
has not been particularly selective with respect to age, though we think it
probable that matriarchs may have been selectively removed from the peripheral
herds.

It has been suggested that the Butiaba Flats population numbering about 1500
elephants has been virtually wiped out by control shooting. It may be that other
unit populations or 'clans' at the edge of the elephant range were also eliminated
in this way, and accounted for most of the control shooting. In that case the
hunting mortality component of total mortality for the remaining population
may have been small.

10.2.   Age and sex structure of elephant populations

The age structures of the samples from M.F.P.S. ($n = 800$) and B.C.F.R.
($n = 303$) have been analysed for males and females separately. Reasons have
already been given for believing that the samples, especially those from the
cropping operations (as against those taken on control shooting operations in
B.C.F.R.), are representative of the populations they are taken from.

Histograms showing age-class frequencies are presented in Figs 10.4
and 10.5. The sample cropping was spread over a period of time and so the
frequencies have been adjusted. Thus, in M.F.P.S., 185 were taken in November
1965, and 615 in 1967; in B.C.F.R. 186 were taken in 1966, and 117 in 1967.
In order to make the samples comparable and to combine them, the age structures have been converted to the base year 1966; foetuses due to be born in 1966
have been included in the samples taken in 1965.

The age structures show clearly that there is a sex differential survivorship in
favour of the female. It is also apparent that there are large variations in age-class
size from year to year, and these might be thought to reflect inaccuracies in the

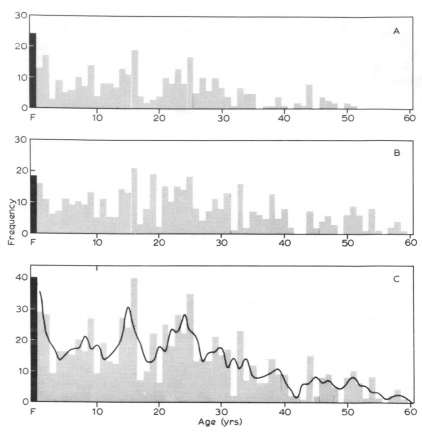

Fig. 10.4. Age structure of elephants cropped in M.F.P.S., converted to base year 1966: (A) males; (B) females; (C) sexes combined and 3-year running average drawn. (F) Foetuses in second half of gestation.

ages assigned, but Laws (1969a) and Laws and Parker (1968) have shown that there are similar large variations in the numbers of foetuses conceived in success- ive years, and in yearling numbers; in these cases the ages assigned are not in any doubt. If, as in M.K.E., 71 per cent of all adult females were in late pregnancy or early *post partum* stages, this is surely conclusive evidence of such fluctuations. To minimize this effect the data for the two sexes have been combined and smoothed by 3-year running averages. A larger series of fluctuations with a wave length of about 6–8 years then became apparent and Laws (1969a) suggested that they represented a series of cycles in recruitment to the population, corre- lated with rainfall cycles of similar period in East Africa.

It should be pointed out that, apart from three known-age wild and captive animals, respectively 6½, 12½, and 27½ years old (Chapter 6), there are no direct checks on the ages assigned to the age groups. However, these were not arbitrary, as Sikes (1968a, 1971) states, but were the result of a careful examination of the

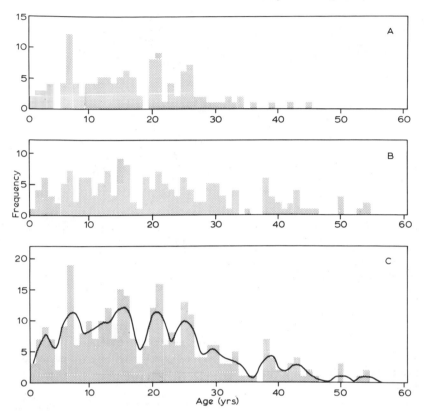

Fig. 10.5. Age structure of elephants shot on control in the Budongo Forest and vicinity. Converted to base year 1966. (A) males; (B) females; (C) sexes combined and 3-year running average drawn.

evidence from a number of different studies, including eye-lens dry weights (Laws 1967), growth ridges on the roots of the teeth (Laws 1966, and unpublished), and apparent rates of growth of a number of structures. The graphs and scatter diagrams in this book, and other unpublished growth curves, as well as the family unit structures (Fig. 7.10) strongly suggest a smooth progressive ageing, rather than a series of steps.

One check on the validity of this interpretation of the fluctuations in age-class sizes would be to re-sample a population and to compare the position of the peaks and troughs in the age frequencies of the two samples. Thus, if the population was re-sampled after an interval of five years, the peaks and troughs should be displaced five years to the right in the age-structure histograms. Unfortunately this has not yet been possible, because the main cropping operations in the Murchison Falls area were completed within two years (and within six months for M.F.P.S.). We have, however, compared the initial samples from M.F.P.N. and M.F.P.S., taken in August and November 1965 (mean month October 1965)

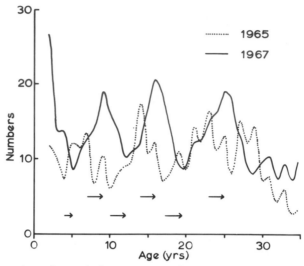

Fig. 10.6. Comparison of smoothed age structures (3-year running averages) for M.F.P.S. females sampled in 1965 and 1967. The arrows indicate displacement of peaks and troughs (see text).

with the sample taken in M.F.P.S. in 1967 (mean month April 1967). It has been necessary to combine the earlier samples in order to obtain an adequate sized sample, but since the climatic fluctuations over the area are similar this is felt to be permissible. The interval between the samples is about 18½ months (1·5 years).

Smoothed curves (3-year running averages from 0 years to 35 years) for these two samples are presented in Fig. 10.6. For the second and third peaks and the first three troughs the mean displacement is 1·9 years; when the next peak is included the average displacement is still 1·9 years. The 1965 sample is less representative above 20 years than the 1967 sample, because the sampling of the bull herds was less random in these early operations when the sampling technique was being worked out. That displacement occurs in the expected direction supports our interpretation of the peaks and troughs in the age distributions, but a further comparison within the M.F.P.S. population over a longer interval is needed. This should be possible if further cropping is undertaken in the M.F.P.S.

This evidence and the three known-age specimens is consistent with a reasonably accurate assignment of chronological ages and seems to leave little room for an explanation of the apparent cyclicity, based on a variation in the time scale applied to the various age groups. Moreover, the peaks in different populations tend to occur at different ages and to vary in intensity from one population sampled to another. It is also relevant that the most productive populations, which show the most precocious puberty, highest fecundity, faster body growth rates, and most stable age structures, are also those which show the least fluctuation in apparent year-class abundance. Final proof is lacking until more known-age animals become available or one of the populations studied is re-sampled, or recruitment to a population is studied over a long period.[†] But we find great difficulty in accepting that the fluctuations in year-class abundance are an artefact.

Whatever the reasons for their occurrence they do complicate analysis of age structures and necessitate considerable smoothing to construct simple population models and to estimate survivorship and mortality rates, and production.

10.3. Population models

Laws (1966, 1969b) has shown that in the elephant the mortality rate for much of the lifespan is nearly constant, so that a plot of the logarithm of sur-vivors against age was linear over the age range 5–50 years, or 20–50 years, for three populations. For a number of elephant populations that have now been sampled we have examined the relation between year-class abundance and age in an attempt to obtain estimates of z, the instantaneous total mortality rate, from the linear segment of the plots. By plotting the natural logarithm of year-class abundance ($\log_e N_t$) against age t, and fitting a regression, z is estimated from the slope $-z$ (Beverton and Holt 1957).

In this method based on the 'catch-curve' of fishery biologists (Ricker 1948), mortality is estimated from the relative abundance of the age groups and a steady state of recruitment and mortality has to be assumed. The effects of trends in mortality rates and trends in recruitment, on the age structure, can be similar and could be important in the analysis. Nor can we rule out the possibility of a curvilinear relation between logarithm of year-class abundance and age. But we feel that for present purposes there is sufficient justification for assuming a log-linear relation over much of the lifespan (Laws (1966) and Fig. 10.7(a) and (b)). Although there are in fact good reasons for not assuming constant mortality (Caughley 1966), such an assumption is unlikely to introduce large errors into the subsequent analysis. The similarity between the results from a number of elephant populations suggests that the adult mortality rates over most of the life-span vary within a relatively narrow range. We have already suggested that the component of total mortality due to controlled hunting operations (with the exception of the Budongo population) is likely to be fairly random with respect to age.

10.3.1. *Numbers*

The following analysis has been confined to the material on female age fre-quencies. In order to eliminate the effects of the large apparent fluctuations in year-class abundance discussed above, and to simplify the calculations, the average $\log_e N_t$ values for 5-year classes were used and slopes estimated (together with

† Douglas-Hamilton (1972) presented data suggesting that the large variation in annual birth rate of the Lake Manyara elephants (directly observed over a period of four years) could be related to rainfall in the year of conception.

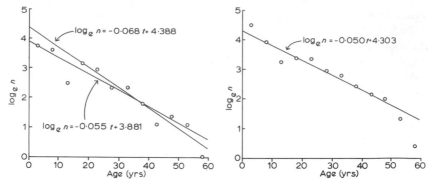

Fig. 10.7. Plots of the natural logarithms of year class abundance against age (5-year class interval) for (a) M.K.C. female elephants, regressions calculated from the age range 0–50 years (below) and 20–50 years (above) are shown; (b) Tsavo (Voi–Aruba) females; calculated regression based on 0–50 years.

Table 10.1.

Estimates of the instantaneous mortality rate z for a series of elephant populations sampled. (Bold type: 'best estimate' on inspection of graphs and correlation coefficients *r*.)

Population	z for different ranges of t			r for 'best estimate'
	0–50	10–50	20–50	
Mkomasi Central	0·055	0·051	**0·068**	− 0·938
Mkomasi East	0·050	**0·060**	0·080	− 0·912
Tsavo Koito	0·050	0·046	**0·063**	− 0·912
Tsavo Koito[1]	–	–	**0·063**	− 0·740
Tsavo McKinnon Road	0·038	0·041	**0·059**	− 0·993
Tsavo Aruba–Voi[2]	0·050	0·042	**0·054**	− 0·992
Zambia Luangwa	0·040	0·044	**0·063**	− 0·536
M.F.P.N.	0·034	0·035	**0·052**	− 0·922
M.F.P.N.[1]	–	–	**0·052**	− 0·604
M.F.P.S.	0·026	0·039	**0·060**	− 0·851
M.F.P.S.[1]	–	–	**0·052**	− 0·567
B.C.F.R.	0·034	0·049	**0·062**	− 0·927
M.F.P.S. + B.C.F.R.	0·028	0·040	**0·058**	− 0·932
M.F.P.S. a[2]	0·027	0·040	**0·057**	− 1·000
M.F.P.S. b[2]	0·026	0·045	**0·062**	− 1·000
Murchison Falls Park[3]	0·048	0·058	**0·063**	− 0·992
Queen Elizabeth Park[3]	0·042	0·051	**0·054**	− 0·992

Notes. Except where otherwise indicated z is estimated from grouped data.
(1) z estimated from ungrouped data
(2) Age composition derived from aerial photographs using age/length key (Laws 1969b)
(3) z estimated from data on found jaws, representing natural deaths presented by Laws (1966)

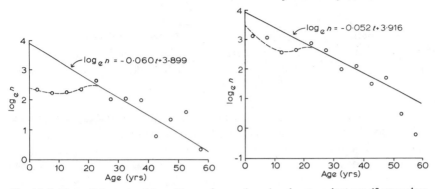

Fig. 10.8. Plots of the natural logarithms of year class abundance against age (5-year class interval) for (a) M.F.P.S. female elephants; (b) M.F.P.N. female elephants. Regressions calculated for age range 20–50 years.

95 per cent confidence limits) by fitting regression lines, using the method of least squares, to the segments 0–50 years, 10–50 years and 20–50 years of the age structures. Even with the grouped data there is considerable variability caused by the peaks and troughs in the age structures, in other words by apparent fluctuations in recruitment. Some examples are shown in Figs 10.7 and 10.8 and the results are summarized in Table 10.1. We are indebted to Dr. J. Hanks, Department of Veterinary Medicine, Cambridge, for providing data on which the Luangwa Valley estimates are based. The other data are original. Animals aged more than 50 years have been omitted from the analysis because there is good evidence for an increased mortality rate in the oldest animals (Figs 10.7(b), and 10.8(b); Laws (1966)).

In some samples the plots suggested a near log-linear relationship over the whole lifespan (e.g. M.K.C., Fig. 10.7(a)). In others the linear segment is restricted to older animals owing to reduced recruitment (e.g. M.F.P.S., Fig. 10.8(a)). The correlation coefficients were used to help decide which was the 'best estimate'. Thus, in general the estimate of z associated with the highest value for r, the correlation coefficient, was adopted. But these differences were often very slight. For M.K.C., for example, r was −0·938 for the regression fitted to the range from 20–50 years, and −0·934 for 0–50 years. The Luangwa Valley data give puzzlingly low correlation coefficients for grouped data. The range of r for the 'best estimate' of z for the data derived from cropping six populations is −0·851 to −0·938, whereas for Luangwa the highest value for r (for $t = 0$–50) is −0·646 and for $t = 20$–50 only −0·536. The discrepancy suggests that the Luangwa sample may be anomalous and suspect.

Confidence limits are not given in Table 10.1, but they ranged from ± 0·027 to ± 0·035, and the 'best estimate' values of z are not significantly different ($p > 5$ per cent). Very much larger samples (which are unlikely to be obtained) would be needed to establish differences, because of the large fluctuations in recruitment.

Exceptions are the data from found jaws from Murchison Falls Park and Queen Elizabeth Park (Laws 1966), where there is a considerable smoothing effect introduced by the method of analysis. For Murchison Falls Park z is estimated at 0.063 ± 0.002 and for Queen Elizabeth Park, 0.054 ± 0.002. These values are for the sexes combined and because of the sex difference in mortality are probably slightly higher than for females alone. Also, for the data obtained by applying age/length keys to lengths measured from aerial photographs, there is again a considerable smoothing effect inherent in the method.

In the case of M.F.P.S., M.F.P.N., and Tsavo Koito, estimates of z have also been made for ungrouped data, over the age range 20—50 years. As expected the correlation coefficients are very much lower, respectively $- 0.567$, $- 0.604$ and $- 0.740$, and not dissimilar from the *grouped* data from Luangwa.

The range of estimates of z then, from the log-linear segment, is from 0.052 to 0.068, corresponding to annual survival rates (e^{-z}) of 0.949 to 0.934, or annual mortality rates of 0.051 to 0.066, that is 5.1 —6.6 per cent. It is particularly interesting that the estimates for Murchison Falls Park and Queen Elizabeth Park, derived from ages at death, are so similar to those derived from the age structures in life (annual mortality rates of 0.063 and 0.054 respectively) and this supports the belief that the sampling by cropping was near random. The present analysis also confirms and extends the earlier report by Laws (1969b, Figure 9) that the age-frequency curves for elephants over 15 years old in six populations were very similar. If this is so it implies not only that mortality is rather constant, but that all populations have had similar age structures from 50 years ago until the effects of decreased recruitment show, for example in M.F.P.S. about 20 years ago.

In an attempt to explain what may have happened to the M.F.P.N. population, models were constructed, assuming a value for z (from ungrouped data of Table 10.1). This value was calculated from the linear segment (20—50 years), representing animals born before recruitment began to decline, and the assumption is made that recruitment was then constant (that is before 1946), and that adult mortality has remained fairly constant. The basis of these assumptions is the similarity of adult age structures in the different populations sampled, which implies either similar rates of increase or stability. First, in constructing a model representing a hypothetical population of M.F.P.S. before recruitment began to decline, year-class abundance was calculated from the equation $N_t = N_0 e^{-zt}$, with an assumed value for N_0 of 1000. The resulting curve is shown in Fig. 10.9 (dotted and solid line; right-hand scale). It was adjusted by calculating female natality, assuming sexual maturity at 12 years, a 50 per cent pregnancy rate of mature females (mean calving interval about 4 years), and a sex ratio at birth of 1:1. This gave a natality of 1197 and involved a slight adjustment of the origin (Fig. 10.9, right-hand scale) and early mortality rates. The tail was adjusted slightly, allowing for increased mortality in old age. This model represents a steady-state population, with recruitment at birth balanced by deaths.

Male survivorship was assumed to be identical with that of the female up to

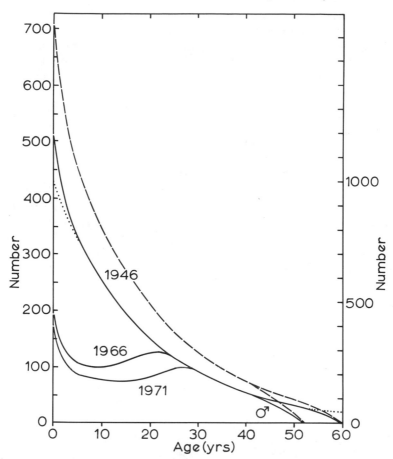

Fig. 10.9. Hypothetical population models (numbers) for the North Bunyoro elephant population in 1946, 1966, and 1971. Solid lines—population structure estimated from year class abundance data derived from sample cropping in 1965–7, and extrapolation. Broken line—makes allowance for numbers taken in control shooting operations since 1946. Dotted line—estimate based on instantaneous total mortality rate of 0·052 ($N_t = N_0 e^{-zt}$). A sex difference above 40 years is indicated. See text for explanation.

40 years, when an increased mortality rate results in no survival beyond 52 years (Fig. 10.4). These adjustments make little difference to the subsequent arguments and the model is not entirely arbitrary because it is very similar to the pattern represented by the year class abundances in some other current populations (e.g. Fig. 10.7(a), M.K.C.). For this population the sample showed relatively little scatter about the linear regression of $\log_e N_t$ on age ($t = 0–50$) of slope −0·055 ($= −z$), and the correlation coefficient $r = −0·934$. Similarly for M.K.E. ($t = 0–50$, $z = 0·050$, and $r = −0·913$), for Tsavo Koito ($t = 0–50$, $z = 0·050$, and $r = −0·885$) and for Tsavo Aruba-Voi ($t = 0–50$, $z = 0·054$, and $r = −0·992$).

M.K.C. and M.K.E. are productive populations (apparently the most productive yet examined), with relatively early puberty and high pregnancy rates (Chapter 9). It seems reasonable to assume that other populations, including M.F.P.S., were similar before decreasing range and habitat change resulted in declining recruitment, the latter brought about by deferred puberty, lower pregnancy rates, and increased calf mortality. This hypothetical model is considered to approximate to the structure of the North Bunyoro elephant population about 1946 or earlier, and will be referred to below as the 1946 population. Habitat change was noted before 1946 and serious damage by 1949 in North Bunyoro (Chapter 1).

Next, the model was adjusted to describe the situation in 1966, by taking into account the 5-year means of year-class abundance for the first third of the lifespan, showing reduced recruitment (pecked line in Fig. 10.8(a)). The 1966 N_t values from 3–23 years were determined graphically. Female natality was then calculated assuming sexual maturity at 18 years, 28·6 per cent pregnant (mean calving interval 7 years) and a sex ratio at birth of 1:1 (as discussed in Chapter 9). This gave a natality of 457 and year-class abundance was adjusted by interpolation up to four years as shown.

	1946 model		1966 model	
t	N_t	Mortality rate	N_t	Mortality rate
0	!197	0·13	457	0·20
1	1040	0·10	380	0·15
2	940	0·09	330	0·15
3	901	0·05	287	0·10
4	856	0·05	261	0·05

If recruitment has in fact been declining in this population for some 20 years (Fig. 10.8(a)), then the model mortality rates for 1966 will be lower than the true rates, and suggest that there has been an increase in total calf mortality from 28·5 per cent ($t = 0$–4) to $> 42·9$ per cent, possibly almost a doubling since 1946. This model is also presented in Fig. 10.9; we are on firmer ground than with the hypothetical 1946 model because the 1966 model is based on an established age structure and other parameters.

Since 1966 we consider that the post-weaning mortality rate has probably remained constant at about 5 per cent annually and that other parameters have· not changed greatly (age at sexual maturity, pregnancy rate, and sex ratio), so we can construct a model for the 1971 population. The sizes of all year-classes above 4 years old in 1966, influenced by reduced recruitment since 1946 (i.e. those less than 24 years in 1966), will have declined in the intervening five years. This decline can be estimated by $1 - e^{-zt}$, that is $1 - e^{-0·26}$, or 22·9 per cent. Natality estimated as for the 1966 model is 407 and year-class abundance up to four years was calculated using the 1966 apparent mortality rates. This model also is presented in Fig. 10.9. Note that it has been assumed that mortality and age-class abundance of the older animals (born before 1946) has remained constant. Because the earlier analysis of data from a number of populations indicated a range of 5·1—6·6 per cent for mean *adult* annual mortality rates up to 50 years, it is suggested that errors are in any case likely to be small.

These models suggest that relative natality fell from 1197 in 1946, to 457 in 1966, and to 407 in 1971, decreases of 62 per cent and 66 per cent respectively. They also suggest that recruitment at 4 years fell from 856 in 1946, to 261 in 1966, and to 212 in 1971, that is by 70 per cent and 75 per cent. Although the models are necessarily very crude and the estimates not very reliable (largely due to the apparent or real fluctuations in recruitment discussed earlier, and the number of assumptions made in order to construct them—particularly the 1946 model) it cannot be doubted that there has been a great change in population structure over 20—30 years and a significant reduction in natality and recruitment. Although this was a necessary consequence of lowered reproduction rate, discussed in Chapter 9, the models give an indication of the possible extent of the effect on population size and structure. Further cropping, by establishing current age structure, would enable the validity of the post-1966 models to be tested.

The year-class abundance values presented so far have been related to the initial arbitrary values for a cohort of 1000 (adjusted to 1197) in 1946. The next step was to sum the N_t values, for both sexes, for each of the three models in order to obtain three relative population sizes. For 1966 this totalled 21 195 and since the actual population size at about that time has been estimated at approximately 9400 (Chapter 5) a correction factor of 0·443501 (9400 ÷ 21 195) has been applied to the three models to derive approximate estimates of true population sizes. The left-hand scale in Fig. 10.9 relates to these, and the correction indicates a population size in 1946 of about 16 000.

However, a further adjustment is necessary to allow for the reduction in population size between 1946 and 1966 due to control shooting and sport hunting operations. In an earlier section of this chapter it was calculated that this factor was responsible for a net reduction of about 6000 elephants, unbiased with respect to age. This was a very rough estimate because detailed records of elephants shot from this population were not available, but only for Bunyoro District as a whole, and it was assumed that such mortality was additive to natural mortality. It was judged that about three quarters of the elephants taken in Bunyoro were from this population, but if substantially less (or more) than 75 per cent of the total for Bunyoro were taken in North Bunyoro, it would affect the estimate proportionately, as would errors in the estimated natural mortality rates and the estimate for unrecorded deaths due to wounding. However, 6000 is our 'best estimate' and implies a population of about 22 000 elephants in North Bunyoro before 1946. The structure of this population is thought to have been similar to that of the 1946 model already presented. Hunting mortality is thought to have been unbiased with respect to age (except possibly in the forest) as discussed above, and an adjusted model is shown by the pecked lines in Fig. 10.9.

On the basis of these models, then, it is suggested that population size decreased from about 22 000 in 1946 to 9400 in 1946 and to 7900 in 1971. This would represent a decrease of 57 per cent between 1946 and 1966, of which about half (27 per cent) could be due to control shooting and sport hunting. The estimated 1971 population is 36 per cent of the hypothetical 1946 population, a decrease of 64 per cent. Natural regulation alone could be responsible for a population decrease of about 41 per cent to 1966 and about 51 per cent to 1971 (in actual numbers from about 16 000 to some 9400 and 7900).

If the models can be accepted, a very substantial adjustment, aided by the control shooting operations, has evidently still been inadequate to permit a stable population to develop in balance with the environment—for reasons which will become apparent when we discuss standing crop biomasses rather than numbers.

However, it must be pointed out that in constructing the models we have been forced to assume various functional relationships, and to use estimates of parameters which may or may not be reliable. We are aware that the most serious potential sources of error lie in the assumption of a stable population in 1946 and in the time scale applied to the age criteria used to establish age structures. There are other potential sources of error inherent in a cross-sectional study such as this, although we are encouraged by some confirmation provided by an outstanding longer-term behavioural study recently completed by Douglas-Hamilton (1972).

We therefore regard this as a first attempt to describe the long-term dynamics of an elephant population in other than qualitative terms, and our intention is to extend and quantify our concept of the general nature of the population response to increasing density and habitat change, first presented by Laws and Parker (1968). It is perhaps best regarded as a theoretical exercise to describe in quantitative terms what might have happened. In the process we may seem to give a spurious impression of accuracy which does not exist, in spite of our disclaimers; we do not wish to claim such accuracy. It will be for future studies to supply more reliable estimates of density related parameters, which may result in minor or major modifications or to this model being superseded by a different one. If our work stimulates others in this way we shall have achieved our purpose. Further cropping to be undertaken in 1973 in M.F.P.S. (Eltringham, personal communication) will provide a test for our prediction of the 1971 population structure.

The 1966 model should give a reasonable approximation, because it is based on direct sampling, and although the future predictions are susceptible to testing, the back extrapolation to 1946 is more doubtfully valid. However, an independent computer simulation study carried out by Fowler and Smith (1973) supports our findings. These authors depend to some extent on biological parameters estimated from field studies, including our own, and their method uses a variable Leslie matrix determined as a function of population density.

They took our crude estimated age distribution for 1945 (Laws and Parker 1968) and fed the relevant parameters into their computer programme. With no other modifications they observed little change in population size over time. They then increased the elephant density linearly from 2—3 per square mile in 1945 to 10 per square mile in 1965. Although the assumption of a linear trend may be grossly in error, as a first approximation it nevertheless 'produces results not unlike those observed in the field'. The observed and predicted age distributions in 1965 are similar and Fowler and Smith (1973) conclude that their model is useful as a predictive tool. Laws and Parker (1968) also made predictions and published crude estimated age distributions for the future, assuming no further change in reproduction and mortality (that is no further change in elephant density) and the computer simulation gave very similar results.

This approach emphasizes the need to direct research towards reliable esti-mates of relevant parameters and to elucidating density-dependent or habitat-dependent relationships. Further cropping would also make it possible to test the predictions.

10.3.2.   *Standing-crop biomass*

With the reservations mentioned above, the numerical models can now be converted to biomass models, which are more meaningful in relation to the environment, for our purposes. In Chapter 8 we presented growth curves, and mean weights at age have been applied to the age frequencies for each age and sex class to obtain population biomass ($\Sigma N_t w_t$). The nutritional status of the population in 1946 is likely to have been very much better than in 1966 or 1971. In order to allow for this, 'optimum' weight at age (calculated in Chapter 8), from comparison with the M.K.E. elephants, have been applied to the 1946 model. In practice this involves increasing the weights by 8·9 per cent. As the weight-growth curves were established by weighings in the wet season they should be reduced, by perhaps 5 per cent, to obtain year-round average values. In the ensuing discussion uncorrected seasonal values are used, but it should be remem-bered that for annual values the results should be adjusted.

The resulting standing crop biomass-at-age curves are presented in Fig. 10.10, where the broken line shows the adjustment of the 1946 model to allow for a net reduction in population size due to control operations, as explained earlier. In 1946 then, the biomass peak was at age 13 years, and the secondary peak at 23 years is due to the supposed male post-pubertal growth spurt. The effect of the reduced recruitment since then has been to postpone the biomass peak to 25 years in 1966 and to about 28 years in 1971.

Population standing crop biomass, rounded to the nearest 1000 kg is esti-mated at $41{\cdot}789 \times 10^6$ kg in 1946, $20{\cdot}996 \times 10^6$ kg in 1966, and $19{\cdot}442 \times 10^6$ kg in 1971. These estimates represent a decrease in standing crop biomass of

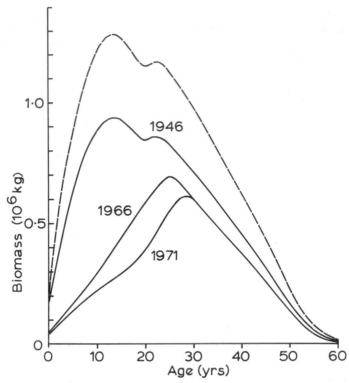

Fig. 10.10. Estimate of standing crop biomass at age for three hypothetical population models of the North Bunyoro elephants (sexes combined). Broken line – allowance made for numbers taken on control shooting operations.

49·8 per cent to 1966 and 53·5 per cent to 1971, slightly less than the percentage decrease in population numbers (Table 10.2).

Mean elephant weight is easily calculated ($\Sigma N_t\, w_t \div \Sigma N_t$), and it is found that there has been an increase in unit weight, according to the models, from 1894 kg in 1946 to 2234 kg by 1966, and to 2461 kg in 1971. This is, of course, caused by the reduced recruitment so that the contribution of the lighter age classes has been reduced, leaving a preponderance of the heavier, older animals in the population.

The elephant range has decreased from an estimated 6300 square kilometres in 1946 to 3200 square kilometres in 1966 (Chapter 1, Fig. 1.4), and to an estimated 2800 square kilometres in 1971. Applying these estimates to population size gives mean elephant densities of 3·50 per square kilometre in 1946, 2·94 per square kilometre in 1966 and 2·83 per square kilometre in 1971, a decrease of about 20 per cent from the 1946 value. However, the increase in elephant unit weight has had the effect of limiting the reduction in weight per unit area. The mean unit weights per square kilometre are estimated at 6633 kg in 1946, 6561 kg in 1966, and 6965 kg in 1971. Over twenty years a very slight reduction is indicated—only 1·1 per cent up to 1966—and by 1971, with continued contraction of the range, an increase of 5 per cent. This is a crucial factor in the continued habitat deterioration caused by the elephant population. The standing crop biomass per unit area appears to have changed very little since the habitat deterioration began and so the change has been progressive. Clearly, the reason for the failure of the control shooting and the reduced recruitment to lower the standing crop per unit area is that the range available has been contracting. By 1966 the range had shrunk to an estimated 51 per cent of its area in 1946, and even less of the pre-1946 range, and the population standing crop biomass to 50 per cent of its size in 1946, the former development effectively nullifying the latter regulatory adjustment. As we have seen, habitat damage had already begun in 1946 and was severe in places by 1949. Furthermore, the rate of reduction of the elephant range has not been uniform, and at times when the contraction was more rapid there would be a consequently higher standing crop per unit area, thus temporarily accelerating the rate of habitat change.

These results are summarized in Table 10.2, where the effects of reducing the population to 4000 by 1975 by cropping are also predicted. By then it is esti-

Table 10.2

Summary of conclusion derived from population models. The 1975 figures relate to the future population should the proposals made in Chapter 12 be put into effect

		1946	1966	1971	1975
Area of range (km^2)		6300	3200	2800	2600
	%	1·000	0·508	0·445	0·413
Population size ΣN_t		22 000	9400	7900	4000
	%	1·000	0·427	0·359	0·182
Population biomass $\Sigma N_t w_t$					
(10^6 kg)		41·789	20·996	19·442	9·844
	%	1·000	0·502	0·465	0·204
Mean weight $\bar{w}$ (kg)		1894	2234	2461	2461
	%	1·000	1·180	1·299	1·299
Weight/unit area (kg/km^2)		6633	6561	6965	3790
	%	1·000	0·989	1·050	0·571
Density (N/km^2)		3·50	2·94	2·83	1·54
	%	1·000	0·840	0·809	0·440
Production (10^6 kg)		1·789	0·805	0·647	−
	%	1·000	0·450	0·362	−
Production (kg/elephant)		111·4	85·6	84·5	−
	%	1·000	0·768	0·758	−
Production (kg/km^2)		390	251	231	−
	%	1·000	0·643	0·592	−
Transfer (10^6 kg)		1·789	1·315	1·167	−
	%	1·000	0·735	0·652	−

mated that the elephant range will have decreased to, at the most, 2600 square kilometres, or 41 per cent of the 1946 area. At a level of 4000, the population would comprise about 18 per cent of the 1946 total, and its standing crop biomass would be about 20 per cent of the 1946 level. The mean elephant unit weight will probably be rather less than the estimated 1971 unit weight, and the density about 1·54 elephants or 44 per cent of the supposed 1946 level. The weight per unit area after this reduction is estimated at 3790 kg per square kilometre, or 57 per cent of the 1946 level. Only a substantial reduction, of this order, in the pressure on the vegetation is likely to permit habitat recovery, but this will be discussed in Chapter 12 after we have examined, in Chapter 11, the effects of the elephant population on the North Bunyoro habitats.

10.3.3.   *Annual production*

Annual production is the total growth increment of a population in a year. The only estimate of the annual production of an elephant population of which we are aware was made by Petrides and Swank (1966), for a population model constructed for the Queen Elizabeth Park elephants for 1957. However, although this was a valuable attempt to derive values for production and energy relations in the elephant, it was largely based on observational data on age classes and inadequate information on growth and other parameters. Although the present data are also less complete than we could have wished, it seems worthwhile to examine this aspect of the models we have set up.

Despite current interest in the flow of energy within ecosystems very few analyses of this kind are available for mammal populations. Davis and Golley (1963) summarized some results for small mammals and give a synthetic analysis for the whitetail deer *Odocoileus virginianus*. Buechner and Golley (1967) give a preliminary estimate for the Uganda kob *Adenota kob*, and Jordan, Botkin, and Wolfe (1971) have recently published figures for the moose *Alces alces*.

We presented data on mortality, growth, and standing crop in earlier sections. Annual production has been estimated from:

$$\sum_{0}^{60} \bar{N}(w_{t+1} - w_t) \text{ where } \bar{N} = (N_t + N_{t+1})/2$$

that is, the sum, over all age classes and both sexes, of the product of the average weight increment over one year and $\bar{N}$, the average year-class abundance at that age. The sums were calculated using a desk computer. The results are presented in Fig. 10.11 and Table 10.2 for the three population models.

For the 1946 model, the production is estimated at $1\cdot789 \times 10^6$ kg, for 1966 at $0\cdot805 \times 10^6$ kg and for 1971 at $0\cdot647 \times 10^6$ kg, respectively 4·3 per cent, 3·8 per cent, and 3·3 per cent of the standing crop biomass. This represents a decrease to 45 per cent and 36 per cent of the supposed 1946 annual production and is primarily due to the decrease in 0—20 year age classes (which are the most rapidly growing) and in population size, but also to the suggested decrease in growth rate. Production is highest in the first year and there is a secondary peak

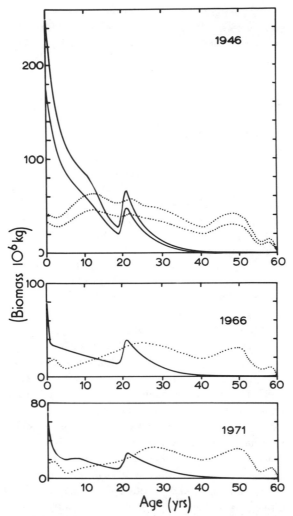

Fig. 10.11. Growth increment (solid line) and biomass transfer (dotted line) for three eleph-ant population models. The upper curves for 1946 indicate allowance made for the effect of control shooting on population size.

just after 20 years, corresponding to the supposed male growth spurt. By 30 years the annual increment is low and has fallen almost to zero by 40 years.

The estimated annual production per unit elephant has also been calculated. It fell from 111 kg in 1946 to 86 kg in 1966 and to 84 kg in 1971, a fall to about three-quarters of its former value. Annual production per unit area has also declined, from 390 kg per square kilometre in 1946 to 251 kg per square kilometre in 1966 and to an estimated 231 kg per square kilometre in 1971—a fall to ap-proximately three fifths of the earlier value.

If the proposals for reducing the elephant population made in Chapter 12 are implemented, then by 1975 the annual production should be no lower than in 1971, probably somewhat higher, because there should be a small response by then in terms of increased recruitment and possibly increased growth.

10.3.4.   *Biomass transfer*

The live weight of elephant dying each year was computed by calculating:

$$\sum_{0}^{60} \bar{w}\,(N_t - N_{t+1}), \text{ where } \bar{w} = (w_t + w_{t+1})/2$$

that is the sum, over all age classes and both sexes, of the product of the number dying between successive age classes t and $(t + 1)$, and their average weight $\bar{w}$. In calculating biomass transfer for the year classes influenced by declining recruitment, negative values are obtained if the actual year-class abundance figures are used in the calculations, because from 5 years to 25 or 30 years the year-class abundance at age $(t - 1)$, N_{t-1}, is greater than that at age t, N_t (Fig. 10.9). For the purposes of this computation, in the case of the 1966 and 1971 models, for the age ranges 5–24 years and 5–30 years respectively, N_{t+1} has been calculated from N_t by applying the survival rate $e^{-0.052} = 0.9493$. The results are presented in Fig. 10.11 and Table 10.2 for the three models.

For 1946, biomass transfer is estimated at 1.789×10^6 kg, balancing production, because this model is constructed as a stable population. For 1966, transfer is estimated at 1.315×10^6 kg, 63 per cent higher than production; and for 1971 at 1.167×10^6 kg, that is 80 per cent higher than production. Over the 25 year period, transfer by death is thought to have decreased to about two thirds of the 1946 value, due to the decline in recruitment and population size, and the suggested decrease in body size at age.

In 1946 transfer peaked at about the 13-year class and again at about 48 and 58 years, the latter peaks corresponding to the increased mortality in old males and females respectively. There is a slight increase in biomass transfer at the time of the supposed male growth spurt. In the 1966 model the peak in biomass transfer was at about 25 years and in 1971 at about 28 years, reflecting a progressive decline in recruitment. The slight peaks in old age remain, because the age structure in the latter half of the lifespan has not altered. Apart from the growth increment due to the male growth spurt, biomass transfer exceeded production after the 14 year age class in all three models.

10.3.5.   *Energy relations*

The biomass and weight data can now be used to estimate energy values, using generally accepted figures for mean calorific values, and then efficiency ratios calculated. The results are crude because it is necessary to make a number of approximations in the absence of direct information, and the models themselves are only approximate, but the exercise seems worth while.

We have presented estimates of standing crop biomass, annual production (or growth increment), and biomass transfer on death, and have estimated the area occupied by the population at various stages in its recent history (Table 10.2). These data were then converted to grams per square metre per year and then to kilocalories per square metre per year, adopting the conversion value of 1·5 kilocalories per gram of live elephant tissue (Petrides and Swank 1966). The results are summarized in Table 10.3.

Estimates are now needed for food consumption, faeces produced, energy assimilated, and energy required for maintenance.

Table 10.3
Summary of data on the energy relations of elephant populations

		North Bunyoro 1946	North Bunyoro 1966	North Bunyoro 1971	Q.E.P.[1] 1957	Q.E.P.[1] Adjusted[4]
Standing crop	biomass	6·63	6·56	6·96	4·8	—
	energy	9·95	9·84	10·45	7·1	10·0
Food consumed	wet weight	103·3	101·9	105·3	71·6	—
	energy	>103·3	101·9	<105·3	71·6	100·8
Faeces	wet weight	58·0	57·2	59·2	40·2	—
	energy	>69·6	68·7	<71·0	48·3	68·0
Assimilation	energy	>33·7	33·3	<34·3	23·3	32·8
Maintenance	energy	>33·1	32·9	<34·0	23·0	32·4
Growth	weight	0·390	0·251	0·231	0·229	—
	energy	0·585	0·377	0·347	0·343	0·483
Transfer	weight	0·390	0·411	0·417	—	—
	energy	0·585	0·617	0·626	—	—
Net balance	weight	0·0	−0·160	−0·186	—	—
	energy	0·0	−0·240	−0·279	—	—

Notes. (1) Data from Petrides and Swank (1966) for Queen Elizabeth Park (Q.E.P.)
(2) Weights are $g/m^2/year$; energy as $kcal/m^2/year$
(3) kcal estimated as 1·5/g for live elephant, 4/g for dry weight green forage, and 4·8/g for dry weight faeces (Davis and Golley 1963; Petrides and Swank 1966; Benedict 1936). Dry weight food intake estimated as 0·25 × wet weight food
(4) Last column, standing crop uprated to 10·0 $kcal/m^2$ for better comparison with North Bunyoro model populations

10.3.5.1. *Food consumed.* In Chapter 8 the average daily food intake was estimated at 3·94 per cent body weight for males and 4·68 per cent for females. These percentages were applied to the standing crop biomass estimates for male and female components of the populations, and then raised to give an annual total. The resulting figures are wet weights and the results are given in Table 10.3. Food consumption per unit area has apparently been remarkably constant, and this reflects the constancy of the standing crop per unit area; the values for stomach fill, on which the daily intake is based, were obtained in 1966. The use of the same percentage values for 1946 and 1971 is only justified by the absence of other data and it is possible that in 1946 food consumption was higher, and in 1971 lower than in 1966.

The data of Buss (1961) on stomach fill, which were collected in 1958–9, were discussed in Chapter 8 and summarized in Table 8.1. In proportion to live weight they were substantially higher than recent data indicate. Also, as we pointed out, there is almost certainly a seasonal difference in the quantity of food consumed, and certainly a difference in the quality of the food, both seasonally and over the years, which should be reflected in the energy value. The directions of probable differences in energy values are indicated in Table 10.3.

Dry weight of green forage is approximately 25 per cent of wet weight and its dry-weight energy value is estimated at 4 kilocalories per gram. Thus the estimated energy values for food consumed (kilocalories per square metre per year) are numerically equivalent to wet weight (grams per square metre per year).

10.3.5.2.   *Faeces.* In estimating the amount of faeces produced we have followed Petrides and Swank (1966) in applying Benedict's (1936) findings, since these provide the only relevant data. Through feeding experiments with Indian elephants *Elephas maximus*, he showed that each unit dry weight of droppings was equivalent to 1·78 dry-weight units of forage consumed. The dry-weight food consumed (i.e. 0·25 × wet weight) has therefore been multiplied by 0·562 to estimate dry weight of the faeces eliminated, and an estimate of faecal energy obtained by adopting Benedict's value of 4·8 kilocalories per gram dry weight. We again have reservations about extrapolating the 1966 food consumed to obtain faecal data for 1946 and 1971, and reservations about using Benedict's experimental data obtained by using dry hay and with a different species. In the absence of better data there is no choice. The results can be refined when better data become available.

10.3.5.3.   *Assimilation and maintenance.* Assimilation is estimated as the difference between the energy value of the food consumed and the energy value of the faeces eliminated. Almost all the energy assimilated goes to maintenance, determined by subtracting growth (or production) energy from assimilation.

10.3.5.4.   *Efficiency ratios.* In Table 10.4 efficiency ratios, calculated from the energy data in Table 10.3, are presented for the three North Bunyoro population models and compared with data for the Queen Elizabeth Park population in 1957 (Petrides and Swank 1966), and with data for three other herbivores. For valid comparisons of stable populations only the 1946 elephant model can be used.

10.4.   Discussion

In a recent publication one of us discussed the relation between an elephant population and its environment in the following terms (Laws 1969b).

The recent studies indicate that the growth of elephant populations probably follows a sigmoid curve, and for the purpose of analysing overpopulation, the

Table 10.4

Summary of energetic efficiency ratios for four elephant population models, compared with other herbivores

	1946	1966	1971	Q.E.P. 1957[1]	Alces alces[2]	Odocoileus virginianus[3]	Microtus pennsylvanicus[3]
Growth/standing crop	0·059	0·038	0·033	0·048	0·25	0·5	2·5
Transfer/standing crop	0·059	0·063	0·060	–	0·18	–	–
Assimilation/standing crop	3·38	3·38	3·28	3·3	–	33·9	87·5
Food consumed/standing crop	10·38	10·36	10·08	10·1	–	41·4	131·6
Growth/food consumed	0·0057	0·0037.	0·0033	0·005	–	0·012	0·020
Assimilation/food consumed	0·326	0·326	0·326	·326	–	0·80	0·70
Maintenance/food consumed	0·320	0·323	0·323	·321	–	0·75	0·68
Growth/assimilation	<0·017	0·011	>0·010	·010	–	0·016	0·029

Notes. (1) Data from Petrides and Swank (1966)
(2) Data from Jordan, Botkin, and Wolfe (1971)
(3) Data from Davis and Golley (1963)

logistic equation is useful because it contains a parameter (K) which can be
equated with 'carrying capacity' [Odum and Odum 1959]. This can be defined
in various ways, but is used here in the sense of 'the level of population at which
a steady state is possible in a given ecosystem' [Fosberg 1961]. An often expressed criticism of the logistic equation is that it is empirical, but this is no
great disadvantage in the present context. The theory assumes that populations (P) grow towards a finite upper limit (K), set by the area, resources
and other parameters of the environment (Text-fig. 10a) [our Fig. 10.12]. In a

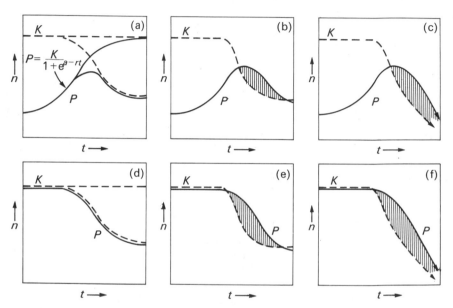

Fig. 10.12. Hypothetical population responses to decreasing carrying capacity K (see text).
(From Laws (1969b).) Reproduced by permission from *J. Reprod. Fert.* Supplement 6, 528.

population introduced into a new environment, growth is initially rapid, but as
the population grows, increasing 'environmental resistance' slows down the rate
of increase until the population is in equilibrium ($P \simeq K$). Exact equilibrium is
rarely, if ever achieved under natural conditions, so there are oscillations in both
P and K. In the case of elephant, the slowing down in response to environmental
resistance is brought about by the changes in reproductive patterns described,
and probably also by increased calf and adult mortality.
    Now suppose that K decreases for any reason before the population reaches
equilibrium; for example, in a uniform habitat, reduction in the area available
will cause a proportionate decrease in K. Provided there is sufficient time for
homeostatic mechanisms to come into operation the population will come into a
new equilibrium with the new value of K (Text-fig. 10a). But suppose that K
decreases more rapidly than the homeostatic response can come into operation;
then population response will lag behind and there will be a period when $P > K$,
when the habitat will be over-used and damage may ensue (indicated by the shaded

area in Text-fig. 10b). If this is not too serious, or prolonged, or if the climatic component of K improves, then a new balance may be reached. However, if the habitat damage is considerable, or if there is a reduction in rainfall (for example), then we may find a progressively worsening situation with K decreasing at an increasing rate and, in turn, habitat damage increasing rapidly (Text-fig. 10c). This could, in an extreme case, lead to the value of K for a particular species in that area falling to zero—as for elephant if Tsavo became a near desert. In the process, the K values for other species could change in a similar way.

A similar process, starting with an equilibrium population and its hypothetical response to decreasing values of K is illustrated in Text-fig. 10(d) to (f).

This is, of course, an oversimplification for the purpose of discussion; for one thing, the curves would not be smooth but would reflect climatic fluctuations, variations in the rate at which the area component of K decreased, and the suppression of predation (poaching). But it serves to clarify thinking on the 'elephant problem' and as a basis for the construction of population models. It also means that, if elephant population growth is adequately or approximately described by the logistic, and if we can obtain estimates of r and P, then an approximate value of K can be calculated from the equation. If reduction cropping were to be undertaken it should, therefore, aim at reducing P so that $P < K$ in as short a time as possible.

It is of course possible that in elephants, as in some other ungulates, the decreasing phase of the logistic curve is not attained and numbers exceed carrying capacity before the changes in recruitment occur. This is more likely in situations where the elephant range is limited and movement cannot contribute to the adjustment of density. Laws (1970a, b) suggested that migration or dispersal was an essential part of the natural regulatory mechanism, bringing undisturbed elephant populations into balance with the habitat, and that regulation by changing birth rates and early mortality rates alone in response to density-induced effects on the habitat was inadequate to bring about an equilibrium situation. Myers (1973) has also argued that movement is an essential part of the regulatory process. If so, the lack of opportunity for such dispersal would strengthen the arguments in favour of management by reduction cropping and subsequent sustained cropping.

Although we are not much nearer to a reliable estimate of the current value of K and there are difficulties in determining r for a declining population, with recruitment apparently varying from year to year, the studies described in this chapter help us to understand the nature of the regulatory processes and explain why, even with far-reaching adjustments of reproductive and mortality rates, this elephant population has not achieved stability at a lower level in the absence of the opportunity to disperse. Indeed, the natural regulatory processes have been reinforced by the control shooting operations—wasteful, inefficient, and inhumane though they have been. (These operations are not to be confused with reduction cropping by complete population units, which, besides its efficiency and economic value, *has been carried out humanely*. This method also has the great virtue that a population can be reduced rapidly without altering its composition, so that natural regulatory mechanisms are not disturbed.)

In earlier chapters the changes in reproductive rates caused by deferred puberty and reduced fecundity have been discussed. What evidence we now have strongly suggests that adult annual natural mortality rates of elephant populations are low and fluctuate only within narrow limits (5–7 per cent), but that calf mortality may increase significantly as the habitat changes. The population models suggest that calf mortality may have doubled since 1946. Such differential mortality is known from other species; in the case of the elephant, the longevity of the species means that it takes many years for reduced recruitment to have a significant effect on the standing crop biomass, which is in turn directly related to the degree of use of the habitat resources. Thus, standing crop biomass in the 1946 model peaks at about 13 years and, if the models are accepted as valid, a 64 per cent reduction in population size (partly due to control shooting) has been accompanied by only a 53 per cent reduction in standing crop biomass, This, despite the fact that natality has apparently been reduced to about 34 per cent of the estimated 1946 level and recruitment at 4 years to no more than 25 per cent of the earlier level. It is clear that, even in the hypothetical extreme case where reproduction ceases and there is no recruitment, the standing crop biomass would continue to decline slowly, until the year groups born before there was a substantial decline in recruitment had passed through the population.

In the case of North Bunyoro we can make a fairly good estimate of the size of the range available to the elephant population at various times in recent history. It has shown a contraction from more than 6300 square kilometres prior to 1946 to under 3000 square kilometres today—an estimated decrease of some 55 per cent. Concurrently standing crop biomass has decreased through natural and human agencies by an estimated 53 per cent, and our studies suggest that the biomass per unit area may now be as high, or possibly higher, than when the habitat change began. (We accept that our figures can only be rather crude approximations and dependent on the assumptions inherent in the models.) Elephant density has perhaps decreased by about a fifth, but the mean elephant unit weight has apparently increased (due to the greater average age of the surviving animals) by nearly a third. The annual production (growth increment) of the population has decreased to an estimated 36 per cent of the earlier value, but in terms of unit area only to 59 per cent.

Our analysis of the energy relations of the population adds relatively little to the conclusions of Petrides and Swank (1966). In view of the observational nature of their study and the inaccuracy of some of their assumptions (e.g. the growth curve adopted), the similarity in the results is remarkable. In Table 10.3 their results have been uprated to correspond to a standing crop of 10·0 kilocalories per square metre, for a better comparison with the North Bunyoro models. Their estimate of food consumed is very similar to the present study, although reached independently and by a different method, and their production estimate is intermediate between those for the 1946 and 1966 North Bunyoro models. Given the similar food consumption, however, the similarity between the figures for faeces, assimilation, and maintenance is to be expected, since they were arrived at by a similar process.

Although the net energy balance between the annual production and transfer shows a substantial deficit, it is negligible in relation to the amounts of food consumed and the maintenance energy.

As Petrides and Swank (1966) have pointed out, the elephant has a very high standing crop, some 7·5 times that of the whitetail deer. We can compare the efficiencies of the hypothetical stable 1946 elephant population with the other herbivores. Annual production per unit standing crop was about an eighth of that of the deer and a quarter of the moose value. Assimilation in relation to standing crop was only a tenth that of the deer, but the food consumed per unit standing crop was only a quarter that of the deer (and a thirteenth that of the mouse). Growth in relation to food consumed was about half that of the deer. For a given quantity of food, assimilation and maintenance energy were about four tenths that of the deer, but the proportion of assimilated energy which goes into growth appears to be the same in the elephant and the deer.

The average standing crop biomass in the riverine zone of the M.F.P.S. was estimated at 280 kg per hectare in 1967, of which elephant comprised 16 per cent (and hippopotamus 68 per cent). In the rest of the area the standing crop biomass averaged 102 kg per hectare, of which 84 per cent was due to elephant (see Chapter 4, Table 4.3). Even if (as the comparison with whitetail deer—a ruminant—might suggest) the elephant population eats only one fourth as much per unit of standing crop as the other species present, then over nine tenths of the range it is responsible for about 57 per cent of the forage consumption per unit area. By virtue of its size and relatively unspecialized digestive tract, it is able to feed on all strata of vegetation from ground level to about 8 metres above ground. In the next Chapter we examine the effect of the very large elephant standing crop on the habitats of North Bunyoro.

10.5. Summary

Since 1925, over 16 000 elephants have been shot on control in Bunyoro, and operations in and around the Budongo Forest are discussed. The objective of the recent shooting was to prevent elephants from entering the forest, but this was not achieved, although there has probably been a change in the routes they use. At least one local group of about 1500 elephants has been eliminated by shooting. The inefficiency and inhumanity of control shooting (as opposed to cropping) is emphasized and it is concluded that in addition to 10 476 recorded as shot on control in Bunyoro since 1946, some 17—23 per cent died unrecorded. Making allowance for several factors it is estimated that the real reduction in population size from this cause in North Bunyoro has been about 6000 since 1946, and that this can be considered to have been random with respect to age.

The age and sex structure of several elephant populations has been studied. There is a sex-specific difference in favour of the female. Difficulties in using the age structures for estimating mortality rates and constructing models are discussed. These difficulties are largely due to uncertainties about the reality of the apparent fluctuations in recruitment, which could be caused by quite small errors in assigning ages. However, these apparent or real fluctuations do not significantly affect the conclusions reached on the basis of the population models.

By plotting the natural logarithms of year-class abundances against age for female elephants, estimates of z (the total instantaneous mortality rate) for adults are obtained for a number of elephant populations that have been sampled. These estimates apply to the year classes born before recruitment was reduced when, it is assumed from the log-linear relationship, the population was in a steady state with zero rate of increase and stationary age distribution. (If mortality due to control shooting is small and random with respect to age, then z estimated in this way approximates to m, the instantaneous natural mortality rate.) Apart from an increase in mortality after 50 years of age, mortality appears to have been constant over most of the lifespan. The range of estimates of z is 0·052—0·068, corresponding to annual mortality rates of 0·051—0·066.

Models for the M.F.P.S. population have been constructed for 1946 (or earlier), 1966, and 1971. The adult mortality rates appear not to have altered significantly, but calf mortality has apparently increased by more than 50 per cent (perhaps as much as 100 per cent) since 1946. Together with deferred maturity and reduced fecundity, this has led to a massive decline in recruitment. It is estimated that relative natality may have fallen to 34 per cent of the 1946 level and relative recruitment at four years to 25 per cent of the earlier level. Population size is estimated to have decreased from 22 000 in 1946 to 9400 in 1966 and to 7900 in 1971, that is by 64 per cent. Less than half of this decrease was due to control shooting and sport hunting. Natural regulatory mechanisms alone were apparently responsible for a decrease in the residual population of about 51 per cent up to 1971.

Owing to the contraction of the elephant range, this has still been insufficient to permit a stable population to develop, and an attempt has been made to quantify the factors involved. The numerical models were converted to biomass models and standing crop biomass-at-age curves were constructed. Estimates of total standing crop biomass are $41·8 \times 10^6$ kg in 1946, $21·0 \times 10^6$ kg in 1966, and $19·4 \times 10^6$ kg in 1971. As a result of reduced recruitment the age class biomass peak has been pushed back from 13 years in 1946, to 18 years in 1971, and unit elephant weight has increased from 1894 kg in 1946 to 2461 kg in 1971. Despite the decline in elephant numbers, the reduction of the elephant range has meant that the elephant standing crop biomass per unit area has remained almost the same in 1966 and 1971 as in 1946. Inevitably the habitat change, which began before 1946, has been progressive and only a substantial reduction in standing crop biomass per unit area, by cropping, can permit habitat recovery.

Estimates of annual production for the North Bunyoro elephant population are given as $1·789 \times 10^6$ kg in 1946, $0·805 \times 10^6$ kg in 1966, and $0·647 \times 10^6$ kg in 1971. Biomass transfer by death is estimated at $1·789 \times 10^6$ kg in 1946, $1·315 \times 10^6$ kg in 1966, and $1·167 \times 10^6$ kg in 1971. Energy relations have been explored and efficiency ratios compared with available data from other mammals. In elephants, about one third of the food consumed is used for maintenance and the energy value of the food consumed annually is about ten times the standing crop energy value.

Finally we discussed the reasons for the failure of the elephant population regulatory mechanisms, reinforced by control shooting, to produce a population in balance with the environment. Elephant have a high standing crop biomass and although the net energy balance between growth and transfer shows a substantial deficit, this is negligible in relation to the amounts of food consumed and the maintenance energy requirements. The longevity of the species means that it takes many years for reduced recruitment to have a significant effect on standing crop biomass. In the case of the North Bunyoro population, the reduction of the area available to elephants has meant that since the deterioration of the habitat began, there has probably been no significant decrease in the quantitative food intake per unit area by elephants. Browse and herbs form a preferred part of their diet, and have been progressively and selectively over-used; we believe that this is the major cause of the habitat changes in North Bunyoro, described in the next chapter.

11. Habitat changes

It was proposed that the management cropping programme involving hippopotamus and elephant, begun in 1965 in the Murchison Falls National Park, should
be accompanied by a concurrent programme of research on the habitats, so that
the impact of cropping could be monitored and understanding of the dynamics
of habitat change be achieved. The habitat changes that have occurred involve
overgrazing, and erosion near the River Nile (see Chapter 2, Plate 2.8), under
the influence of hippopotamus, and destruction of woody vegetation over the
area exposed to elephant (Plate 11.2). With the exception of an aerial survey in
1967 involving the photography and analysis of transects, described below, and
the setting up of two experimental plots in 1965 and twelve in 1967, this urgently
needed research has not yet been implemented. In 1966 the Forest Department
initiated an investigation of elephant demage in the regeneration areas.

11.1. Aerial photographic survey

The aerial survey was directed towards quantifying the process of destruction
of woody vegetation, and this section gives a preliminary account of the method

PLATE 11.1. *Terminalia* woodland M.F.P.N. with elephant-barked trunk in foreground.

and results. It was financed by the Uganda National Parks and Wildlife Services Ltd. We hope that a more detailed analysis will be published by R. M. Watson, who carried out the photography, supervised the interpretation (by Mrs. Watson and Miss V. Breen), and made a preliminary analysis of the results. This section is based on his report to Wildlife Services Ltd.

It is hoped that the National Parks will have these transects photographed and analysed at intervals in the future. It would also be valuable to have ground controls made along the transects.

11.1.1. *Methods*

Sixteen transects were photographed, of which eight were south of the Victoria Nile, in Bunyoro, and therefore the basis of this account. They were selected to cover regions of significant habitat change. All transects were intended to be straight lines between or through the points given below, but the navigational problems inherent in flying light aircraft in turbulent conditions preclude absolute precision. The positions of the transects were:

S1 31° 31′ 30″ E / 02° 10′ 0″ N to 31° 39′ 22·5″ E / 02° 04′ 15″ N.
S2 Paraa Beacon 2495 feet, to 31° 41′ 0″ E / 02° 19′ 45″ N.
S3 10 miles south along main Butiaba road from the Weiga Bridge.
S4 Murchison Falls to Wairingo Beacon 2567 feet.
S5 31° 51′ 30″ E / 02° 22′ 00″ N through triangulation point 3097 feet to Park boundary.
S6 31° 52′ 30″ E / 02° 22′ 15″ N through Rabongo Beacon to edge of cultivation.
S7 Rabongo Beacon 1239 feet to 32° 11′ 15″ E / 02° 13′ 00″ N.
S8 31° 49′ 30″ E / 01° 58′ 00″ N through Lukohe Hill to Escarpment.
The transect locations are plotted in Fig. 11.1.

The method was developed by Watson (1968) for the Tsavo Research Project in Kenya. Photography was carried out at 305 metres (1000 feet) with an F.24 aerial camera, fitted with an 8 inch lens. Frames along the transect were photographed at 7½-second intervals which gave approximately 10 per cent overlap between successive frames. The film used was Kodak Super XX topographic film; the exposure was 1/1000 second with lens aperture f.8. The scale of the photographs is about 1:4000 and gives a circle of confusion of about 0·6 metres (2 feet).

The negatives were processed in standard 5 inch film developing tanks using D 19 B developer. A set of prints was made on Grade 2 Bromide paper, using Kodak DA 163 developer. These prints were discarded after interpretation, since this process entails marking the print extensively, but the negatives serve as a permanent record of the transects. They are the property of and are stored by the Uganda National Parks.

Interpretation of the prints follows the general lines of interpretation of the Tsavo National Park transects (Watson 1968). The following data were taken from each frame:

(1) number of mature trees with crown diameters in excess of 8 metres;

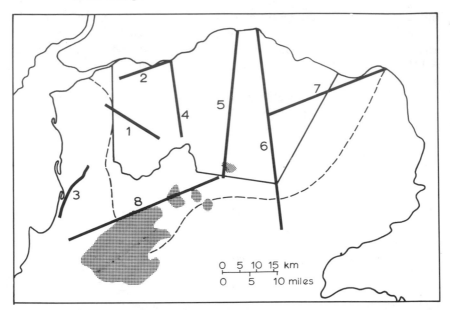

Fig. 11.1. Location of aerial photographic transects in the North Bunyoro elephant range. Shaded areas—forest; National Park boundary shown; broken line—limits of elephant range.

(2) number of small trees and bushes with crown diameters in excess of 1 metre;

(3) number of dead trees in two categories, standing and lying;

(4) numbers of termitaria and their type;

(5) number of large animal tracks intersecting a cross with arms of 4·1 centimetre length, placed in the centre of the frame (each track was counted only once, even if it intersected the cross more than once);

(6) where large areas of erosion, or large numbers of trees or bushes occurred (so that counting of individual crowns was impossible), an estimate of the percentage cover for erosion, trees, bushes, and grassland was made by means of a point intersect method.

For information under (1)–(4), subsampling was carried out where necessary to avoid counting very large numbers. Notes were made for each frame on the general topography, drainage situation, roads etc.

Copies of the raw data are held by Uganda National Parks and by Wildlife Services Ltd. The preliminary analysis involved the calculation of the exact scale of each transect with the aid of 1:50 000 maps. In some cases a large scale change took place along the transect and in such cases the mean scales in 10-frame intervals were used for subsequent computations. The scale change occurred because the aircraft was not fitted with a radio altimeter for indicating camera to ground heights, and over the undulating terrain it was not possible to keep the above ground height constant. This affected the scale and means also that there is not a constant relation between frame number and distance traversed. Thus, the number of frames per kilometre averages about 2·5 for transects S1, and S3—S6, but only 1·25 for transect S2 and about 1·9 for S7 and S8.

The descriptions given below have taken this variability into account, by relating features on the aerial photographs to the topographic map. The raw data were converted to density data in metric terms, using a programmed desk calculator. The density data for transects S4, S5, and S6 have been presented graphically, as 4-frame means, in Figs 11.2—11.4.

11.1.2.   *Results*

The total area of the sixteen transects was calculated to be 250·4 square kilometres (96·7 square miles), and the summed lengths of all transects was 455·8 kilometres (283·2 miles). The south bank transects totalled 130·2 square kilometres (50·3 square miles) and 237·1 kilometres (147·3 miles). The area of the south bank elephant range outside the forest is about 2850 square kilometres (1100 square miles), giving a sampling intensity of approximately 4·6 per cent.

Transect S1 is predominantly grassland and does not approach the River Nile. There is a markedly higher density of woody vegetation about the middle of the transect, bushes and small trees (single frames up to *ca* 2600 per square kilometre) and large trees (up to 500 per square kilometre) coinciding with higher ground to the west of the Joliya River. Damage to trees (as represented by dead tree densities) increases as the transect enters the Park and is maximal on high ground north-west of the Wairingo River (up to 526 per square kilometre) (Plate 11.2). The density of current elephant use (as represented by tracks per kilometre of intersect) increases as the transect enters the Park, progressively increases towards the east, and falls in the Wairingo valley.

Transect S2 is characterized by very low densities of mature trees and dead trees, but high densities of small trees and bushes which increase towards the

PLATE 11.2. Dead *Terminalia* trees in Wairingo woodland, M.F.P.S.

River Nile (to 2500 per square kilometre). There is a consistent 5–10 per cent level of erosion along the transect; track densities are fairly high.

Transect S3 follows the main Butiaba road external to the park, and is outside the present elephant range. There is a constant high level (*ca* 1500 per square kilometre) of woody vegetation in the form of bush thickets, but no extensive tracts of large trees, except at the northern end of the transect where the road crosses low lying grassy swampland for 2·5 kilometres, with 20–73 large trees per square kilometre, increasing to 187 per square kilometre at the Weiga River. Other drainage lines which intersect the transect are associated with a few large trees (16–48 per square kilometre). There are no large animal tracks, no erosion, and virtually no dead trees along the transect.

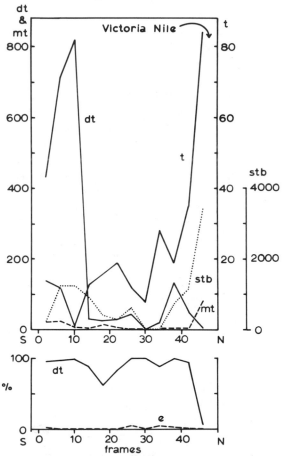

Fig. 11.2. Transect S4. Summary of the results of interpretation of aerial photographs by 4-frame means; the orientation (south to north) is indicated. *Above.* Numbers of: dt—dead trees per square kilometre; mt—mature living trees per square kilometre; stb—living small trees and bushes per square kilometre; t—tracks per kilometre. *Below.* dt—dead trees as percentage of dt+ mt; e—erosion per cent.

Transect S4 (Fig. 11.2) runs from the Victoria Nile to Wairingo Hill. Fairly
high densities of woody vegetation, both small trees and bushes (up to 4800 per
square kilometre) and large trees (up to 150 per square kilometre) are associated
with the Nile valley slopes, but progressing southwards very low densities of
mature trees are recorded (< 10 per square kilometre), with a slight increase
towards the Park boundary (20 per square kilometre). The densities of dead trees
increase dramatically near the Wairingo River to over 1000 per square kilometre),
representing the former Wairingo woodland (Plate 11.2).

Current animal use of the transect shows an increase from near the Park
boundary to the River Nile, where very high track densities are recorded, with two
areas of low density apparently associated with proximity to a road. Erosion is
slight, ranging from 2–10 per cent in 5 out of 48 frames.

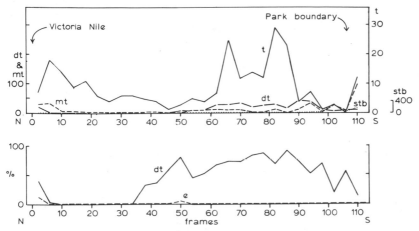

Fig. 11.3. Transect S5. Summary of the results of interpretation of aerial photographs by
4-frame means. Explanation as for Fig. 11.2.

Transect S5 (Fig. 11.3) runs southwards from the Nile to the Park boundary.
Woody vegetation is at a very low density throughout the transect with a slight
increase towards the Park boundary (mature trees to *ca* 100 per square kilometre;
small trees and bushes to *ca* 250 per square kilometre). There are also slightly
higher densities near the River Nile (respectively 30 per square kilometre and
20 per square kilometre). Densities of dead trees show a small increase up to the
Park boundary. The density of animal tracks decreases from the river to the
middle of the transect and then increases to high levels towards the Park boundary,
when it again falls to a low level. There are small amounts of erosion close to the
Nile.

Transect S6 (Fig. 11.4) runs from the Nile southwards, across the Park boundary
into cultivated land. Densities of large trees are very low south from the Nile
until some distance outside the Park, when there is a sharp increase to high tree
densities (over 400 per square kilometre and up to 900 per square kilometre)

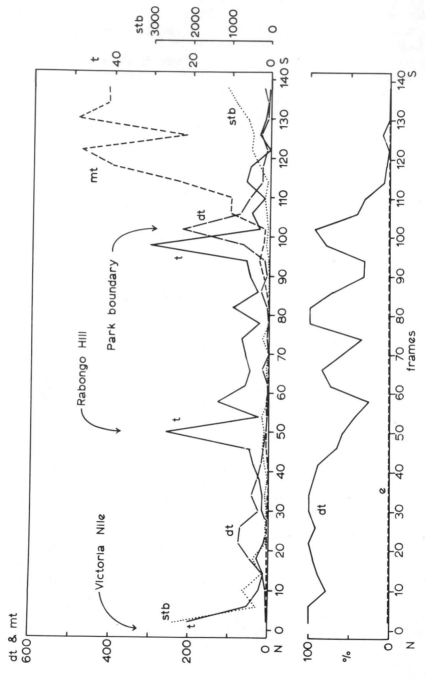

Fig. 11.4. Transect S6. Summary of the results of interpretation of aerial photographs by 4-frame means. Explanation as for Fig. 11.2.

(Plate 2.6). Small trees and bushes are at very high densities on the Nile valley slopes (up to 5800 per square kilometre) (Plate 2.8) but decrease to very low densities over most of the transect until there is a progressive increase in density outside the park (to over 2000 per square kilometre). Dead trees show two areas of high density, one between 10–15 kilometres south of the Nile, the other just outside the Park boundary along the northern edge of the dense woodland.

Track densities are relatively high on the Nile Bank, but low immediately south of the river, showing a gradual increase southwards to the Park boundary; there are peaks at about 25 kilometres (northern slopes of Rabongo Hill) and 50 kilometres south of the Nile (just inside the Park). From about 55 kilometres the track densities decrease as the transect enters more cultivated areas. There is very little erosion along this transect, but in general erosion tends to be concentrated on valley slopes near the Nile, and this transect follows the line of a ridge near the river. Also it originates in Section 7 which has the lowest grazing density of hippopotamus within the Park, 9·6 per square kilometre (24·8 per square mile).

Transect S7 runs from east to west across the Park boundary to the main road near Karuma Falls. There are low densities of woody vegetation in the western half of the transect and an increase to very high values (up to 87 per cent cover) east of the Park boundary. This increase is very abrupt in the case of small trees and bushes. Dead trees are at low densities throughout. After a very high density associated with the slopes of Rabongo Hill (up to about 90 per kilometre), animal tracks progressively increase from west to east up to about 7 kilometres from the Karuma Falls, when they decrease. This decrease is presumably associated with an increase in human activity towards the Karuma–Kiryandongo road. Some erosion was recorded where it passes near the river at Goragung Rapids, associated with high hippopotamus densities in Section 2 (see Chapter 4, Table 4.2).

Transect S8 runs from west to east across the northern edge of the Budongo and Pabidi Forests. Densities of large trees fluctuate markedly as the transect cuts across parts of the forest (Plate 2.3) and dense woodland (100 per cent canopy cover). Outside the closed forest and woodlands, the average density of large trees varies (between *ca* 25 per square kilometre and *ca* 600 per square kilometre). Densities of small trees and bushes decline from west to east up to the Masindi-Paraa road (from 2700 per square kilometre to none), after which there is a slight increase (to *ca* 300–400 per square kilometre). Densities of dead trees are fairly low and show no obvious trends, as are track densities which show no clear pattern of use.

The eight north bank transects will not be described in this paper, but it is hoped to deal with them in a projected paper on the Murchison Falls, North elephant population, and that a detailed analysis will be published in due course by R. M. Watson. It is worth-while (in discussing the results for the south bank transects) to summarize the general picture they present, when appropriate, because it is probably similar to the past situation on the south bank.

Large tree densities have been shown to be low inside the Park boundary on the south bank, but tend to be higher outside, often with an abrupt change coinciding, by and large, with the perimeter of the elephant range. A similar pattern characterizes the distribution of small trees and bushes, except that high densities are always found in the immediate vicinity of the River Nile.

The density of woody vegetation is much higher on the north bank but shows marked peaks and troughs in the distribution of numbers per unit area. As in the south, the north bank transects show an increase in woody vegetation outside the Park boundaries, except where settlement precludes this, and in general this change is more marked in the less wooded western part of the area.

In some dense woodlands on the north bank, there is a high-density understory, but in others a low-density one. This variability probably indicates different use by animals in the past and/or different burning histories. The densities of small trees and bushes are much more variable than those of mature trees and they appear to be more subject to local fluctuations in numbers, in relation to drainage situations, soil types etc.

The use of the area by elephant in the last five years, as indicated by dead-tree densities shows a less even distribution than current use, as indicated by track densities. This may indicate that tree damage is a phenomenon not exclusively associated with feeding. The situation in Murchison Falls Park is in striking contrast to that in Tsavo National Park where Watson (1968) concluded, on the basis of the density distribution of dead trees along two transects, that 'elephant have operated with exceptional uniformity along the transects over . . . several years'.

There was, however, a great variability in track densities which showed a correlation with the presence of water holes. This is to be expected if tracks are indicative of regular movements (as to and from standing water or shade) rather than of feeding activities. Alternatively, in Murchison Falls Park there may have been changes in pattern of use in the last two years, or some localized feeding preferences may be in operation.

In the Murchison Falls National Park tree damage appears to be greatest on the edge of the remaining woodlands; it probably represents a dynamic state in which a zone of damage progresses through woodland leaving behind a much changed habitat.

Current use as indicated by track densities is in general greater in the south and probably more uniform on the north bank than on the south (where there are more pronounced peaks and troughs). This is especially marked near the Victoria Nile where the peaks tend to be on average 50 per cent higher than on the north bank. Track densities on the north bank tend to follow tree densities but in the eastern transects where large-tree densities are highest, they show a tendency towards an inverse relationship with tree densities. This is consistent with the hypothesis that lower track densities are found where there is less need to travel to seek food or shade. The greatest track densities on the south bank near water may be due to the fact that the shading properties of the denser woodland in the north reduced the need for water, and therefore the frequency of movements in relation to water.

This situation may be compared with the higher track densities in parts of the Tsavo National Park (Watson 1968), where movements in relation to shade and water are much more frequent and extensive. In other words the higher track densities in the Tsavo area are associated with greater mobility rather than higher population densities. Track densities are probably inaccurate for establishing local feeding densities, since feeding elephants wander and do not make tracks. In the Murchison Falls Park, with water so widespread, tracks are in general more likely to be associated with shading activities and so can be used as indications of large-scale use.

In general, however, the areas of high elephant use recorded by track densities coincide with areas which aerial observations of elephant distribution indicate to be more heavily used by elephants (see Chapter 7, Fig. 7.2).

Aerial transects of this kind are providing a great deal of meaningful data on the dynamics of habitat change in the Murchison Falls National Park. There is little doubt that ground controls and periodic repetition of the photography would enable the major parameters of habitat change under the influence of hippopotamus and elephants to be established for the area. In any event, a base line has been established from which to judge the impact of management procedures.

11.2. Woodland to grassland

What evidence there is indicates that forest, woodland, or bushland existed over much of North Bunyoro until recent years (see Chapter 2 for definitions of these vegetation types). Consideration of the species now present as relics would indicate that the area was formerly fairly heavily forested. Individual *Chlorophora excelsa* are found with clean boles for 18 metres (60 feet) indicating a former forest or heavy bush cover during their growth (Plate 11.4). Root coppices of *Spathodia campanulata, Phyllanthus discoideus*, and *Markhamia platycalyx*, all species of thicket or forest, are found growing under open conditions. A few living and many standing dead trees provide evidence of about 25 former patches of gallery forest east of Rabongo Hill. There are now only eight definite patches. Stands of *Mitragyna stipulosa*, a swamp forest species, have been found in seasonally wet areas.

The degeneration or disappearence of woody vegetation over large areas is therefore attributable to a factor (or factors) that has (or have) only appeared in this century. Buechner and Dawkins (1961) were of the opinion that elephant were the primary instigators of the change, in which fire played an important secondary role. Buss (1961) held the converse opinion that fire played a primary part and elephant were secondary.

The progressive radial increase in tree cover and variety away from the focus of the elephant concentration has already been described and supports the view of Buechner and Dawkins. The lack of previous work prevents accurate description of the degeneration of woodland and it is not known which species of the original complex were the first to go. However, it is possible to reconstruct the general process by examination of elephant use of the dominant tree and shrub species. The majority of trees growing in the grassland show elephant damage.

This takes two forms—the older stems have bark removed and the young saplings are heavily browsed. No species was noted to be completely free from damage, but the heaviest bark damage appears on *Terminalia glaucescens* and *Combretum binderanum*. During the period 1965—7 elephant were seen browsing on the foliage of mature *Terminalia* infrequently, although young saplings are heavily browsed. However, during the dry season and early rains (often after the burn when no grass is available) elephant removed and ate bark, chiselling it off the boles with their tusks, either by means of several gouged strips or by completely removing bark from a substantial part of the trunk. By so doing they expose the cambial layers and living tissues of the tree, and make distinctive scars (Plate 11.1).

This de-barking renders the tree vulnerable to fire, to which this species is normally very tolerant, and kills it if bark ringing is complete. The majority of deaths of *Terminalia* in the area are attributed to this activity, since browsing normally merely limits the height of growth. It is of interest that in some areas where the *Terminalia—Combretum* cover has been removed, for example south-west of Lukohe Hill and the former woodlands of the Wairingo Valley, dense stands of heavily browsed fire-resistant *Lonchocarpus laxiflorus* have developed. These are 2—3 metres (6—10 feet) in height and do not appear to develop beyond this. A stand measured by Buechner and Dawkins (1961) was found to be of the same height in 1966. Elephant rather than fire are responsible for this suppression.

The incidence of living and dead trees was discussed in the previous section where it was concluded that a zone of damage progresses radially through the woodlands so that tree damage is greatest on the edge of surviving woodlands. Such a zone was sampled by us in 1967. Using the incidence of dead and scarred trees as an indicator of elephant use, a classified count was conducted from the north of the Budongo Forest along its western boundary.

The count was made from the track running along the perimeter of the Budongo Forest from near Lukohe Hill in the north-east to where the track enters the forest between the Sonso and Bubwe Rivers, a distance of about 23 kilometres (14 miles) (see Chapter 5, Fig. 5.6). Standing mature *Terminalia* trees within 50 yards of the track were recorded as dead, living scarred, and living unscarred. The results are presented in Table 11.1 on the basis of four sections, each about 5 kilometres (3 miles) long, north and east of the Waisoke River; south-west of this river; north-east of the Sonso River; and south-west of the Sonso River. The condition of 558 trees was recorded along this transect.

It can be seen that in the north 95·5 per cent were dead, 4·5 per cent scarred, and none unscarred. This picture gradually reverses until the converse is true, with 1·8 per cent dead, 24·1 per cent scarred, and 74·1 per cent unscarred. South of the Sonso River, *Terminalia* trees are found inside the forest which has enveloped them in its expansion. The progressive changes in this area should be compared

Table 11.1

Proportion of mature Terminalia glaucescens *in three categories of damage, counted within 50 yards of the Forest Reserve perimeter track* (see Fig. 5.6)

Sector	Unscarred		Scarred		Dead		Total	
	No.	%	No.	%	No.	%	No.	%
A. North-east of Waisoke R.	0	0·0	6	4·5	127	95·5	133	100·0
B. South-west of Waisoke R.	12	5·5	148	67·9	58	26·6	218	100·0
C. North-east of Sonso R.	6	6·3	78	82·1	11	11·6	95	100·0
D. North-west of Sonso R.	83	74·1	27	24·1	2	1·8	112	100·0

with the current intensity of elephant use, as indicated by the distribution of elephant shot on control in and around the forest (Fig. 5.10). Parallel with the rise in living and unscarred *Terminalia* trees is an increase of shrubs and other tree species. The aerial photographic transects show this increasing density of living large trees (the great majority *Terminalia*) and bushes at the periphery of the elephant range.

It would appear however, that although the scarring is important, it is not the only factor responsible for the death of the trees. Many trees were found with extensive old scars which yet retained considerable vigour. Others show little bark-stripping damage (less than 15 per cent) but they have died. Nor does age appear to affect the time of death; young, apparently vigorous trees have been found dead, after suffering only a small amount of scarring, whereas old, non-vigorous stems on which girdling is almost complete are still alive. Trunks of *Terminalia* trees which we felled and sectioned with a power-saw showed the marks of old scars; one laid down over ten years previously (on the basis of annual rings in the wood) extended over 90 per cent of the circumference at that time, yet had healed and been covered with healthy tissue.

These data and the results from the aerial transects clearly indicated that the radial pattern of the vegetation is elephant induced, and provide the most likely explanation for the disappearance of the woodland. As the elephant have over-browsed the woodland, so the grass stratum has become more continuous, and fire progressively more intensive (by virtue of the increased amount of fuel) so that the remaining vegetation is largely composed of fire-resistant species. Fire has therefore accelerated the change. It is also worth making the point that the majority of fires originate close to human habitation and that this encircles the present elephant range. Were fire the primary cause of the change from woodland to grassland, the radial pattern should be the reverse of that observed, with denser and more varied vegetation at the centre of the area.

Thus, fire plays an important contributory part in the death of the tree cover. The susceptibility of individual trees depends on the extent to which the tissues exposed by elephant damage are subject to fire; a tree with little scarring but subjected to a fierce burn is more likely to die than a tree with perhaps a greater amount of scarring that is not burnt. Although fire is not the primary cause of the tree deaths it is therefore of great importance, but only after barking by elephants has occurred. In southern Bunyoro the *Terminalia* cover is dense and where cultivation is not in progress, is expanding; to the south of Budongo Forest areas of *Terminalia* are being colonized by *Maesopsis eminii* and are changing towards high forest, yet these areas have been subject to the same burning schedule as North Bunyoro. The obvious difference between the two areas is that one carries a high density elephant population whereas the other does not.

Buechner and Dawkins (1961) concluded that once the vegetational succession had been deflected in this way by elephant, fire alone could maintain a sub-climax state. This may be the case in the giant *Pennisetum* grasslands, where the dominant grass may be capable of inhibiting the regeneration of woody plants (Eggeling 1947b), but there are examples from the tall *Hyparrhenia* zone where, despite annual burning, the elimination of elephant has been followed by a pronounced trend towards woodland.

In 1966–7 the National Parks constructed experimental vegetation plots at Chobe, M.F.P.N., from which elephant were excluded. Of three exclusion plots established in grassland, one has not been burnt, one early burnt, and one late burned. In all three, tree regeneration is marked and some acacias are several feet high. The Chief Warden, R. J. Wheater, commented (*in litt.*) 'the Chobe plots indicate quite clearly, even to the layman, that fire does affect the species of grass present, but seems to make little difference to the growth of fire resistant woody vegetation'. Spence and Angus (1971) have recently presented the results of recording these plots, and similar plots in woodland, in 1967 and 1969.

Between the Rift Escarpment and the south-western third of the Budongo Forest (see Chapter 2, Fig. 2.1), where fires are annual but at minimal intensity as a deliberate policy of early burning by the Forest Department, there is a dense regeneration of shrub and tree growth, now over 3 metres (10 feet) high, particularly of fire-resistant species like *Combretum* and *Lonchocarpus.* Elephant have been progressively eliminated from this area during the past 5–10 years both by denial to them of the Butiaba Flats below and by intensive 'control' shooting.

Another example is a strip less than a mile wide along the western side of the Karuma–Kiryandongo road (Fig. 2.1) in grassland and bushed grassland. In this strip relatively dense tall unbrowsed stands of *Lonchocarpus laxiflorus* have become established, probably, it seems, through the development of continuous human settlement along the east side of the road, so that elephant no longer frequent its immediate vicinity. The area is burned annually, with less planning than the former example, but thoroughly.

Elsewhere in the elephant range elephant browsing usually keeps this shrub to within 30–40 centimetres (1 foot) of the ground, (with the exception noted above where browsing has maintained stands at 2–3 metres (6–10 feet) for a decade or more). In the areas of tall, unbrowsed, regeneration the present vegetation is predominantly fire resistant, but the density of shrubs is ousting the *Hyparrhenia* and breaking the continuity of the inflammable grass stratum. In the process the conditions for regeneration of less fire-resistant species are returning. This further supports the contention that elephant are primarily responsible for the present degeneration of woodland in the rest of the area.

11.3.   The forest edge

Langdale-Brown *et al.* (1964) have described the natural barrier to fire that lies around the forests.

In between grassland and forest lie the shrubby species of the forest edge, such as *Vangueria* spp. and *Acanthus pubescens*, welded together into an almost impenetrable barrier by scramblers and climbers. Being light demanders they cannot flourish within the forest, but the side-shade and shelter of the trees delays their desiccation in the dry season and allows them to fulfil the vital role of checking fires and protecting the forest.

The presence of large numbers of elephants destroys this natural firebreak and in turn exposes the forest proper to the influence of fire (Plates 2.4 and 11.4).

The process is described by Beuchner and Dawkins (1961, p. 761):

Along the edges of the forest, elephants consumed and trampled understory trees and shrubs such as *Acanthus pubescens, Randia urcelliformis, Rinorea ardisiaeflora, Rinorea ilicifolia,* and *Caloncoba schweinfurthii.* Large trees along the forest edges including *Chlorophora excelsa, Cynometra alexandri,* and *Pterygota mildbraedii,* were being killed by the combined action of debarking and burning. As a result of the destruction of both large trees and the understory along the margins of the forest, light penetration increased sufficiently to permit the spread of grasses, notably *Panicum maximum,* into the forest. Sufficiently inflammable material is produced to carry the fire from surrounding grasslands ever deeper into the forests.

Our observations lead to similar conclusions. The forest edge in these areas is now indistinct, as grassland has penetrated into the forest which in parts gives the impression of open parkland. Any *Acanthus pubescens* present is yellow and of a very sickly appearance. Where an understory does occur it is a very open shrub layer riddled with game paths and browsed to a height of 2–3 metres (6–10 feet). In this understory *Rinorea* spp. and *Alchornea* spp. are common; *Olea welwitschii* is the dominant tree species. In some areas individuals of large forest species, such as *Khaya grandifoliola* and *Chlorophora excelsa,* now stand in the open surrounded by grass. The termitaria characteristic of forest also now stand in the grassland.

All relict forest patches in the National Park and Karuma Controlled Hunting Area show these signs in an advanced state and it is extremely doubtful whether they have any chance at all of survival with the continued presence of even small numbers of elephant (Plate 11.4). The large forest patch of Pabidi

(Plate 2.3) also shows many signs of decay through elephant use, and also, as mentioned, the north-east section of Budongo.

That elephant are the primary factor in the retreat of the forest is apparent when we consider their distribution and compare it with the distribution and incidence of fire. Elephant are now all but absent on the south-western fringes of Budongo but present all year round in fair numbers (seasonally present in large numbers) on the north-eastern edge. All the grasslands around the main forest block are burned early in December as soon as the rains have finished, and all areas are burned within a few days. This is to 'ensure the prevention of violent late burns, which are likely by the local people and are employed in their hunting' (Philip 1965).

Ramsay and Rose Innes (1963) have studied the effects of various burning treatments in West Africa. They found a 300 per cent increase in number of stems in protected blocks, a 200 per cent increase in early-burnt blocks and an 80 per cent increase in late-burnt blocks. Thus, even with late burning we might expect some increase in the woody vegetation on the north-east margin of Budongo (as in the south-west; see below) and a substantial increase under an early burning regime. As this is not found to be the case, it indicates that fire-resistant species are being heavily browsed by elephants (for which there is independent evidence) and thus have no chance to develop.

The south-west margin of Budongo gives the reverse impression. Here the edge is expanding rapidly and is only controlled by Man's interference in the way of cultivation and roads. Near Busingiro hill, in an area described by Eggeling (1947b) as being grassland in 1946, there is now a forest cover with *Maesopsis* dominant. In 20 years this edge has extended over 30 metres (100 feet). In this area is found the natural succession of Budongo. There is a healthy *Acanthus* margin leading into a *Maesopsis* dominated stand, which in turn leads into the mixed forest with the mahoganies dominant. Relict termitaria of grassland species (*Macrotermes bellicosus*) are found within the advancing forest, and some individuals of *Terminalia glaucescens*, heavily colonized by epiphytes in this situation.

Although we believe that fire is not the primary cause of the recession of the forest edge, it is important to the extent that nearly all of the forest tree species are non-resistant to fire, so that any regeneration of forest trees that does occur will be destroyed if fire penetrates to them.

In summary, then, the pattern is that elephants destroy the fire-resistant woody species along the forest edge, which removes the shading effect of the canopy and allows grass to develop; this grass will be maintained by the annual burning regime and by continued elephant destruction of tree and shrub regeneration; gradually grassland is making inroads into the forest (Plates 2.4 and 11.4).

11.4.   Forest
11.4.1.   *Current management*

The first working plan for Budongo (1935–44) was followed by working plans for the decades 1945–54, 1955–64, and 1964–74. Under the current working plan the objects of management are: '(i) To produce economically the maximum sustained yield of hardwood timber, especially the mahoganies. (ii) To maintain specimens of the characteristic plant and animal communities of Budongo'. (Philip 1965, p. 46).

It is intended that the Budongo Forest should remain in its mixed state and should not progress to a *Cynometra* climax; only in this way can an optimal yield of valuable timber be maintained. If, as Eggeling (1947b) believed, *Cynometra alexandri* is the climatic climax species, then it is only possible to deflect the succession to the mixed forest type by continued intervention. This involves opening the canopy in order to allow optimum growing conditions for the regeneration of desirable timber-producing trees. As the commercially desirable species are mainly light or semi-light demanding species then the greater the canopy opening, the faster the growth of desirable species. Since 1955 this canopy opening has been achieved by felling, followed by the removal of all non-desirable species over 30 centimetres (1 foot) girth at breast height (g.b.h.), by means of a contact arboricide. Further treatment of undesirables with arboricide is carried out at ten-year intervals, should the young regeneration need it.

Immediately after felling and treatment there is a rapid growth of an herbaceous climber tangle. Initially this blankets the area, apart from those desirable stems left after the felling and treatment (Plate 11.3). Gradually the desirable regeneration, particularly species such as *Khaya anthotheca, Chrysophyllum albidum,* and,

PLATE 11.3. Budongo Forest treated compartment with herbaceous climber tangle at ground level.

PLATE 11.4. Herd of about 400 elephants in remains of forest patch at periphery of their range; another forest relic is in the background.

in very open conditions, *Cordia millenii* and *Maesopsis eminii*, begin to show through this herbaceous climber tangle.

Three years after the initial treatment the herbaceous climber tangle is still evident but saplings, particularly those of the species named above, have pushed through and are rapidly outgrowing the tangle. Ten years after the initial treatment the saplings are from pole size (15 centimetres, 6 inches) to 30 centimetres (1 foot) g.b.h. and form a closed canopy; the herbaceous climber tangle underneath has died due to lack of light. Thus under optimal conditions, the canopy, brought down to ground level by treatment, progressively climbs again, and a relatively open understory appears. Although the present system is aimed at producing a uniform stand, this term can only be used loosely, as there will be a difference of up to 2 metres (6 feet) g.b.h. in the size of the final stand trees. This is due to the setting of the felling limits of desirable species at 180 centimetres (5·9 feet) g.b.h.

At present 2000 acres (810 hectare) a year are felled and treated. Owing to the uniformity of the system, these 2000 acres form a continuous block and are adjacent to the 2000 acres treated the previous year. Thus, at any one time there are nearly 10 000 acres or 16 square miles (4050 hectare or 40 square kilometres) of herbaceous climber tangle in one large sector of the forest.

The succession outlined above continues in the absence of elephant, but is seriously deflected or interrupted by the presence of elephant. It has been shown that the range of the elephant herds in Bunyoro and neighbouring districts has been greatly restricted in recent years, and evidence was presented in Chapter 10 showing that the North Bunyoro elephants have been above the carrying capacity of the range probably for at least two decades. This means that the feeding grounds available to them are under considerable pressure from over-use. When one also considers that the greater part of the elephant range is burned annually within a short period (the January–March dry season), then one can see that at the time of this burning there will be very little food available to elephants in the burned areas, and they are under great pressure to move.

The current value of forest to elephant is then evident, as it now presents a relatively large, productive feeding area which is not burned. With the progressive decrease in the amount of woodland, wooded grassland, and grassland available, so the use of the forest has probably tended to increase. By managing the forest so as to create large areas of succulent herbaceous growth, very desirable feeding areas have also been created for the elephants. But only, we believe, for elephant 'clans' normally inhabiting the range in the vicinity of the forest. In the process of feeding in the herbaceous climber tangle, the elephants maintain the secondary growth by breaking off any shoot appearing through the tangle, and thus preventing the ground-level tangle from being overshadowed by an emergent canopy. These climbers and herbaceous plants are very fast growing and productive and easily replace themselves in a short period.

Until recently the main concern of the Forest Department with elephant has been with bark damage to mature stems; this, because it is so noticeable, was thought to be the greatest danger. (There is a parallel here with the recognition of the nature of elephant problems in bushed grassland and wooded grassland (Laws 1969b, 1970b).) Leggat (1965) investigated the damage to stems of six species over 60 centimetres (2 feet) g.b.h., in the Kibale Forest, Toro. The main interest of his work is that he records most of the damage to the stems as being of recent origin. The opposite is true of the Budongo studies, because we believe, there was very little regeneration management work being carried out in the Kibale Forest at the time of Leggat's survey. When young regeneration is available, elephant turn to it.

Meanwhile, visual observations in Budongo had indicated that the progression of a stand from its initial climber tangle to thicket stage was not occurring as expected. Areas which had been felled and treated six years previously still gave the impression of being at the initial herbaceous climber tangle stage. It was noted that any desirable regeneration which did penetrate the climber tangle disappeared again after a few months. Many elephant trails were found in these young regeneration areas and the records showed that many elephants had been shot in these areas. Control efforts were concentrated on keeping elephants out of the regeneration areas rather than shooting them after they had entered. This has been relatively successful and although there has been an increase in the numbers shot, both the numbers and proportion killed in the regeneration areas have declined.

However, it appeared that the elephants were still using the young regeneration areas, and it was thought that they must be doing a disproportionate amount of damage. Buss (1961) has stated that the greatest proportion of the elephants' diet consisted of grass, but under optimal feeding conditions we believe that up to 50 per cent of the annual food intake may be herbaceous—shrub and tree leaves—or woody material (Laws 1970b). In any case the elephants' size alone will result in damage to regenerating saplings.

Eggeling (1947b) has concluded that the climax vegetation of the Budongo Forest is a closed canopy, dominated by *Cynometra alexandri* and *Celtis mildbraedii*, and was of the opinion that this was a natural climax due to progressive floral competition. However, Langdale-Brown *et al.* (1964) remark that 'the very nature and constancy of the climax are in doubt. The lack of reliable annual growth rings is a handicap in studying this, but the stand tables of many of the present dominant species suggest that regeneration is insufficient to maintain the present populations of mature trees, and that they therefore only represent a seral stage in the development of the forest.'

The stand curve for mahogany in Budongo given by Philip (1965, Appendix V) is particularly striking, indicating a population in which recruitment is seriously reduced. Evidently a disturbing factor intervened about 150 years ago, which may well have been elephant (see below). Similarly Osmaston (1959) in discussing the kink in the stand curves for certain species in the Kibale Forest concludes that 'regeneration is normally continuous and was so until about 40 years ago, when some disturbing factor intervened, allowing few trees to pass through the 1 ft girth class. It is possible that this factor is damage by elephant'.

In trial plots in Budongo and Bugoma Forests, elephant use of the regenerating forest dominants has been studied. The results of these preliminary investigations indicate that young *Cynometra* and *Celtis* are damaged far less frequently than other species studied, and the *Cynometra* consocation may represent an elephant deflected climax.

Other elephant-induced climaxes in high forest are known from West Nile District in Uganda, where the best known is said to be the Bula Forest, dominated by *Holoptelea grandis* (Eggeling (1935) not seen by us but quoted by Buechner and Dawkins (1961)). If significant elephant use of the forest could be demonstrated to have occurred over, or beyond, the lifespan of the present forest dominants, there would be strong grounds for believing that the *Cynometra* climax is elephant induced. Furthermore it would be of great interest to establish whether elephant use has remained constant, or changed appreciably over this period.

11.4.2.   *Damage to mature trees*

A preliminary investigation to attempt to establish a history of elephant use of the forest was undertaken in June 1967. The intention was to examine the stumps of felled forest trees for indications of previous damage and to attempt to date these. This is made possible by the prevalence of fungal rot, which infects the de-barking wounds caused by elephant, and makes signs of them conspicuous in cross-sections (Plate 11.5). Growth curves for the trees can be constructed by making use of the extensive data on incremental growth accumulated by the Forest Department, and, from these, estimates of age can be made.

Two types of rot infection were observed; centre rot, which may or may not be related to elephant damage, and buttress rot, which is almost certainly caused by elephant de-barking. Buttress de-barking by elephants has frequently been observed although some (randomly distributed) buttress damage could be caused by falling dead branches or neighbouring trees.

Centre rot may result from damage to leading shoots or branches; it affects 10 per cent of the timber extracted by the saw-millers and a rebate is paid to the millers by the Forest Department for affected timber. There are no extensive data on the incidence of buttress rot, but of 35 mahoganies examined in the present study 33 were affected in this way. Buttress rot is much less important commercially than centre rot, because it is invariably restricted to the base of the bole,

PLATE 11.5. Buttress of mahogany stump, showing rot patches and growth lines.

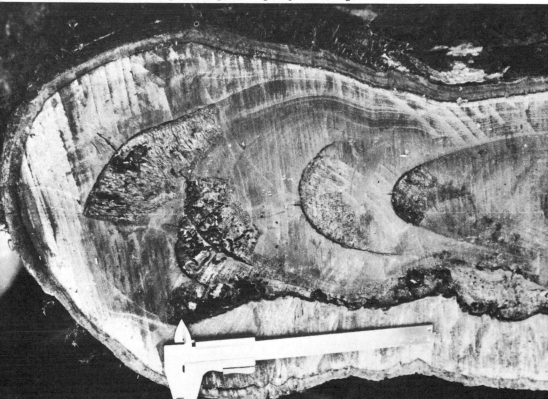

but it may cause splitting of some planks. It is with buttress rot that we are presently concerned.

First, an average-growth curve for the mahoganies was constructed, following a method described by Osmaston (1956). The periodic mean annual increments (p.m.a.i.) of 326 trees of four species (199 *Khaya anthotheca*, 70 *Entandroph-ragma cylindrica*, 42 *E. utile*, and 15 *E. angolense*) measured by the Forest Department over 3- to 5-year periods between 1959 and 1966, were plotted against their median girth above buttress (g.a.b.) measurements. A series of girth classes (of 25 centimetres, 10 inches class interval) were taken and the width of the class was divided by the smoothed averaged p.m.a.i. for that size class. This gives the average time taken for each tree to grow through that class.

Starting from the lower limit of the lowest class as a base, the cumulative 'times' of successive classes were determined. These approximate to the time taken by the mean tree to attain the size of the successive class limits, and can be plotted as a graph of girth at age, converted to radius at age for present purposes, and a smooth curve drawn. From a consideration of the morphology of buttressed trees it seemed reasonable to assume that the diameter above the buttresses (at 3·05 metres, 10 feet height) corresponds to the minimum diameter at buttress level (1·3 metres, 4 feet 3 inches) where the felling cut is made (Fig. 11.5).

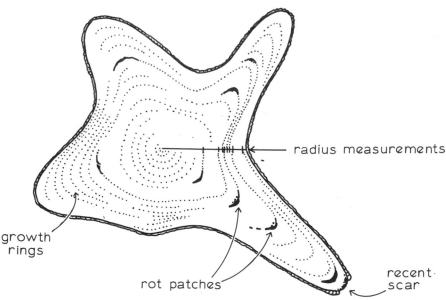

Fig. 11.5. Diagram of a cross-section of a mahogany stump, to illustrate method of relating rot patches to radial measurements and thus to age of tree.

The time taken for initial growth to 25 centimetres (10 inches) girth is problematical because the increment data used include very few trees less than 20 centimetres (8 inches) girth and none less than 10 centimetres (4 inches). There is evidence that under unfavourable conditions, growth may be suppressed for long periods at this stage. We have, more or less arbitrarily, assumed it to be 50 years, although in some cases it might well be as long as 100 years. However, as we are working backwards in the dating, this does not introduce any error, because no trees in the sample showed rot patches at less than 1·22 metres (4 feet) g.a.b.

The p.m.a.i. measurements used relate to six research plots typical of the forest edge (Forest Department research plots, R.P.s 15 and 16), the ecotone between mixed forest and *Cynometra* forest (R.P. 7), mixed forest (R.P. 50), and mature mixed forest (R.P.s 6 and 53). The *Khaya* data came from all plots, but mainly from plots 15, 50, and 53; the *Entandrophragma* measurements came mainly from plot 53, but some from plots 7, 15, and 16. Plots 50 and 53 are very close to the area sampled in this study.

The method of analysis introduces heavy smoothing both because there are large variations in individual p.m.a.i., there are several species in the sample, and because records from the different plots sample different parts of the growth cycle. But in view of the limited numbers examined and the restricted area of sampling, it was not considered worth-while to go into more detail. The objective was merely to establish in general terms whether elephant have been present in sufficient numbers to cause damage, extending over the lifespan of the present dominant trees, and whether or not there has been an increase in damage to mature trees in recent years.

Hummel's study of the 1934—45 increment records (unpublished Forest Department Records) showed that elite emergent *Khaya* reach 3·66 metres (12 feet) g.a.b. in 120 years (others not so elite in 150—80 years) and that the mean annual increment does not fall off until a girth of over 5·49 metres (18 feet) is reached. This is in very close agreement with the present study, which indicates that the average *Khaya* and *Entandrophragma* reach 3·66 metres (12 feet) girth in 155 years. An average girth of 6·10 metres (20 feet) is reached at 300 years. Extremely large specimens recorded by Langdale-Brown *et al.* (1964) are *Khaya anthotheca*, 22 feet g.a.b; *Entandrophragma cylindrica*, 27 feet; and *E. utile*, 20 feet. Conceivably some of the Budongo giants may be well over three centuries old.

It was planned to examine the stumps of mahoganies felled in the forest for buttress rot patches and to attempt to estimate the age at which these were formed, by relating the position of each rot patch on the radius to the radial growth curve (Fig. 11.5). In this way we hoped to be able to examine a large number of trees within the short period available for study. In the event we found that, owing to discoloration, the stump cross-section rapidly deteriorated after cutting, and it was not possible to use stumps from trees felled more than 3—4 days before examination.

In practice, therefore, we accompanied the felling gangs and consequently we were limited to examining 35 recently felled mahoganies (11 *K. anthotheca*), 18

E. cylindrica, 4 *E. utile*, and 2 *E. angolense*), in a restricted area of the forest
(Compartment W 23, Fig. 5.9). This was compensated for by the fact that we
found an unexpectedly high incidence of buttress rot, totalling 152 patches, an
average of 4·34 per tree. The average number for 11 *Khaya* was 6·55 per tree
(range 0–13), and for 24 *Entandrophragma*, 3·33 per tree (range 0–15). This
species difference is highly significant ($\chi^2 = 18·03$, 1 d.f., $p < 0·01$ per cent) and,
since the age structure of the samples is similar (i.e. they have been at risk for an
equal period) we conclude that the two genera are differentially attacked by
elephant; probably this is a function of buttress size.

Our procedure on arriving at the stump to be examined was to measure the
least radius (between buttresses), to the outer edge of the wood and to the outside
of the bark. The rot patches can easily be seen in the cross-sections, and, by the
nature of the damage process, are clearly defined peripherally (Plate 11.5). Thus,
after de-barking and fungal infection, the rot spreads inwards for a distance of
1–5 centimetres to form a crescent of decay. It is sealed off by regrowth of the
cambial layer, a process which may take 5–10 years or more, depending on the
extent to which the tree is damaged. Growth layers visible in the cross-section
clearly demonstrate this process.

The result is that the outside edge of a rot patch is related precisely to the
point in time at which de-barking occurred. Growth rings are conspicuous and the
positions of the rot patches were transferred and marked on a radial line drawn
at the least radius of the stump, by following the relevant growth rings (Fig. 11.5).
The distances of these transferred marks from the centre were then measured to
the nearest millimetre using a steel tape.

The measurements were converted graphically to estimated ages by reference
to the radial-growth curve already constructed. This gave the estimated age of
the tree and its estimated age when each de-barking incident occurred. It was
then a simple matter to work back from the present (1967) and assign a year to
each rot patch. The frequency distributions were plotted for each species separately and since they showed the same general pattern these distributions have
been combined and are shown in Fig. 11.6.

No rot patches were found at a lesser distance from the centre than 20 centimetres, corresponding to a g.a.b. of 1·22 metres (4 feet) and an estimated age of
about 70 years. It is assumed that large buttresses do not develop before this age
and we advance the following argument as a possible explanation for the absence
of barking incidents in the early years. A tree with a smooth rounded bole has
its circumference totally available to elephant tusking. At this stage it is liable to
up to 100 per cent girdling damage, or substantially more than a heavily buttressed
tree on which only the outer part of each buttress is at risk.

The younger trees are at greater risk from elephant and from rot because the
scar inflicted will be a proportionally greater part of the girth of the trunk. Also,
because rot will travel as quickly through a small bole as through a large one, the
smaller bole will be destroyed sooner. Consequently the younger damaged trees may

not survive to maturity. Thus the buttressed trees with scar damage are thought to be those that passed through the first 70 years without bole barking. Those that were barked did not survive, or at least too small a proportion of them to be recorded in our sample. The number of mahogany saplings in regeneration areas relative to the numbers of mature trees indicates a low survival to maturity (see Tables 11.2 and 11.3). But this is a complex and dynamic situation and other areas show an excess of mature trees over small ones (e.g. Langdale-Brown *et al.* 1964, Fig. 6).

A correction has been made to the raw data on the temporal incidence of de-barking to allow for the initial 70 year period. A cumulative frequency distribution of recruitment of trees into the buttressed size classes (i.e. at 70 years of age) is shown in Fig. 11.6. It represents the potential numbers of trees in the sample that, on this basis, could show rot patches in successive years. The numbers of rot patches actually recorded for each year have been expressed as a proportion of the number of trees at risk to obtain a relative damage index, and the results are presented in Fig. 11.6. This gives a crude, approximate estimate of the relative incidence of de-barking. A small number of rot patches estimated to date from 1780–1810 suggest a damage index of 0·50 and may possibly relate to a drier period when elephant made more use of the forest. The data representing the period 1885–1900 have been combined.

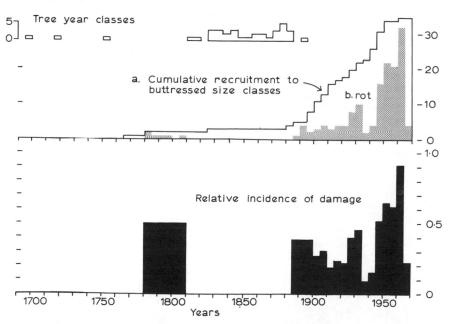

Fig. 11.6. *Top.* Estimated ages of trees examined in the Budongo Forest rot patch investigation. *Middle.* a. Cumulative recruitment of these trees to buttressed size classes (at 70 years); and b. estimated incidence of rot patches by years. *Bottom.* Relative incidence of damage; indices calculated from (b) above as proportion of (a). Values for 1780–1810 and for 1885–1900 averaged in calculating the damage index.

Table 11.2

Budongo C.F.R. Summary of size classes of elephant damage
Cpt. W 18 35·475 acres, 2½ per cent total area of compartment

Species	Total no. stems	Total no. damaged	Percentage damaged	Size classes all stems†							Size classes damaged stems†						
				Sap	Pole	1	2	3	4	5+	Sap	Pole	1	2	3	4	5+
Chlorophora excelsa	10	3	30	9	1						3						
Entandrophragma (all spp.)	30	10	33	29						1	10						
Khaya anthotheca	599	211	35	593	5					1	209	2					
Lovoa (all spp.)	—	—															
Olea (all spp.)	286	86	30	172	57	35	13	7	2		50	19	10	1	5	1	
Albizia (all spp.)	74	49	66	72	2	1					47	2					
Antiaris toxicaria	173	100	58	166	1	1		1	1	3	96	1			1	1	1
Piptadeniastrum africanum	—	—															
Cordia millenii	64	39	61	51	9	2				2	33	4					2
Holoptelea grandis	72	18	25	24	16	20	6			6	6	5	5	2			
Maesopsis eminii	86	43	50	20	38	15	4	4	3	2	10	20	6	3	1	2	1
Morus lactea	13	11	85	10	2			1			8	2			1		
Newtonia buchananii	—	—															
Guarea cedrata	374	151	40	260	95	12	3		1	3	103	44	2	1		1	
Trichilia spp.	81	55	68	80						1	54						1
Aningeria altissima	4	3	75	4							3						
Chrysophyllum albidum	768	457	60	439	231	56	21	6	6	9	235	181	30	7		1	3
Chrysophyllum purpureum	21	11	52	17	1					3	10	1					
Chrysophyllum sp. nov.	3	3	100	2			1				2			1			
Erythrophleum guineense	42	24	57	17	17	4	4				9	11	3	1			
Mildbraediodendron excelsum	35	18	52	32						3	17						
Schrebera arborea	5	1	20	1					1	3			1				
Total	2740	1293	47	1998	475	146	52	19	13	37	905	292	57	16	8	6	9
Mean/acre	77·2	36·4		56·3	13·4	4·1	1·5	0·5	0·4	1·0	25·5	8·2	1·6	0·5	0·2	0·2	0·2

† See Appendix E

Table 11.3

Budongo C.F.R. Summary of size classes of elephant damage
Cpt. N9 30·55 acres, 2½ per cent total area of compartment

Species	Total no. stems	Total no Damaged	Percentage damaged	Size classes all stems†							Size classes damaged stems†						
				Sap	Pole	1	2	3	4	5+	Sap	Pole	1	2	3	4	5+
Chlorophora excelsa	3	1	33	1						2	1						
Entandrophragma (all spp.)	51	27	53	48	1					2	26	1					
Khaya anthotheca	195	50	26	180	2			1	2	10	40	1				1	8
Lovoa (all spp.)																	
Olea (all spp.)	80	7	9	49	10	8	3	4	3	3	5	1	1				
Albizia (all spp.)	39	5	13	37	1					1	5						
Antiaris toxicaria	185	45	24	185							45						
Piptadeniastrum africanum																	
Cordia millenii	51	12	24	17	23	9	1			1	2	7	2				1
Holoptelea grandis	107	10	9	28	22	16	16	5	9	11	5	2	2	1			
Maesopsis eminii	48	9	19	1	6	18	1	3	6	13	1	1	4			1	2
Morus lactea	76	51	67	57	12	3		3		1	36	9	3		2		1
Newtonia buchananii																	
Guarea cedrata	172	22	13	143	15	12				2	21	1					
Trichilia spp.	78	26	33	77	1						25	1					
Aningeria altissima	36	3	8	36							3						
Chrysophyllum albidum	626	130	21	486	76	28	14	8	7	7	96	29	3	1	1		
Chrysophyllum purpureum	50	12	24	45			1		2	2	11					1	
Chrysophyllum sp. nov.	13	6	46	13							6						
Erythrophleum guineense	31	3	10	22	2	3		1		3	3						
Mildbraediodendron excelsum	9	3	33	7	1					1	2	1					
Schrebera arborea	14	1	7	7	4	2	1				1						
Total	1864	423	23	1439	176	99	37	25	29	59	334	54	15	2	3	3	12
Mean/acre	61·0	13·8		47·1	5·8	3·2	1·2	0·8	1·0	1·9	10·9	1·8	0·5	0·1	0·1	0·1	0·3

† See Appendix E

We conclude that significant elephant use of this part of the Budongo Forest covers at least the past two centuries (from 1780) and possibly longer. The relative damage index suggests that from 1885 to 1925 there was a decreasing trend of elephant damage, and subsequently an increase over the past two decades. It is tempting to attribute this increased use of the forest by elephant to the Game Department policy of confinement, which dates from 1925 (Chapter 1).

Finally, in the last few years there has been a sharp drop in the incidence of barking damage. This may be related to the reduction of the Butiaba Flats elephant population by control measures and to the attraction exerted by the young regeneration areas for elephant, leading to a reduction in use of high mature forest. Unfortunately this pilot study does not take us very far back in time, owing to the relatively low average age of the trees in the sample that we were able to study (*Khaya*, 133 years; *Entandrophragma*, 122 years); nor does it relate to more than two stands of trees in a restricted part of the forest. In future felling operations involving larger and older stands of trees in a variety of locations it would be worth-while to repeat this pilot study.

11.4.3.   *Damage to regeneration*

In 1966 it was decided to sample the young regeneration areas in three compartments of Budongo Forest to find out:
  (a) how much damage and what type of damage was occurring;
  (b) which commercially desirable species were being damaged; and whether any species were immune;
  (c) whether damage was limited to a particular size group of trees; and
  (d) what effect the elephants were having on the structure of the stand.

Three areas of the Budongo Forest were selected for sampling for elephant damage, comprising Compartments W 18, N 9, and N 7 (Fig. 5.9). These areas were not randomly selected, but were chosen primarily because routine diagnostic sampling was being carried out in them at the time, so that additional sampling could be carried out at little extra cost. In addition Compartment 8 of Bugoma Central Forest Reserve was sampled for comparison. Sampling procedure was simple and is described in Appendix E. *Only desirable species were recorded.*

In its original state, Cpt. W 18 was primarily mixed forest with some dense patches of *Cynometra alexandri.* Felling of desirable species took place in 1960–2 and was preceded in 1960–1 by a silvicultural treatment which involved poisoning all non-desirable species over 30 centimetres (1 foot) girth. Sampling was carried out in 1966. There have been frequent elephant movements reported from this area, which is nearer to the main elephant population than the two other compartments sampled (Figs 5.9 and 5.10).

Compartment N 9 has both mixed and colonizing forest as it borders on the grassland. Treatment in 1958 preceded felling in 1958–9 but was not carried out in the northern half of the compartment as this forest was considered to be too young to benefit from the treatment. The treatment of the mixed forest consisted of poisoning all non-desirable species of 5—60 centimetres (2—24 inches) g.b.h. and all the *Cynometra alexandri* over 60 centimetres (24 inches) g.b.h.; many of the *Cynometra* survived the treatment. Felling was light, little being removed from the colonizing forest. Few elephant movements have been recorded in the northern half of the compartment. Sampling was carried out in 1966—7.

Compartment N 7 had some very dense *Cynometra alexandri* groups in its original state. The treatment carried out in 1957—8 consisted of poisoning all non-desirables of 5—15 centimetres (2—6 inches) g.b.h. and all *Cynometra alexandri* over 60 centimetres (24 inches) g.b.h. The *Cynometra* were not frilled (ring barked) and hence few died. Felling of desirable species in 1958—9 was fairly heavy and although the treatment was light and did not result in a heavy canopy opening, large gaps were made by the removal of the large mahoganies in the felling. Sampling was carried out in 1966.

Bugoma Central Forest Reserve is a forest of very similar composition to Budongo, but not as rich in mahogany species; *Khaya anthotheca* is rarely found. The forest lies 64 kilometres (40 miles) to the south-west of Budongo, some 8 kilometres (5 miles) from the escarpment, and is also in Bunyoro District. Owing to the intervening habitation and cultivation, there is no longer any movement of elephant between Budongo and Bugoma, although this may formerly have taken place. Bugoma Compartment 8 is primarily mixed forest, but as it borders on grassland it does have some colonizing forest. It is expanding fairly rapidly and a large number of *Maesopsis* stems (> 74 per hectare, > 30 per acre) over 30 centimetres (1 foot) girth are found on the edges. Felling took place in 1956—7 and treatment followed in 1965. In the treatment all non-desirable species over 30 centimetres (1 foot) g.b.h. were killed. Obligatory felling removed all desirable timber species over 150 centimetres (5 feet) g.b.h. Elephant droppings have been found in the compartment, but little damage is evident on casual observation.

Thus the degree of canopy opening increases over the series Budongo Compartments W 18, N 7, N 9, to Bugoma Compartment 8.

11.4.3.1.   *Number of stems per acre.* The volume of timber removed per acre in the felling varies considerably between the compartments, (from 217 to 456 cubic feet per acre). Examples of the data available for all the species involved are given in Tables 11.2—11.5, and we will consider here only the total effect of the damage. At present the total number of stems per acre is: Compartment W 18—77·2; N7—66·7; N 9—61·0; Bugoma 8—62·3 (Table 11.6) respectively 190·8, 164·8, 150·7, and 153·9 per hectare). The extent of the canopy opening is directly correlated with the number of stems per acre. In Bugoma 8 (62·3 stems per acre) where the canopy opening was in two stages (felling and treatment being separated by 8 years), the effect is similar to that of a light canopy opening as in Compartment N 9 (61·0 stems per acre), except that the distribution of size classes is less skewed.

Table 11.4

Budongo Central Forest Reserve. Sample of elephant damage
Cpt. W 18. 35·475 acres, 2½ per cent total area of compartment

Species	Total no. desirables	Total no. damaged	Size of damaged stems†							Type of damage†					Survival†					Age†	
			Sap	Pole	1	2	3	4	5+	a	b	c	d	e	i	ii	iii	iv	v	R	O
Chlorophora excelsa	10	3	3								2			1		2			1	1	2
Entandrophragma (all spp.)	30	10	10								8	1		1		8	2			1	9
Khaya anthotheca	599	211	209	2						6	195	5	1	4	7	173	25	2	4	25	186
Lovoa (all spp.)	–	–																			
Olea (all spp.)	286	86	50	19	10	1	5	1		2	76	6	1	1	1	50	22	10	3	3	83
Albizia (all spp.)	74	49	47	2				1			49				3	43	2	1		6	43
Antiaria toxicaria	173	100	96	1			1	1	1	3	96			1	2	91	7			8	92
Piptadeniastrum africanum	–	–																			
Cordia millenii	64	39	33	4					2		37	1		1		23	13	3		6	33
Holoptelea grandis	72	18	6	5	5	2					10	6		2	1	12	3	2		2	16
Maesopsis eminii	86	43	10	20	6	3	1	2	1	1	30	10	1	1	8	20	11	3	1	5	38
Morus lactea	13	11	8	2			1				9	2				8	2	1		1	10
Newtonia buchananii	–	–																			
Guarea cedrata	374	151	103	44	2	1		1		2	124	11	1	3	2	112	32	3	2	9	142
Trichilia spp.	81	55	54						1	1	52	1		1	3	44	8			5	50
Aningeria altissima	4	3	3								3				1	2					3
Chrysophyllum albidum	768	457	235	181	30	7		1	3	5	421	24	7		19	311	90	34	3	16	441
Chrysophyllum purpureum	21	11	10	1							11					11					11
Chrysophyllum sp. nov.	3	3	2		1						2			1					1		3
Erythrophleum guineense	42	24	9	11	3	1					16	5	3		3	13	7		1	5	19
Mildbraediodendron excelsum	35	18	17			1					17	1				16	1		1	1	17
Schrebera arborea	5	1		1					1		1					1					1
Total	2740	1293	905	292	57	16	8	6	9	20	1159	83	14	17	50	942	225	59	17	94	1199
Mean/acre	77·2	36·4	25·5	8·2	1·6	0·5	0·2	0·2	0·2	0·6	32·6	2·3	0·4	0·5	1·4	26·6	6·4	1·5	0·5	2·7	33·7
% of total number damaged		100	71	24	4	1	–	–	–	2	90	6	1	1	4	73	18	4	1	7	93
% of total number stems		47	33	11	2	1	–	–	–	1	41	3	1	1	2	34	8	2	1	3	44

† See Appendix E.

Table 11.5

Budongo Central Forest Reserve. Sample of elephant damage
Cpt. N 9. 30·55 acres, 2½ per cent total area of compartment

Species	Total no. desirables	Total no. damaged	Size of damaged stems† Sap	Pole	1	2	3	4	5+	Type of damage† a	b	c	d	e	Survival† i	ii	iii	iv	v	Age† R	O
Chlorophora excelsa	3	1	1								1							1		1	
Entandrophragma (all spp.)	51	27	26	1						1	25		1		1	17	7	1	1	2	25
Khaya anthotheca	195	50	40	1				1	8		34	13	3		10	17	15	5	3		50
Lovoa (all spp.)																					
Olea (all spp.)	80	7	5	1	1						4	2		1		2	4		1		7
Albizia (all spp.)	39	5	5								5					4	1				5
Antiaris toxicaria	185	45	45							1	43		1		1	24	9	9	2	2	43
Piptadeniastrum africanum																					
Cordia millenii	51	12	2	7	2				1		6	5	1				2	7	3		12
Holoptelea grandis	107	10	5	2	2	1				1	6	2	1			2	4	2	1		10
Maesopsis eminii	48	9	1	1	4			1	2		2	7			3	3	2	1		1	8
Morus lactea	76	51	36	9	3		2		1		36	8	7		1	22	10	17	1		51
Newtonia buchananii																					
Guarea cedrata	172	22	21	1						1	19	2	1		1	9	10	2			22
Trichilia spp.	78	26	25	1							23	1	1		1	18	6	1			26
Aningeria altissima	36	3	3								3						1	1	1		3
Chrysophyllum albidum	626	130	96	29	3	1	1				108	8	14		7	46	52	23	2		130
Chrysophyllum purpureum	50	12	11					1			8	2	2		2	4	3	3	1	1	11
Chrysophyllum sp. nov.	13	6	6								5		1		1		1	2			6
Erythrophleum guineense	31	3	3								3					3					3
Mildbraediodendron excelsum	9	3	2	1							3					1	1	1			3
Schrebera arborea	14	1	1								1					1					1
Total	1864	423	334	54	15	2	3	3	12	4	335	50	33	1	29	174	128	76	16	7	416
Mean/acre	61·0	13·8	10·9	1·8	0·5	0·1	0·1	0·1	0·3	0·1	11·0	1·6	1·1	–	1·0	5·7	4·2	2·4	0·5	0·2	13·6
% of total number damaged		100	79	13	4	–	1	1	2	1	80	12	7	–	7	42	30	17	4	2	98
% of total number stems	100	23	18	3	1	–	1	1	1	–	18	3	2	–	2	9	7	4	1	1	22

† See Appendix E

Table 11.6
Total number and percentage of stems by size classes

| Cpt. | Sapling | | Pole | | Girth classes (ft) | | | | | | | | | | Total | |
| | | | | | 1 | | 2 | | 3 | | 4 | | 5+ | | | |
	Per acre	(%)	Per acre	(%)	Per acre	(%)	Per acre	(%)	Per acre	(%)	Per acre	(%)	Per acre	(%)	Per acre	(%)
W 18	56·3	73	13·4	17	4·1	6	1·5	2	0·5	–	0·4	–	1·0	2	77·2	100
N 7	51·1	77	7·5	11	4·6	7	1·4	2	0·5	1	0·2	–	1·4	2	66·7	100
N 9	47·1	77	5·8	10	3·2	5	1·2	2	0·8	1	1·0	2	1·9	3	61·0	100
Bugoma 8	35·3	57	7·4	12	6·6	11	5·6	9	3·2	5	1·9	3	2·3	3	62·3	100

The similarity of the percentage size distributions of stems per acre in the three
Budongo samples, as contrasted with Bugoma, is of considerable interest. Theoreti-
cally Budongo Compartment N 7 should be of similar composition to Bugoma
Compartment 8, as their present canopy openings occurred within eighteen
months of each other. Budongo Compartments N 7, N 9, and W 18 show a high
stocking of saplings (47·1—56·3 per acre) as compared to Bugoma Compartment 8
(35·3 per acre) and a much lower stocking of size classes of 30 centimetres (1 foot)
girth´and over (respectively 7·5—8·1 per acre and 19·6 per acre).

It would appear that in the Budongo compartments many of the stems are not
being allowed to grow beyond pole size. Compartments N 7 and N 9 would be
expected to show a greater percentage of stems in the 30 centimetre (1 foot)
and 60 centimetre (2 feet) girth classes than Bugoma Compartment 8, as the
former compartments had a greater initial canopy opening (because felling and
treatment were carried out at the same time). However, the respective percentages
are 9, 7, and 20. The Budongo compartments are also lacking in stems of 90
centimetres (3 feet) girth and over.

Two explanations occur to us; either that the felling resulted in stems of these
size classes being destroyed, or that these age groups of trees were destroyed by
elephants in the past. The former can largely be ruled out because in Bugoma,
Compartment 8 (where the felling limits were lower and a larger number of trees
were removed with consequent heavier felling damage), there are more trees in
the larger size classes than at Budongo. We believe that owing to heavy elephant
damage in the past, the young stems have not developed into the large size classes.
If this is true then it contradicts the view that because elephants have used the
forest in the past no action is required now; it would indicate that action should
have been taken some time ago.

Comparisons of the dominant species in each compartment are given in
Table 11.7. In order of the greatest number of stems per acre they are:
Chrysophyllum albidum, Khaya anthotheca, Antiaris toxicaria, Guarea cedrata,
Olea welwitschii, Cordia millenii, Chrysophyllum perpulchrum, and
Entandrophragma sp. The last two species were not recorded in the three Budongo

Table 11.7
Total number of stems per acre, and number undamaged, by species

| Species | Budongo | | | | | | Bugoma | Budongo average | |
| | Cpt. W 18 | | Cpt. N 9 | | Cpt. N 7 | | Cpt. 8 | | |
	Total	Undamaged	Total	Undamaged	Total	Undamaged	Total	Total	Undamaged
Chrysophyllum albidum	21	9	21	16	14	8	–	18·7	11·0
Khaya anthotheca	17	11	6	5	15	8	–	12·7	8·0
Antiaris toxicaria	–	–	6	5	8	2	9	4·7	2·3
Guarea cedrata	11	6	6	5	3	2	–	6·7	4·3
Olea welwitschii	8	6	–	–	4	2	8	4·0	2·7
Cordia millenii	–	–	–	–	4	1	–	1·3	0·3
Chrysophyllum perpulchrum	–	–	–	–	–	–	8	–	–
Entandrophragma spp.	–	–	–	–	–	–	5	–	–
Total	57	32	39	31	48	23	30	48·1	28·6

samples. As can be seen from Table 11.7 the composition of the Budongo compartments is very similar, with *Khaya anthotheca* and *Chrysophyllum albidum* the dominant species. They form nearly 50 per cent of the stand in each case. At Bugoma no dominant species can be singled out.

The vast majority of the *Khaya anthotheca* and *Chrysophyllum albidum* at Budongo are in the sapling and pole size classes. In a part of Siba Forest where there are no elephants, an enumeration immediately following felling and treatment showed that sapling-sized specimens of these two species formed over 50 per cent of the total numbers of the desirables. If these species are dominant from the time of treatment why is it that they have not progressed to any great extent to the pole and 30 cm (1 foot) girth size classes in Budongo? Under normal conditions *Khaya anthotheca* grows at a rate of about 30 centimetres (1 foot) girth every ten years. That it has not done so can only be due to suppression by the elephants, which break off the leading shoots and do not allow any emergence from the herbaceous climber tangle. By their movements, elephants also tend to compress the tangle, which in turn leads to the suppression of *Khaya* and other desirables.

11.4.3.2.   *Damage.* Of the Budongo compartments sampled, N 9 stands out as subject to least damage (Table 11.8). The reason for this is obscure, but it may be relevant that in the management programme this compartment developed the smallest canopy opening, as only half of it was treated and felling was light; there may be a balance between the degree of canopy opening and the amount of elephant damage. Heavy canopy opening results in a large amount of damage and a light canopy opening produces a small amount of damage. However, it has already been seen that the lighter the canopy opening, the smaller the amount of regeneration obtained. The optimum canopy opening could perhaps be found by experimental management.

The greatest amount of damage occurs in the smaller size classes, particularly the sapling class, because these are the size classes that would be destroyed if elephants were feeding (the leading shoots can easily be reached). Stems of 30 centimetres (1 foot) and over show much less damage than smaller stems, which would indicate increasing relative immunity from damage for stems over 30 centi-

Table 11.8
Total number of stems damaged by size classes

Cpt.	Sapling Per acre	(%)	Pole Per acre	(%)	1 Per acre	(%)	2 Per acre	(%)	3 Per acre	(%)	4 Per acre	(%)	5+ Per acre	(%)	Total Per acre	(%)
W 18	25·5	33	8·2	11	1·6	2	0·5	1	0·2	–	0·2	–	0·2	–	36·4	47
N 7	27·7	42	3·9	6	1·2	2	0·6	–	0·2	–	–	–	0·7	1	34·3	51
N 9	10·9	18	1·8	3	0·5	1	0·1	–	0·1	–	0·1	–	0·3	1	13·8	23
Bugoma 8	3·5	6	1·7	2	1·3	3	0·6	1	0·1	–	0·1	–	0·2	–	7·7	12

Girth classes (ft)

metres (1 foot) girth. None of the species sampled was free from damage. There
was, however, a considerable variation in the amount of damage, some species
being more susceptible than others. The species most liable to damage were
Morus lactea, Albizia spp. *Cordia millenii,* and *Trichelia* spp. Those least affected
were *Olea welwitschii, Holoptelea grandis,* and *Schrebera arborea. Guarea cedrata*
could also be considered as fairly free from damage. It is of considerable interest
that in Budongo neither of the two dominant species of timber producers (*Khaya
anthotheca* and *Chrysophyllum albidum*) are among those species most liable to
damage.

From an economic point of view, the composition of the stand is greatly altered
when one takes account of the number of damaged stems, because any future
treatment will have to aim at removing these. Thus in Budongo removal of the
damaged stems would give the numbers of undamaged stems per acre, considering
only the more common species, shown in Table 11.7. Not only would the number
of stems be reduced (on average from 48 to 29 per acre) but the stand composition
would be affected. *Chrysophyllum albidum* and *Khaya anthotheca* would remain
the most common species and continue to form 50 per cent of the stand, but the
species which suffer least from elephant damage (*Guarea cedrata, Olea welwitschii,*
and *Holoptelea grandis*) would form a greater percentage of the stand than they
did previously. Considered as percentages of the total numbers of stems and of
the total number of undamaged stems these three species contribute to the stand
as shown in Table 11.9.

Table 11.9
Total stems and proportion undamaged as percentage of the stand for three species

| Species | Compartment | | | | | |
| | Total no. | | | Percentage undamaged | | |
	W 18	N 7	N 9	W 18	N 7	N 9
Guarea cedrata	14	5	9	15	8	10
Olea welwitschii	10	6	4	14	6	5
Holoptelea grandis	3	1	6	4	1	7
Species combined	27	12	19	33	15	22

Thus, as a result of elephant damage these three species probably make a
greater contribution to the stand than they otherwise would, and continued
elephant use might well result in these species coming to form an even greater
proportion of the stand, to the extent that they might become dominant. This is
not a purely hypothetical view, because Buechner and Dawkins (1961) and
Stuart-Smith (1966) have noted that the Rabongo forest shows a domination of
Holoptelea grandis, with the *Khaya* spp. being mere remnants. Such forests are also
found in West Nile where elephant damage has been heavy in the past (Eggeling

1935). It would appear that the exploited areas of the Budongo forest are rapidly changing and that to allow elephants continued use of the forest will result in a fairly rapid transformation from its present state to one in which *Guarea cedrata, Olea welwitschii,* and *Holoptelea grandis* are dominant.

The type of damage is considered in Table 11.10, which shows the percentages of different types of damage. That the vast majority of the damage consists of

Table 11.10
Summary of types of damage

Cpt.	(a) per acre	%	(b) per acre	%	(c) per acre	%	(d) per acre	%	(e) per acre	%
W 18	0·6	1	32·6	41	2·3	3	0·4	1	0·5	1
N 7	0·9	1	31·2	47	1·7	3	0·3	–	0·2	–
N 9	0·1	–	11·0	18	1·6	3	1·1	2	–	–
Bugoma 8	0·4	1	6·6	10	0·7	1	–	–	–	–

Notes. The percentage is based on the total number of stems
     (a) Leader broken, no new one grown
     (b) Leader broken, new one grown
     (c) Bark removed
     (d) Branch pulled off
     (e) Tree trampled or uprooted.

damage to the leading shoots is of great importance. It amounts to 47 per cent of the total number of stems in Budongo Compartment N 7, and confirms that elephants are using these areas for feeding purposes. Studies of their movements show that elephants remain in the forest for several days at a time, and suggests that they are able to subsist on a diet of leaves, herbaceous, and woody material. It indicates that elephants do not necessarily need or prefer a largely grass diet as Buss (1961) believed, but can adapt their feeding habits to very different conditions. It has already been pointed out by Laws and Parker (1968) and Laws (1969b) that the high proportion of grass in the stomachs of Murchison Falls National Park elephants is probably unnatural (due to restriction of range and change of habitat) and that vegetation change in the direction of grassland is causally related to the decline in elephant populations (see also Chapter 8).

Virtually all species in which stems over 30 centimetres (1 foot) girth occurred were subject to bark damage. It was noted that although *Guarea cedrata, Holoptelea grandis,* and *Olea welwitschii* suffered less damage than other species, they were still subject to bark stripping. The majority of this was old damage, which probably occurred before the felling and treatment were carried out (as the rot investigation also indicated), and it seems probable that this stripping only occurs when supplies of other food materials are scarce. In the woodland and wooded grassland areas, de-barking shows a seasonal pattern. The creation by forest management of herbaceous tangle has evidently abolished the need for bark eating.

That the majority of the stems are still in the sapling size class, in spite of the fact that it has been up to nine years since felling and treatment, would indicate that there has been a considerable loss of incremental growth due to elephant damage. Repeated breaking of the leaders resulted in many of the stems remaining at sapling size, in spite of their being several years old, and many of the stems showed several past breaks. A new leader normally grows after the break except in cases where suppression by climbers or other tree species occurs. It is evident, therefore, that if *Holoptelea grandis* is less damaged than the other species, then it will gradually outgrow the damaged species, and will suppress them by cutting down the light reaching them, eventually to destroy them.

Very few stems are damaged to the extent that they are killed. The majority of dead stems found were mainly killed by trampling; a few stems were found, however, which had been pulled right out of the ground.

11.4.3.3. *Chance of survival.* Table 11.11 presents data on the estimated chance of survival, based on the total number of stems of desirable species for the four compartments sampled. Columns (*iii*)–(*v*) show the number of stems which already have defective timber. At present, in the three compartments at Budongo we have:

	W 18	N 7	N 9
Percentage timber defective	11	20	12
Percentage trees damaged but timber still stands	36	31	11
Percentage trees not damaged	53	49	77

At present, as far as timber production is concerned, there is no cause for great concern, as any defective stems could be removed in future treatments; the number of stems affected is still small enough to allow this. However, should more damage occur, then it will not be long before nearly 50 per cent of the timber is defective. This would then become serious, as any future treatment would be confined only

Table 11.11

Estimates of chances of survival of damaged stems

Cpt.	(i) per acre	%	(ii) per acre	%	(iii) per acre	%	(iv) per acre	%	(v) per acre	%
W 18	1·4	2	26·6	34	6·4	8	1·5	2	0·5	1
N 7	4·1	6	16·4	25	8·3	12	5·2	8	0·3	–
N 9	1·0	2	5·7	9	4·2	7	2·4	4	0·5	1
Bugoma 8	0·5	–	3·0	5	3·0	5	1·1	2	0·1	–

Notes. The percentage is based on the total number of stems

    (*i*) excellent chance;
    (*ii*) good chance;
    (*iii*) fair chance but timber will be defective;
    (*iv*) slight chance, timber useless;
    (*v*) no chance.

to the removal of elephant-damaged stems, and would not liberate greater numbers of non-defective desirables (because the optimum conditions for regeneration have passed).

11.4.3.4.   *Age of damage.* The majority of the damage was found to be over six months old. No conclusions could be drawn from this study, as it was found impossible to determine at all accurately when damage had occurred unless it was within the past few weeks. However, the results of the investigation into the distribution and occurrence of rot patches in cross-sections of the trunks of felled mature mahoganies in Compartment N 8 indicated that there had been a dramatic decline in bole and buttress damage over the past ten years (Fig. 11.6); that is, since management began.

11.4.3.5.   *Cynometra alexandri.* The damage investigations described above relate to desirable timber-producing species, but during the enumerations of Compartments N 9 (Budongo) and 8 (Bugoma), an enumeration was also carried out to establish how much damage was being done to the dominant undesirable species, *Cynometra alexandri.* The method employed was the same, and the same plots used as in the study of desirables.

   This investigation showed that damage to *Cynometra alexandri* was very slight (Table 11.12). Thus the percentages of this species damaged were only 7 per cent and 2 per cent respectively in Compartments N 9 and 8. When all species were included, the total percentages damaged were 23 per cent and 12 per cent respectively (Table 11.8). The type of damage to *C. alexandri* was again mainly to the leading shoots (Table 11.13). The enumeration of the chance of survival showed that, of the stems damaged, the majority were in the three categories of most serious damage (Table 11.14). No recent damage was found.

   Another undesirable, *Celtis mildbraedii*, was sampled at Bugoma Compartment 8, where it was found that out of a total of 482 stems only 21 (4 per cent) were damaged. There are no figures available for Budongo.

   These data are extremely interesting and show that the amount of damage done in both compartments to *Cynometra alexandri* is the lowest for any species studied. We have here a species which is very common in Budongo Compartment N 9 and common in Bugoma Compartment 8, yet it is not greatly subject to elephant damage. Where damage occurs it is mainly confined to the breaking of leaders of saplings and very little damage occurs to the older stems, which have survived this.

   Cynometra alexandri is more common than any of the other dominant species in Budongo. As a fully grown adult it forms almost pure stands and, due to its dense canopy, prevents the regeneration of any of the desirable species in its shade. Where there is a plentiful light supply, the desirable species, such as *Khaya anthotheca,* will normally outgrow *Cynometra alexandri.* However, conditions are not normal and it has been shown that *Khaya anthotheca* and other desirable species are being damaged by elephants to such an extent that

Table 11.12

Damage to size classes of Cynometra alexandri

Cpt.	Total no. stems per acre	Total no. damaged stems per acre	Size class all stems per acre†							Size class damaged stems per acre†						
			Sap	P	1	2	3	4	5+	Sap	P	1	2	3	4	5+
N 9	23·9	1·7	17·5	0·7	0·4	1·3	0·8	1·1	2·1	1·2	0·2	–	0·2	–	0·1	–
Bugoma 8	4·8	0·1	3·4	1·4	–	–	–	–	–	–	0·1	–	–	–	–	–

†See Appendix E

Table 11.13

Type of damage to Cynometra alexandri

| Cpt. | (a) | Type of damage† (stems per acre) | | | (e) |
		(b)	(c)	(d)	
N 9	–	1·3	0·3	0·1	–
Bugoma 8	–	0·1	–	–	–

† See notes to Table 11.10

Table 11.14

Estimates of chance of survival of damaged stems of Cynometra alexandri

| Cpt. | (i) | Survival† (stems per acre) | | | | Total |
		(ii)	(iii)	(iv)	(v)	
N 9	–	0·1	0·8	0·6	0·2	1·7
Bugoma 8	–	0·1	–	–	–	0·1

† See notes to Table 11.11

they cannot outgrow the other emergent species. If *Cynometra alexandri* is then virtually undamaged by elephant, it is likely that a stand of almost pure *Cynometra* will quickly develop.

Is it not possible that in the past, elephant selectively destroyed the regeneration of the economically desirable light and semi-light demanding species when they occurred in gaps created by falling trees, thus leaving *Cynometra* to become dominant? If this were the case then it would appear that the *Cynometra alexandri* forest could be an elephant-induced deflected climax and not the climatic climax as stated by Eggeling (1947b). It would help to explain the apparent lack of mahogany and other light or semi-light demanding species of over 60 centimetres (2 feet) girth.

In Budongo Compartment N 9 the total number of stems per acre including *Cynometra alexandri* is 84·9, and 15·5 of these are damaged. To the total number of stems *Cynometra* contributes 28 per cent, but considering only the undamaged stems it makes up 47 per cent of the stand. One can see that further elephant damage would result in the proportion of *Cynometra* increasing even further.

These results are of course based on too small an area to give incontrovertible results and the views put forward in the preceding paragraphs are speculative. The quantitative results obtained are, nonetheless, of great interest and indicate that further study is urgently needed. If it is confirmed that, over wide areas, *Cynometra alexandri* is relatively free from elephant damage, when other species are available, it would have an important bearing on the past, present, and future structure of the forest. It should be noted that, in forests where elephant damage is extreme (for example in the Rabongo Forest) then more intensive damage to *Cynometra* does occur, but attacks on this species seem to occur only as a last resort after other species have been selectively affected.

11.4.4.   *Damage caused by buffaloes*

Only slight damage to the forest is caused by buffalo, and this mainly to the former loading areas and grassy patches. By continually cropping, these buffalo prevent the regeneration of tree seedlings and maintain these clearings in their grassed state. This is not serious because the area affected is small, and it could easily be reduced by restricting the number of loading bays made by the loggers.

During the study of elephant damage in Compartment W 18, records were also made of buffalo damage. It was found that damage to tree species was slight and confined to those stems occurring at the edges of paths. Only 30 stems were found damaged in 14·4 hectares (35·5 acres), *Cordia millenii* being the most damaged species, mainly because it is a fast-growing light demander which occurs along the edge of the tracks. The main damage was to the stem by rubbing, and 50 per cent of damaged stems showed rub marks. Other desirable timber producing species found damaged were *Guarea cedrata, Khaya anthotheca, Chrysophyllum albidum, Maesopsis eminii, Holoptelea grandis, Erythrophleum guineenze,* and *Entandrophragma* spp.

None of the other desirable species were found to be damaged. It would appear that buffalo confine their activity to the grassy areas and that their increase in numbers is mainly due to the increasing management of the forest, which has resulted in the creation of more areas of grass. It is desirable, however, to enlarge our knowledge of the ecology of the buffalo, as there is a possibility that if their numbers continue to increase there may be overgrazing, leading to pressure on the herbaceous vegetation of the young regeneration areas.

11.5.   Other effects of elephant use

In areas heavily used by elephant they create and enlarge numerous waterpans. This is achieved through their habit of frequently plastering themselves with mud, scooped up from puddles and thrown over the body; and also by drinking water with mud in suspension. This process enlarges the original depression until it will hold substantial amounts of water. The location of these pools in the Murchison Falls Park is often along the top of a ridge, or the upper reaches of a valley, and must play a significant role in the over-all ecology of the areas in which they occur, particularly in relation to the needs of other animals.

11.6.   Discussion

Buechner and Dawkins (1961, p. 764) suggested that 'the role of elephants probably shifted in the process of vegetation change from an initial triggering action, in the presence of fire, to one of accelerating the change, finally becoming nonessential in the perpetuation of grasslands. In contrast, fire increased in importance as the vegetation changed, and currently it is an essential factor in the maintenance of grassland vegetation.' We do not agree that elephant ultimately become non-essential in the perpetuation of the *Hyparrhenia* grasslands—at least, not so long as there is a stock of woody species available for recolonization (present as geophytes or patches of woodland or bush). As soon as elephant are removed, there is a regrowth of bush, despite persistent and intense fires (Plate 2.10). We even doubt whether this is necessarily the case in the *Pennisetum* stands, as there are no large areas comparable to the *Hyparrhenia* grasslands.

With the continued contraction of the elephant range (Fig. 1.4) the densities of elephant over the available range have probably continued to increase, or to remain stable, in spite of the decrease in the absolute size of the elephant population, while at the same time the woody vegetation resources of the range have further decreased.

The relative use of woody growth by elephant (expressed as a proportion of the standing stock of trees or bushes) has certainly increased and we consider that the role of elephant is currently much more important than that of fire in suppressing the regeneration of woody vegetation. There is sufficient root coppice growth of 30 species (Buechner and Dawkins 1961) to allow the re-establishment of woodland if elephant alone can be controlled, although re-establishment will probably be more rapid and more diverse if fire is also controlled. If elephant use is reduced, fire-resistant trees and shrubs appear and lead to the development of a less flammable environment in which less fire-tolerant plant species can grow. The mean annual rainfall is high enough to support heavily wooded grassland, woodland, and forest, as in the past, if this biotic influence can be controlled.

Under continued annual burning, fire-sensitive species will disappear leaving the fire-resistant species, particularly *Terminalia glaucescens, Lonchocarpus laxiflorus, Pseudocedrela kotschyi, Stereospermum kunthianum, Combretum binderanum, C. gueinzii,* and *C. molle* as potential components of the future woody vegetation. Of these Buechner and Dawkins (1961, p. 762) consider *Lonchocarpus laxiflorus* to be the most successful in surviving annual fires. 'Some patches are so dense that seemingly they will develop into closed woodland.' However, in the face of heavy browsing by elephants this prediction has not proved accurate.

The time of burning is important, early burns tending to promote the establishment of fire-resistant species (and disappearance of fire-sensitive species), while late burning is so fierce that even fire-tolerant species are retarded.

However, the control of burning alone is unlikely to result in a sustained increase of woody vegetation, for some of the surviving woody species, such as *Lonchocarpus laxiflorus,* are preferred foods of elephants. Buechner and Dawkins (1961) remark in connection with *Lonchocarpus laxiflorus*: 'the foliage and stems of this species are utilised so readily that unbrowsed individuals are seldom

Table 11.15

Densities (converted to number per square kilometre) of woody plants recorded in study plots Murchison Falls National Park 1958

| Species | Sample plots | | | | | | |
	1	2	3	4	5	6	7
Prosopis africana	—	2100	—	—	—	—	—
Ficus dicranostyla	200	—	—	—	—	—	—
Ficus sp.	100	100	—	—	—	—	—
Stereospermum kunthianum	—	—	—	17 200	—	—	—
Terminalia glaucescens	4800	2900	—	31 400	22 000	72 400	—
Borasus aethiopum	—	—	25 700	—	—	—	—
Crataeva adansonni	—	—	1100	—	—	—	—
Combretum gueinzii	200	—	—	—	—	50 000	13 800
Combretum binderanum	—	—	—	—	43 000	65 200	18 000
Acacia sieberiana	—	—	200	—	—	—	—
Lonchocarpus laxiflorus	—	—	32 600	22 200	6900	26 400	32 600
Harrisonia abyssinica	—	—	—	9700	—	—	—
Strychnos innocua	—	—	—	—	130 000	—	—
Grewia mollis	—	—	—	—	10 500	—	—
Securidea virosa	—	—	—	—	—	—	41 400
Others recorded	—	—	—	12 400	47 200	85 400	43 600
Totals (all species recorded)	5300	5100	59 600	92 900	236 000	299 400	149 400

Notes. Description of plots:

(1) living large trees, *Terminalia glaucescens* woodland at Wairingo Ranger Post

(2) living large trees, *T. glaucescens–Prosopis africana* Woodland at Pandera (Murchison Falls Park, North)

(3) *Borasus aethiopum–Lonchocarpus laxiflorus* regeneration, Te Okuto, (Murchison Falls Park, North)

(4) geophytes, *T. glaucescens* woodland at Wairingo Ranger Post (as (1))

(5) geophytes, *Terminalia–Prosopis* woodland at Pandera (as(2))

(6) geophytes, grassland derived from *T. glaucescens* woodland, Wairingo Ranger Post

(7) geophytes, grassland derived from wooded grassland, Wairingo Ranger Post.

The totals refer to (1) 4 species; (2) 3 species; (3) 4 species; (4)–(7) 21 species.

Data extracted and converted from Buechner and Dawkins (1961).

found, yet the heavy foraging does not prevent heavy growth and spread of coppicing.'

We disagree with these authors, believing that in the past decade there has been a decrease in the densities or at least a significant suppression of growth of this species, probably mainly due to overbrowsing by elephant. Thus, in the vicinity of Wairingo it no longer forms large dense stands as reported, and illustrated by Buechner and Dawkins. In contrast, in other areas where fire is frequent, but elephants have recently disappeared or are at low densities, tall dense stands of this shrub are growing up. The spatial change in the densities of small trees and bushes at the periphery of the elephant range shown by the aerial transects (e.g.

Figs 11.2—11.4) is largely due to *Lonchocarpus* and *Combretum* plants.

Buechner and Dawkins (1961, p. 755) examined photographic evidence of vegetation change, based on comparison of aerial photographs taken in 1932 and 1956. In the Te Okuto area (M.F.P.N.) they compared the numbers of trees, by five crown-diameter classes in six 10-hectare samples. Trees under 9 metres (29·5 feet) diameter were too small to be seen clearly and the numbers recorded may not be accurate. For five plots the reduction in number of trees with crown diameters over 9 metres ranged between 53 per cent and 95 per cent in the 24 year period; for the remaining plot there was an increase of 73 per cent, due to maturation of smaller trees.

Over-all, the numbers of large trees decreased by 50 per cent (from 440 to 219, or in terms of density 733—365 per square kilmoetre). Including those trees under 9 metres crown diameter, the decrease was 52 per cent (from 864 to 416, or 1440—693 per square kilometre). This represents an average exponential rate of decrease of about 3 per cent a year, but there has probably been a progressive increase in this rate, so that in the later part of the period it was probably greatly in excess of the average rate. The area sampled was designated as wooded in Vandeleur's map of 1895 (Vandeleur 1897). Although they relate to an area north of the river and refer to a restricted locality, these data give some indication of the possible rate of change of woodland on the south bank of the River Nile between 1932 and 1956.

Buechner and Dawkins (1961, p. 756) also sampled the vegetation by means of ten 0·1 hectare (0·25 acre) plots in *Terminalia* woodland near Wairingo Ranger Post, and ten plots in *Terminalia—Prosopis* woodland at Pandera (M.F.P.N.). In all plots they recorded the number of stems of trees living geophytically, and in the first three series of plots they recorded data on individual trees (size, vigour, damage etc.). Their data for the frequency of the more abundant species are summarized in Table 11.15, in which the numbers have been converted to densities to facilitate comparisons.

In the Wairingo woodland plots 29·4 per cent of *T. glaucescens* trees were dead and in the Pandera series 23·7 per cent; in the first series of plots 16·7 per cent of four other species were dead and in the second series 43·6 per cent of three other species; combining all species, the percentages dead were 28·4 per cent and 33·8 per cent respectively. We do not know how long dead trees survive the annual burn, but on average it is probably not more than 3—5 years.

Buechner and Dawkins (1961) noted that in 1958 all trees of all species at Wairingo were scarred by elephant.

Altogether the 48 living *T. glaucescens* trees examined contained at least 75 completely closed old scars. Evidently the trees have been under attack for several decades. Old scars that had partially healed numbered 25 and fresh scars numbered 20 for the 48 trees. The fresh scars varied from occasional single gouges . . .to large rectangular patches from which the bark had been removed completely over an area 30 by 60 cm or greater . . . Frequently bark was stripped from 1 to 3 m above the ground, and occasionally to a height of 5 m.

These authors remark that some individual trees recover from scarring, but that once girdled over 50 per cent of the girth there was little prospect of recovery. They suggested that the degree of exposure to fire resulted in variation in survival after barking, but conclude that 'from the present condition of *T. glaucescens* it is evident that under current conditions of annual burning the woodland at Wairingo will change drastically in another decade or two'.

In fact it has changed even more rapidly than they forecast. From the aerial photographic transects (S 4) carried out in 1967, the density of dead and living mature trees (crown diameter more than 8 metres) at the Wairingo Beacon, within *ca* 500–1000 metres of the 1958 plots, averaged 430 per square kilometre and 20 per square kilometre respectively. Thus 95·6 per cent were dead compared with 23·7 per cent in 1958. The average density over eleven frames (8·3 kilometres, 5·2 miles) from north to south of the Wairingo River was 667 per square kilometre, of which 97·5 per cent were dead. The maximum densities on this woodland transect were 1060 per square kilometre, about 3 kilometres (1·9 miles) north of the Wairingo River, of which 98·3 per cent were dead. This is the area which ground observation also now shows to have the highest density of trees. There were an estimated 5300 ± 5298 ($P < 5$ per cent) living mature trees per square kilometre in the Wairingo woodland in 1958, mostly severely barked, and of low vigour.

Even allowing for the considerable sampling and geographical variability affecting the comparability of the 1958 and 1967 estimates, there has clearly been a very heavy die-off of trees in this former woodland area in the past decade, which is indeed obvious even to a casual observer (Plate 11.2). This may well represent as much as 99 per cent mortality suffered by the stands alive in 1958, most of which probably occurred in the first half of the decade.

In studying the effect of elephant on the former woodland and wooded grassland, we are dealing with an historical situation with its roots in the past (at least fifty years ago) and a cycle of deflected succession that is almost complete. It is no longer possible to study the early stages of this process in action in Bunyoro, although there may be areas in Acholi (north of the Victoria Nile) where such an investigation could be conducted.

The situation in the forest is, however, still dynamic and progressive, and gives many pointers to an understanding of the selective damage process as it has probably affected the former woodland. The complicating effect of fire is absent in the forest and this both clarifies understanding and decelerates the rate of change in forest (where the longevities of the dominant plant species involved are in any case much higher as compared with woodland). In both cases the magnitude of the changes is primarily due to human intervention; in the former woodland by restriction of the elephant range, as discussed in Chapter 1, and in the forest by creating (virtually instantaneously) large areas of secondary herbaceous growth which have attracted elephant concentrations, a development enhanced by the fact that they are under pressure in other parts of their range.

Care must be taken in the use of the results from the forest study. The areas were not randomly selected and so the results obtained may not be representative of the regeneration areas as a whole. Some important points have been made nonetheless, notably concerning the widely differing end-effects of elephant use on high forest, the forest edge, and woodland. In high forest it appears that elephants may be responsible for the dominance of *Cynometra alexandri* in forests over a very large area of Africa (where climatic and edaphic conditions are suitable); in contrast, at the forest edge and in woodland, in conjunction with fire, they have caused the development of open tall grassland in North Bunyoro. Greater elephant densities, especially if associated with regular burning, would probably result in the degeneration of *Cynometra* stands and their possible replacement by tall *Hyparrhenia* or giant *Pennisetum* grasslands, as has apparently occurred in parts of North Bunyoro. The respective parts played by man and elephant in this latter cycle are not yet known.

This comparison of the effects of elephant on forest and woodland suggests that artificial reduction of elephant numbers and control of fire could deflect the forest succession or prevent change from forest or woodland to grassland, if action were taken early enough. Once the process of habitat change has progressed beyond a certain point, much more drastic action is necessary to reverse the change. The lesson to be learnt, and applied in other areas, is surely that we should take effective action at an early stage in the process as soon as extensive damage becomes evident.

That damage to the forest is serious cannot be doubted. If the present rate of damage continues, it will not be long before a marked deterioration in the structure of the forest, from an economic point of view, is manifest. While the damage to the forest edge and the surrounding grassland is perhaps the most spectacular, the most visible, and most urgent from the point of view of conservation, another immediate cause for alarm concerns the damage to the young regeneration areas in the forest.

The results of the forest studies suggest that there are correlations between the degree of canopy opening, damage by elephants, and regeneration of economically desirable species of trees. If the point of optimum balance, from a management point of view, could be found, then elephant control measures (short of complete elimination) might be greatly simplified.

The damage caused by elephants is causing a proportional change in the species composition of the forest. It is to be expected that this change will accelerate as more of the dominant species are damaged. Damage is mainly confined to the smaller size classes which are those stems within easy reach of elephants, and would appear to result from the elephants seeking food because it consists mainly of broken leading shoots. No species was found which was free from damage, but some species were more liable to damage than others.

Damage to the commercial timbers is 12·14 per cent by volume and mainly concerns the most valuable mahoganies. This represents an annual revenue loss of over £10 000, but not all of this may be attributable to elephant. However it can be rectified to some extent, as much of the damaged material can be removed in future treatments, but further elephant damage will result in a progressive increase in the amount of damaged timber (A. W. M. Watt, *in litt.*).

11.7.   Summary

The analysis of the ecology and population dynamics of the elephants indicates that they are at densities far in excess of the carrying capacity of the habitats. It was therefore necessary to consider the dynamics of the habitat changes in some detail.

The grassland and wooded grassland range was studied extensively by means of 16 aerial photographic transects, totalling 456 kilometres and sampling 250 square kilometres. Half were in M.F.P.N. and half in M.F.P.S. In interpreting the results, quantitative records of numbers of mature trees, small trees and bushes, dead trees, and animal tracks, were made. Large tree densities were shown to be very low inside the National Park (M.F.P.S.) boundary, but higher outside, often with an abrupt change coinciding with the perimeter of the elephant range. A similar pattern characterized the distribution of small trees and bushes, except that high densities are also found in the immediate vicinity of the River Nile, correlated with erosion and hippopotamus overgrazing. Recent tree damage, indicated by the proportion of dead trees, is greatest at the edge of the remaining woodland (in both M.F.P.N. and M.F.P.S.), suggesting that this is a dynamic process which passes radially through the woodland, leaving behind a much changed habitat. In the Wairingo woodland for example, nearly all the living *Terminalia* trees present in 1958 have died.

These changes are correlated with the distribution of elephant, and the radial, centrifugal pattern shows that fire is not the primary cause of damage, because most of the fires originate near human habitation which encircles the elephant range. Even in the presence of fire, tree regeneration is prevented only where elephant occur. Over parts of the periphery of the range, where elephant are now absent owing to the contraction of their range, and in experimental plots, where elephant are excluded by ditching, burning does not prevent regeneration of the fire-resistant species, although it does retard it.

Significant elephant use of the forest covers at least the past two centuries. Where they are present in numbers elephants destroy the fire-resistant species along the forest edge, which removes the shading effect of the canopy and allows grass to develop, destroying the natural fire barrier of the forest edge. Where fire is present, but elephants are absent, as along the south-west edge of the Budongo Forest, the forest is expanding. In the managed compartments, felling and treatment opens the canopy and promotes an herbaceous climber tangle from which emergent species carry the canopy upwards again. Some 40 square kilometres of very desirable elephant feeding grounds have been created in this way and in the process of feeding there, elephants interrupt the succession.

The amount of regeneration (number of stems per unit area) is directly correlated with the extent of canopy opening. Elephant selectively damage the smaller (sapling) size classes, mainly by breaking the leading shoots, and there is also a considerable loss of incremental growth. Elephants are also species selective and this leads to changes in the composition of the stands, so that commercially undesirable timber species become predominant. The presence of elephant is thus incompatible with economic timber production. The undesirable *Cynometra alexandri*, is the least damaged of any species studied, and it is suggested that the ironwood forest may be an elephant-induced deflected climax, rather than a climatic climax. Much greater elephant densities, especially in association with burning, probably result in the replacement of the *Cynometra* stands in their turn by giant *Pennisetum* grasslands, as illustrated by the many forest remnants in the area.

12. Economic and ecological considerations

12.1. The grasslands and woodlands

The area considered in this section is the area of the National Park and the surrounding unoccupied areas, including parts of the Karuma Falls Controlled Hunting Area, but not the grassland of the Pabidi and Budongo Central Forest Reserves, or the Bukumi-Bungungu Controlled Area. The Forest Reserves are considered separately.

12.1.1. *General considerations*

The aesthetic and cultural grounds for maintaining wildlife and National Parks have been eloquently expressed (Darling 1960, 1970; Huxley 1961; Dassman, 1963, 1968), and we intend to confine our comments to ecological and economic factors. This does not mean that we think that aesthetic factors are unimportant. In the long term we believe the converse to be true, but the survival of the natural habitats and their wildlife depends on events in the next decade, when immediate economic considerations are likely to be of overriding importance in a developing country.

The potential value of the three National Parks to the Uganda economy is unquestioned. There are 2760 square miles (7148 square kilometres) of land under this form of land-use, making up only 3·7 per cent of the total dry land area of Uganda (74 739 square miles; 193 573 square kilometres). The potential revenue from tourism has been predicted at £4 798 000 for 1970; £14 298 000 for 1975; and £42 609 000 by 1980. The value of the longer-term extrapolations is extremely questionable, since there are a number of possible disturbing factors,† but the 1970 estimate (which was attained) represents a gross return of £1738 per square mile, since the vast majority of tourists came to see the wildlife in the National Parks. The 1975 projection represents a gross return per square mile of over £5000 (but now certainly will not be attained).

These figures compare with a current gross return of £422 per square mile for the Budongo Forest, the richest forest in East Africa, and a gross return at maturity of £383 per square mile from a proposed ranching-game cropping development plan for the Murchison Falls Area, advanced by the Agricultural Development Service (attached to the World Bank's Permanent Mission in East Africa) (Anon 1967). Even in 1964, with the gross revenue from tourism running at about one tenth (£1·3 million gross) of the forecast potential for 1975, tourism was roughly competitive with other forms of land-use in the area, in relation to the over-all economy of Uganda.

† Some of these have already come into effect and since this was written, tourism has virtually ceased as an industry in Uganda, although in Kenya the forward-look estimates have been exceeded.

Clearly, even the net profits from tourism are potentially vastly greater than those from other forms of land-use and bring in much needed foreign exchange. As long as the revenue from tourism continues to rise, the economic argument in favour of conservation and tourism, as opposed to other forms of land-use, will continue to strengthen. This economic argument alone is sufficient reason for making great efforts to preserve and develop the National Parks and to maintain or improve the habitat and faunal diversity.

There are grounds for supposing that the income from tourism is presently divided between the Queen Elizabeth Park and Murchison Falls Park in rough proportion to the respective land areas. (For various reasons the Kidepo Valley National Park is not yet even at its current potential in terms of visitors.) Thus the ratios between the respective areas of these two Parks, 1:1·95, and between the number of visitors entering them, 1:1·70[†] are roughly comparable.

On this assumption the Murchison Falls Park, South represents a potential value of £4 million gross per year in 1975, since its 810 square miles comprise 29·4 per cent of the National Parks estate in Uganda. There is a comprehensive Development Plan for the area, prepared by R. J. Wheater (1968a), and major attempts to develop tourism are being made, but there is also an imperative need to conserve and if possible to extend the woodland habitats.

An early requirement is for a Management Plan on the lines of the Working Plans produced by the Uganda Forest Department, or the Management Plans for Nature Reserves in the United Kingdom (Eggeling 1964). The *pro forma* Management Plan for the Queen Elizabeth Park drafted by J. M. Boyd (1965) at the request of one of us, R.M.L., would be a useful framework. However, no action has yet been taken on this and there is a very urgent need for decision and action on the over-population problems of the Murchison Falls Park. Tackle (1968) has emphasized the relationship between research and administration, the need for action before it is too late, and the danger of waiting too long for research results.

The Controlled Hunting Areas are currently managed solely for sport hunting, as discussed in Chapter 3. The area west of the Park is already almost completely pre-empted by settlement (fishing villages, subsistence agriculture, and grazing). The only form of revenue from these areas is from hunting licences.

Unfortunately the Game Department has been unable to provide us with data separately for the Karuma Falls and Bugungu Controlled Hunting Areas or for the other parts of the elephant range under discussion. Figures for total numbers of elephant shot annually on control or under licence in Bunyoro as a whole are presented in Appendix D. The Game Department has provided figures (*in litt.*) for revenue collected in Bunyoro from Supplementary Licences, Controlled Hunting Area Permits, Animal Fees, Minister's Permits, and fees from cropping

† These figures are for 1959–60, the last year before instability in the Congo and Toro District upset the comparison and caused wide fluctuations in the Queen Elizabeth Park entrance figures. In 1962–63, a relatively stable year, the visitor ratio between the two parks was 1:2·24.

projects. These elephants must have been taken mainly from either the populations with which this book is concerned or from the much smaller herds centred on the Bugoma Forest. The stated revenue from May 1962 to December 1968 was £31 145.

This revenue does not include the sale of ivory obtained from control shooting operations, which the Department estimate at £22 500 a year (S. Ruhweza, personal communication). At an average of 625 elephant per year shot on control, this amounts to £36 per elephant, that is an average of approximately 8–9 kg (18–20 lb) of ivory per tusk. For this 6½ year period then, the total gross revenue reported from elephant in Bunyoro was at least £177 395, from 4914 animals.

We found it difficult to accept these figures which seem very high. On further enquiry M. G. Trussler, Deputy Chief Game Warden (*in litt.*) stated

I have dug around in our files to ascertain the number of elephant shot in Bunyoro during the period 1st January, 1963 to 31st December 1968 and you will be pleased to know that it is not as high as you were given to understand. During this period, local licence holders shot 207 and Uganda Wildlife Development hunters took a further 115, making a grand total of 322.

This gives an average of 54 per year over a six year period, compared with 74 per year which the earlier figures indicated.

Assuming, however, that these figures are correct, even this gross revenue compares with a potential gross revenue for this number of elephants if fully utilized (Appendix F), of £481 572.[†]

It can be argued that control shooting is very wasteful and unsatisfactory and it has been suggested (Brown 1968) that in certain areas it might be more profitable to compensate for loss and damage. Brown has discussed the problems and economics of game control in greater detail than is possible here.

In practice, sport hunting contributes to the tourist receipts discussed in Chapter 3, although visitors' licences (as opposed to residents') represent a relatively small proportion of the fees. However, there are other reasons for encouraging sport hunting and it is more realistic to recalculate the value only of the elephant presently shot on control, as if they were the basis of efficient cropping operations of the kind mounted in the Murchison Falls National Park in recent years. Instead of a gross revenue of £22 500 a year they could be expected to produce £61 250 a year, or 2·7 times the stated gross revenue.[†] Moreover, if a more efficient and humane method of cropping were adopted we estimate that a further 20 per cent of elephant that are wounded in current practice, die slowly and are lost, would be utilized. Unfortunately, there is insufficient information to enable these figures to be presented on a unit area basis for comparison with other forms of land-use.

As pointed out in the previous chapter there is a very serious problem of maintaining the habitats in the face of increasing pressure, mainly from settlement

† Much more of course at current (1973) ivory prices.

and cultivation. The economics of the Controlled Hunting Areas are so arranged as to produce revenue for the Local Administration, to encourage their interest and cooperation in the conservation of game. We believe that if this revenue can be increased, the changes of the survival of these areas as habitats for wild animals will be improved. Even if, as seems likely, the human population pressure is too great to permit the long-term survival of the game in these areas, the cropping of elephant, hippopotamus, and buffalo, as proposed below would reduce the pressure this will bring to bear on the National Park habitats in the near future.

The alienation of the area west of the National Park (the Bukumi-Bugungu Controlled Area) is now almost complete and a boundary effect is already becoming obvious. As cultivation comes to occupy more and more land up to the Park boundary, the conflict between wildlife (particularly elephants) and subsistence agriculture can be expected to intensify. Crop destruction will become an important source of friction, and poaching forays into the Park potentially even more frequent than at present. This would in a relatively short time become prejudicial to the future of this section of the Park, and through political pressure to an even larger area. The National Park authorities should take the initiative now, while there is still time.

We have therefore recommended that the construction of an elephant-proof barrier (fence and/or ditch) should be commenced as soon as possible, the barrier to extend initially along the Park boundary from the Victoria Nile to the Weiga Swamp. This is a distance of some 26 kilometres (16 miles) and might involve a capital cost of up to £16 000 and a recurrent annual cost of £1000. Subsequently this barrier could be extended to link up with the proposed barrier along the northern boundary of the Forest Reserves, preferably with small adjustments to the National Park boundary.

Before embarking on this project, advice should be sought from other conservation authorities which have successfully completed and maintained effective elephant barriers (e.g. Aberdares National Park, Kruger National Park, Kenya Forest Department). A joint approach at the planning stage by Uganda National Parks and Forest Department would minimize costs, and the construction would probably best be achieved by employing an outside contractor.

The study described in this book has demonstrated that, owing to restriction of range, the elephant population from an area of over 6300 square kilometres (2400 square miles) has been compressed into a range of some 3200 square kilometres (1200 square miles) over a relatively short period of time. It seems very probable that the range will be further contracted to 2100 square kilometres (810 square miles), the area of the southern part of the National Park, within the next decade. Owing to the progressive and rapid contraction of the range, the natural regulatory processes of the elephant population have not been sufficient to produce a dynamic balance.

The adaptive response of the elephants has in fact been very considerable, involving probable reduction in their growth rate, retardation of the age at first breeding, lengthening of the interval between calves, and probably heavy calf mortality. Unfortunately these processes have not been sufficient to halt or reverse the trend to grassland, although it is known that, even in the presence of regular annual burning, woodland and forest are expanding under the current climatic conditions, in the absence of elephant. However the prerequisite for this expansion—a nucleus of trees or geophytes—may not obtain for much longer.

The evidence presented indicates that the North Bunyoro elephant populations have been declining, in response to this contracting of range, for some 20–30 years. The models proposed by Laws (1969b), and also the discussion in Chapter 10, indicate how this progressive habitat deterioration can occur. Once the population comes to exceed the 'carrying capacity', then the carrying capacity per unit area continues to decline progressively, a process accelerated by the increasing excess of population over carrying capacity.

In the case of North Bunyoro, although the elephant population in absolute terms has been declining for decades, their population density has been increasing due to the rate of contraction of the range available; the density increasing faster than the rate of population response by means of density-dependent (or habitat-dependent) natural regulatory processes.

In short, we have a population crash (which is extended over decades owing to elephant longevity), a progressive destruction of the woodland habitat, and its replacement by coarse grassland. The seriousness of this conservation problem is related to the time scale of the elephant population cycle and of tree regeneration. Thus, even if elephant were completely eliminated, it would probably take at least 50 years for stands of mature woodland to develop.

In the parallel problem of over-grazing (illustrated by the hippopotamus over-population in the Murchison Falls and Queen Elizabeth National Parks) the time scale is much shorter. If erosion has not progressed too far, the rehabilitation of grasslands can be achieved remarkably quickly as the ecological and management studies in the Queen Elizabeth Park (Laws 1968a; Field 1968a) and in Murchison Falls Park (our field observations, and Spence and Angus (1971)) have demonstrated.

Despite the magnitude of the problem, for us to recommend no action would be a counsel of despair, and there is clearly a strong case for reducing the elephant population. The rationale behind this is a need to reinforce the natural regulatory process operating (inadequately because too slowly) to bring about a balance between the elephant population and the habitat. That is to accelerate the population crash, so as to bring the population density to a level below the 'carrying capacity', and to allow habitat recovery to begin. Although we speak of a balance between elephants and habitats, it may be that, especially in a restricted area, a point equilibrium is not possible. If true this does not invalidate our argument, but means that sustained monitoring and management will be necessary to keep the population at or below the carrying capacity and so to achieve an approximate equilibrium state (see Chapter 10).

There is some evidence that habitat recovery could be expected to closely follow significant reduction of elephant densities. Initially this would probably be mainly in the form of escapement of heavily browsed geophytic species from the suppressive effect of elephant and fire. In order to obtain full benefit of these control measures it is imperative that the incidence of fire should also be regulated, and we make specific recommendations on this in later paragraphs. Specific proposals for conservation cropping are made below.

12.1.2.   *Reduction cropping*

12.1.2.1.   *Elephant.* We consider that reduction or conservation cropping should be implemented in two phases with suitable provision for monitoring (by means of research) the population levels and the dynamic response to cropping. The reason for not presenting a detailed and definitive long-term plan at this stage is that, although a fair amount of analytical work has been carried out, it has been achieved, of necessity, in a rather short period. The general nature and possible extent of the response of elephant populations to habitat change (and conversely to cropping) has been elucidated, but experimental work is needed before the temporal relations of these changes can be established. We foresee a long-term plan being refined over a number of years, subject to revision in the light of new evidence, and using the cropping operation as a natural experiment. However, there is clearly an urgent need for action.

The National Parks may come under considerable pressure to undertake selective cropping (or culling), concentrating on certain sex and age groups. We believe that this would be not only wrong in principle, but also impracticable for elephant management. Since this is a recurring theme in discussions about elephant conservation and management, let us consider the argument in detail.

Apart from unsupported and improbable ideas such as the one recently resuscitated by Sheldrick (1972)[†] there have been no supported proposals for achieving population reduction by selective cropping until Fowler and Smith (1973) proposed a management strategy involving age-specific cropping. They developed a method for predicting the nature of the carrying capacity (stable density) and stable age distribution when certain other density-dependent relationships within a population are known. They applied the method to model African elephant populations and concluded that their computer analysis supported the findings of Laws and Parker (1968). They stated that the predicted age structures appeared to converge to the pseudo-stable age structure, which in time will converge to the stable age structure. Like Laws and Parker they concluded that the population age structure will 'most likely remain unstable for quite an extended period of time unless specific management measures are taken'. Populations above a stable

† In 1963 a 'well-known statistician' claimed that the elephant population of Tsavo East National Park, then estimated at 7000, could be reduced by a third (*ca* 2300) over a period of 5 years by means of the selective culling of only 280 animals a year (140 females and 140 males). How this can be achieved has never been explained and the original calculation has not been published.

density level 'should be artificially reduced to levels more compatible with the capacity of the environment', and they discussed a selective management strategy. The aim of this approach would be to remove animals in such a way that the remaining population would approximate to a stable age distribution.

In Fig. 12.1 the models presented in Fig. 10.9 have been converted to a common origin at 1.0 to illustrate this principle. If feasible, such selective reduction would enable a stable situation to be achieved more rapidly, but there are serious practical difficulties in applying highly selective management to social animals such as elephants. We have already discussed the elephant family unit as the basic population unit and the essential need to remove complete family units or bull herds in reduction cropping, in order to avoid disturbance to the surviving

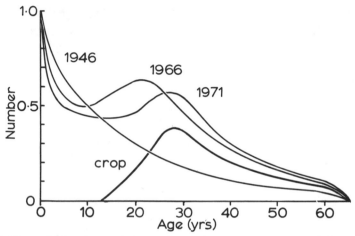

Fig. 12.1. The model female populations reduced to a common origin. The desirable relative age structure of the crop is also shown, representing the proportion of the 1971 population to be removed so that it would approximate to a stable age distribution (1946).

population. Fowler and Smith (1973) recommend the removal of those family units with age structures approximating to the portion of the population to be removed as suggested by the model. In reality the age structure does not follow a smooth curve (Fig. 10.4) and it seemed that the most practical method of selective cropping might be to remove groups led by old matriarchs and to avoid taking those led by younger females.

The feasibility of this method of selection has been tested by subsampling our M.F.P.S. sample of family units, together with any associated bulls, on the basis of their age structure (Fig. 7.10). A simple field criterion might be the age of the oldest female, but comparison of the age structures of groups led by females older than 50 years and less than 40 years of age, showed no obvious differences (Fig. 12.2). Next, from a consideration of the family unit age structures, groups with a higher average age were selected by inspection of Fig. 7.10. Only twelve groups could be selected in this way, comprising a sample only 16 per cent of the

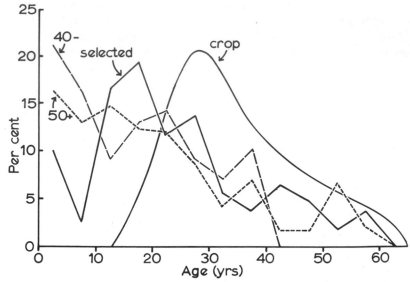

Fig. 12.2. Age structures of subsamples of complete family units (derived from Fig. 7.10) compared with the approximate age structure of the desirable age-specific crop of females (Fig. 12.1). The subsamples are based on the age of the oldest female ($<$40 years or $>$50 years) or by selection of family units that have a higher than average age.

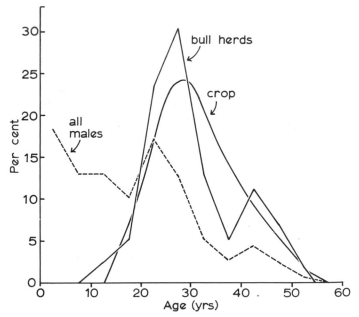

Fig. 12.3. Age structures of bull herds cropped (including single animals) and of all males taken, compared with the approximate age structure of the desirable age-specific crop of males.

total. They showed a more suitable age structure, which was however, still far from that desired for meaningful age-specific cropping. Since the problems of selection in the field are very much greater than in this 'paper' exercise we conclude that selective cropping of complete family units is not practicable as a means of altering the female age structure in the direction of a stable age distribution.

There may be serious objections to selective cropping of males (as suggested by Glover (1963)) or older animals, in that the social organization is highly complex, and selective removal of breeding bulls or leaders from population units would introduce another variable into the problem. The bull herds do in fact approach the desired selective crop much more closely (Fig. 12.3), and it may be advisable in drawing up detailed quotas for the proposed reduction cropping to specify separate quotas, within the over-all quotas, for mature bulls not associated with family units. If family units are taken in reduction cropping (as they must be if it is to be meaningful) then the age structure of the total male crop would depart from the age structure needed to achieve a stable age distribution rapidly.

Thus, the reasons for advocating the taking of complete family units are as follows:
1. The apparently insuperable difficulty of large scale selective cropping of elephants is that of disturbance. If some animals in a group are shot and others allowed to escape, disturbance will rapidly become an important factor, both in relation to cropping success per unit effort, and to tourism. The effect on social structure may be adverse to the over-all aims. These effects would jeopardize and probably wreck the operation.
2. By taking a random cross-section of the population it is possible effectively to reduce the population without initially changing its composition. This will have certain advantages in interpreting the effects of the proposed cropping and of the earlier cropping on population structure and will give an unbiased estimate of the population structure several years after the previous cropping operations (already six years have elapsed). There are no advantages in a biased cropping method, which makes no real contribution to the need for selective cropping outlined above.
3. There is no urgent need to maximize the yield from the cropping operations in terms of biomass and profit. This is outweighed by the need for early action.
4. The proposal of Sikes (1966b) for selective culling is not practicable on this scale, nor in our opinion is it desirable. The arguments under (2) above apply to such culling, and in any case the objective is to reduce the population, not to stimulate recruitment. The reduction of the population to a level approximating to the 'carrying capacity' should have the incidental effect of eventually lowering the proportion of diseased or undernourished animals.

The first phase of the conservation cropping is to reduce the peripheral high-density stratum of the population to the level of the central, medium-density stratum. This means reducing the peripheral density from 3·8 per square kilometre (9·5 per square mile) to 1·9 per square kilometre (5·6 per square mile).

The area occupied by this stratum is 1292 square kilometres (499 square miles) (of which 629 square kilometres, 243 square miles are outside the Park boundaries), holding at a density of 3·8 per square kilometre (9·8 per square mile) a population of 4890 elephants. At a density of 1·9 per square kilometre (4·9 per square mile) this area would hold 2445, so the quota should be 2445, or rounding off conservatively, 2500. The quota should be taken as soon as possible, by the methods outlined below.

The second phase would be to reduce the residual population over the whole range (5159) from an over-all density of 1·9 per square kilometre (4·9 per square mile) to an average density of 1·5 per square kilometre (4·0 per square mile), that is by 18·4 per cent, or 949 (rounding to 1000). This would leave a residual population of about 4200 elephants, or approximately half the present population. This simple calculation ignores the hypothetical response, but if the reduction cropping is carried out within a four year period the immediate effect of a possible change in recruitment would be negligible, and we would expect cropping to result in a net reduction in the population, approximating to the numbers cropped.

The heavy control shooting around the Budongo Forest since 1958 (Fig. 10.1) evidently had little effect in increasing recruitment to the population, at least up to 1966–7 when it was sampled, and has probably caused a net reduction roughly equal to the numbers cropped. The proposed time scale for the reduction is known to be possible, because 1600 elephants and 2800 hippopotamus were cropped in under two years in the previous cropping programme both north and south of the Victoria Nile, and there has been a considerable evolution of hunting and processing techniques since then.

The method recommended is to take complete population units—single animals, family units, and bull herds—as randomly as possible and as extensively as possible within the blocks to which the quotas refer. We see no need to diverge from the system of operation in the earlier cropping, namely to take the first population unit encountered on each occasion in a given area, provided that it is small enough to be taken in its entirety and dealt with in the hours of daylight—in practice this now means a maximum group size of about 25. The herd position must be favourable for hunting and it must be possible to reach the spot with lorries so that the carcases can be utilized.

In Phase 1 the quota should be distributed between the blocks as shown in Table 12.1, the block quotas being based on the percentage distribution of the population. The boundaries of the hunting blocks, related so far as possible to natural features, are shown in Fig. 5.1. An alternative series of quotas to be taken within the National Park, if agreement cannot be reached with the Game Department for cropping outside the Park is also presented. Cropping to these

Table 12.1

Elephant reduction cropping, Phase 1. Recommended quotas by blocks (see Fig. 5.1)

Blocks	Quota (a)	Quota (b)
1b–4–5b$_1$	250	250
5b$_2$–9–10	500	280
6b–7b	650	650
8	650	} 570
3b	450	
Total	2500	1750

Notes. (a) Contingent on hunting both inside and outside the Park
      (b) Inside the Park only

quotas could be begun while discussions proceed on cropping outside the Park, for time is running out.

The previous operations (1965–7) have shown that the method of taking complete population units does not conflict with tourist use. In any case the only area subject to intensive tourist use that is involved in Phase 1 of the proposed cropping programme is Block 1b, which is transected by the main Masindi–Paraa road. It is suggested that the quota for Blocks 1b, 4, and 5b would be taken during the months of lowest tourist use (May and June). The grass is not inconveniently long and rainfall not as high as in October–November.

The distribution of quotas by blocks in Phase 2 is dependent on the results of further aerial counts establishing the distribution of elephants up to three years from the start of Phase 1, and there seems little point in presenting a detailed breakdown of the over-all quota at this stage. The sub-quotas should be calculated in relation to the percentage distribution, by blocks, of the elephant population at the start of Phase 2.

The gross income to be expected from the first two phases of the reduction cropping is £245 000 and £98 000, respectively, totalling £343 000[†]. This is contingent on cropping being carried out by the method recommended in this report, and the carcases being optimally utilized.

In the earlier cropping operations the potential gross return (£98 per elephant,[†] Appendix F), was not achieved by the cropper. The main reason for this was that it was an entirely new venture and there was uncertainty about the contract until the first 400 elephants had been taken. This led to reluctance to invest capital in processing techniques, such as freezing; the skin had never been used before (except for ear skin) and a technique had to be developed (Plate 12.1) and a market found. In the event the cropper overcame this difficulty during

† Now much higher.

PLATE 12.1. Salted elephant hides from cropping operation, Mkomasi.

PLATE 12.2. Preparing salted elephant meat, Mkomasi.

the operation, but the meat was sold very cheaply to local buyers, fetching less than £5 a carcase (Plate 12.2). The National Parks therefore received only £13 075 in fees. However, the real importance of these first operations, apart from the scientific yield, was that a humane and efficient method was developed, and processing techniques were vastly improved.

12.1.2.2.   *Hippopotamus.* The earlier proposals for hippopotamus cropping to restore the riverine habitats by an initial reduction cropping of 4130 hippopotamus have not yet been fully implemented. Only 2908 were cropped over a two year period, 1965–7, and since then, cropping has proceeded at a much slower rate (712 between July 1967 and December 1968). There has been a marked habitat response, but in view of the very high use of the riverine zone by elephant and hippopotamus combined, it is considered that further reduction cropping to a grazing density of 7·7 per square kilometre (20 per square mile) should be undertaken.

Detailed quotas for Sections 1–6 and 9–11 of the Victoria Nile are presented in Table 12.2; Sections 7 and 8 should remain as controls in which no cropping should be carried out. Half of these quotas should be taken south of the river in Bunyoro. The net recruitment under this regime is estimated at 6 per cent per year, an approximate value derived from research on population dynamics (Laws 1968b), from the results of previous counts (1964 and 1967) and the intervening cropping in 1965–7. Table 12.3 shows how the cropping rate necessary to achieve the required reduction was estimated.

Although there are no accurate figures for the number of hippopotamus below Murchison Falls, it was estimated that there were approximately 1375 hippopotamus on the south bank of the Victoria Nile in this area, at a grazing density of 23 per square kilometre (60 per square mile). The target population at 7·7 per square kilometre (20 per square mile) would be about 460 and, if detailed counts confirm this estimate then a net reduction of about 900 is recommended; to be achieved by a gross reduction of 1000 in one year.

Again this study has been, of necessity, incomplete, owing to lack of time and funds. It is therefore very important to monitor the effects of cropping, both on the hippopotamus population and on the habitats and other grazing species. In particular it will be important for the survival of other mammal populations dependent on the short-grass areas, to watch these areas closely. The cropping programme should be used as a natural experiment to establish habitat responses; it should be subject to annual review and in no way be regarded as rigidly fixed. The monitoring can be accomplished by further aerial counts, including an initial count before the cropping begins, by analysis of the crop(for age structure and reproductive parameters), and of the vegetation. The cropping quotas can be refined in the light of this additional information.

It should also be pointed out that the annual quotas are proposed on the assumption that the meat produced will be disposed of for local consumption, as before. There are compelling arguments in favour of this. Present indications,

Table 12.2

Hippopotamus, Victoria Nile, Sections 1–11. Estimated population, target population (at 20 per square mile), and reduction quotas over four year period

Section	Grazing area (sq. miles)	Population 1967	Target population	Net reduction	Gross reduction (4 yrs)	Annual reduction Yrs 1–3	Yr 4
1 } 2	47·0	1479	940	540	780	213	142
3	21·3	1227	426	800	1160	316	210
4	17·0	1112	340	770	1115	304	202
5	17·7	751	354	400	580	158	105
6	16·6	683	332	350	505	138	92
7	17·5	559	(559)	0	0	0	0
8	16·0	694	(694)	0	0	0	0
9	18·1	720	362	360	520	142	95
10	15·1	559	302	260	380	104	70
11	17·7	678	354	320	460	125	84
Total	204·0	8462	4663	3800	5500	1500	1000

Note. Sections 7 and 8 are control sections

Table 12.3

Hippopotamus, Upper Nile: estimate of cropping rate necessary to achieve required reduction

Year	Population size (1)	Crop quota (2)	Residual population (3)	Net increment (4)
1970	8500	1500	7000	470
1971	7500	1500	6000	400
1972	6400	1500	4900	300
1973	5200	1000	4200	300
1974	4500	250	4250	250
1975	4500	250	4250	250

Note. Figures rounded off

$$\text{Net increment} = \frac{\text{columns (1)} + \text{(3)}}{2} \times 0\cdot06$$

based on experience during the earlier cropping, are that the local market will not take many more than 1500 carcasses a year. If alternative arrangements were made for marketing the meat (e.g. distributing further afield) the annual quota could possibly be set much higher, and the required reduction accomplished more rapidly. This would be an advantage.

A realistic gross value to the cropper of the products from an average hippopotamus is estimated at £24 (if the carcase is sold locally) or £44[†] (if an alterna-

† Now likely to be much higher.

tive method of marketing is adopted) (see Appendix F). Thus, over a four year period the estimated gross return from 3750 hippopotamus taken in Bunyoro would be £90 000–£165 000. Assuming costs to account for 50 per cent of this, there should be a net profit of £45 000–£82 500.

From the cropping of some 2900 hippopotamus by Game Management (Uganda) Ltd., between 1965 and 1967 the Uganda National Parks and Game Department received £16 900 in fees. Because this operation was a new venture, techniques had to be developed and new products, including treatment of skin for leather, had to be sought. For these reasons the potential gross return was not in fact realized. Had it been realized the revenue to Parks and Game Departments (£16 900) would represent approximately half the net profits if costs are esti-mated as above at 50 per cent. Previous experience therefore suggests that the estimates given in the preceding paragraph are not over-optimistic.

12.1.3.   *Sustained-yield cropping*

In view of the demonstrated potential of the Uganda National Parks as an economic form of land use in the form of tourism, it might be thought that we are to some extent freed from the necessity of suggesting a solution to the problem of their survival, dependent on the direct economic yield of wildlife. But we do not feel that the National Parks are absolved in any way from maxi-mizing productivity. Tourism is undoubtedly the greatest source of revenue, but it in no way diminishes the potential of cropping, which is an entirely comp-lementary form of land-use and need not conflict with tourism. Success in one field should not be allowed to prevent efforts in other directions. There are in fact other compelling arguments for setting up a programme for sustained-yield utilization of wildlife, of several species, both inside and outside of the National Park.

The National Parks are threatened by poaching by local people living around the periphery. This influence will become progressively more important as the presently unoccupied lands around the National Park become settled. Already cultivation extends up to the Park boundary in some places and, in the absence of a positive policy, the edge effect due to dense human populations surrounding an unsettled area will come to exert an increasingly important influence on the National Park. It may be expected that a zone of at least 4 miles deep will be subjected to the direct effect of intensive poaching, even if there were a tremen-dous increase in the anti-poaching effort by the Administration. There are some 127 kilometres (79 miles) of Park boundary in Bunyoro, so this represents a potential area of at least 780 square kilometres (300 square miles), or 37 per cent of the southern part of the Murchison Falls National Park. Consequently, enhanced seasonal burning will seriously affect an even larger area.

In addition to a probable continuing need for sustained conservation cropping of elephant and hippopotamus, there is thus a further strong argument for rapidly developing a sustained economic yield cropping programme, with the aim of preempting the presently unoccupied lands surrounding the Park—currently an area of some 780 square kilometres (300 square miles), so as to form a 'buffer zone' around the Park to protect it from this disastrous edge effect. A secondary objective of sustained yield cropping would be to demonstrate that the National Parks are of direct economic benefit to local people—a proposition that is by no means obvious at present, because most of the benefits of tourism are not experienced in the vicinity of the Park. Thus, economic justice may not only be done, but also be seen to be done. The availability of a ready supply of cheap meat (Plate 12.2) might also greatly reduce the incentive to poaching.

It would be ill-advised and illogical to restrict this cropping to the peripheral zone outside the Park. If cropping is to be done it should utilize the total resource, not merely a part of it. Provided that realistic and rational quotas are set there would be no danger to the survival of animal populations in the Park. Perhaps the most telling argument in favour of evenly cropping the total resource is that restricting cropping to the peripheral zone outside the park would tend to compound the problems within the park by promoting a centripetal build-up of numbers.

Two of the main animal species that should be exploited (elephant and buffalo) in fact move seasonally in and out of the park and there is likely to be a continuing need for conservation cropping of elephant and hippopotamus within the Park for many years, if not indefinitely. Populations of other species do not justify inclusion in a cropping scheme at present. However, the populations of Uganda kob and hartebeest, each numbering several thousands, would support a large sustained yield if a way can be found to crop them economically. Bindernagel (1968, pp. 164, 165) proposes a cropping rate of 20 per cent for these two species and feels that this may be unduly conservative for the Uganda kob. On the basis of our population estimates (Table 4.1) an offtake of one fifth would represent annual offtakes of 650 and 930 for kob and hartebeest respectively.

12.1.3.1.   *Elephant.* In order to allow habitat regeneration to proceed, it will be necessary to attempt to hold the elephant population at a level below the 'carrying capacity' of the habitat. We estimate that after completing the reduction cropping proposed, the residual population on the south bank might eventually sustain an offtake of 6–8 per cent per year. However, the evidence suggests that initially there would be little increase in recruitment, as the elephant population appears to be regulating maximally in response to the habitat change and high densities, and it is expected to be many years before the habitat is more than marginally favourable to elephant population increase. By virtue of the long-term nature of the change in parameters affecting recruitment, there may well be a period before there is any net population increase to be harvested, and further cropping during this period would produce a further net decrease in the population. For this reason it is important that the dynamics of the population and of the habitat should be closely monitored, by means of aerial counts, by vegetation studies, including aerial photographic transects and ground observations, and by analysis of the crop (age structure and reproductive parameters). The techniques have already been developed and are available for use.

If these further studies confirm that there is a net annual surplus, further cropping operations should be carried out. With a residual population of 4200 elephants, a net annual surplus of 5 per cent would represent an annual quota of, say, 200 animals, representing a gross income of £19 600 a year.[†] It may also be necessary to alter the level of cropping from time to time, in order to maintain or increase the habitat diversity, while conserving the elephant populations.

The quotas should be specified geographically as in the reduction cropping so as to prevent concentrations of cropping effort in areas which are easy of access or otherwise favourable to the cropper. The block quotas should also be subject to annual review as a result of the monitoring operations.

12.1.3.2. *Hippopotamus.* We estimate that, from Year 5 of the cropping programme for hippopotamus above the Murchison Falls, 6 per cent of the population should be cropped annually, that is, 250 animals. This is a conservative offtake and should again be subject to annual revision in the light of information from the monitoring processes. It should be divided proportionally between the respective sections.

A quota of 250 above the Murchison Falls, of which half are to be taken on the south bank, and 25 to be taken on the south bank below the falls, means an annual quota of 150 to be taken in Bunyoro. This should produce a gross return of £3600—£6600 according to the marketing arrangements, although it is unlikely that the more sophisticated methods of marketing would be economic unless other species were also being cropped.

12.1.3.3. *Buffalo.* There is insufficient knowledge on which to base firm recommendations for a sustained-yield cropping programme based on the buffalo populations of North Bunyoro. Thus, only one reliable estimate of the population is available, which is subject to a large confidence interval (14 291 ± 4996, Table 4.1); and practical experience of methods for large-scale cropping of the species is lacking. We do not know whether the offtake should be confined to bachelor males, to mature animals of both sexes, or involve the taking of complete herds; arguments could be advanced in favour of each of these possibilities. Nevertheless it seems that there is a case for embarking on a pilot cropping scheme based on buffalo. However, we are not satisfied that the methods employed by the Game Department cropping scheme in the Aswa—Lolim area are economically or ecologically sound; and even if they are, they may not be applicable to North Bunyoro including the National Park.

To gain some idea of the potential, let us assume that there are 14 000 buffalo in the area, a figure that should be checked by further aerial counts. Let us suppose that 50 per cent of the population are mature animals, at a mean weight of 500 kg and subject to a natural mortality rate of 10 per cent annually (Grimsdell

† Now much more.

1969). Let us also assume, with Reinwald and Hemingway (1968), that the potentially realizable yield is 90 per cent of the total number or biomass of adult animals dying per year. The annual quota to be set (by hunting blocks) would then be 630. At an average gross value of £17 (Appendix F) the value would be £10 710 annually.

12.1.4.   *Summary of proposed cropping programmes*

The estimated reduction and sustained yield cropping outputs from the proposed programme over a 10 year period are as follows:

Years 1–4	*Gross return (U£)*	
3500 elephant	343 000	
3750 hippopotamus	90 000	
2500 buffalo, say,	42 500	
		£475 500
Years 5–10		
1200 elephant	117 600	
900 hippopotamus	21 600	
3800 buffalo, say,	64 600	
		£203 700
Total for 10 year period		£679 200

The potential gross return would be realized only if the operations were planned on this long-term basis, and would be reduced by some £100 000 if sustained cropping of elephants at an annual level of 5 per cent were not indicated. In order to mount an efficient operation and to obtain the maximum return, there would be need of fairly heavy capital investment and heavy recurrent expenses would be incurred. A cost analysis is beyond the scope of this book but we assume that this might be of the order of 50 per cent of the gross return, in which case the net profit for the 10 year period should be about £340 000.[†]

After the initial four years there would be a sudden decrease in the gross return from about £119 000 per year to about £34 000 per year (or to £14 000 per year if sustained cropping of elephant is not undertaken).

During the period of sustained-yield management, the costs are expected to be lower than during the initial period, but even if they remain at 50 per cent, the net return from 2727 square kilometres (1053 square miles) is £17 000 per year (£62 per square kilometre, £160 per square mile). This compares quite favourably with the expected net annual income per square mile from the Budongo Forest over the period of the current working plan, 1964–74 (Philip 1965).

It is not for us to decide how the programme should be implemented, but we would recommend that the initial cropping at least should be carried out by private enterprise under contract to the National Parks and under the control of the Parks Administration, in conjunction with the National Parks Conservation

† Very much higher at current (1973) prices. See Appendix F.

Cropping Unit. Again the Budongo Forest shows a precedent for this type of private enterprise, the saw-millers operating on a royalty system. This has also worked well in relation to cropping in Murchison in recent years. In this connection Reinwald and Hemingway (1968) remark:

this is the scheme best suited to private enterprise. A Game Department or National Park which has arrived at a conservation decision that required the removal of so many head of an animal in so many years' time, in order to reduce a herd, would be well advised to set a fair price on these animals and allow them to be harvested by an experienced private firm whose aim would be to make a profit out of them at the price they bought them. National Parks and Game Departments, after all, are not in the hunting or meat packing business, and as amateurs on a scheme of only a few years' duration are not likely to prove as economically efficient as a private firm that is continuously engaged in such schemes.

The National Parks cropping unit could collaborate in the large-scale reduction cropping and so acquire the expertise necessary to perform the subsequent sustained cropping operations.

Reinwald and Hemingway suggest that continuous conservation cropping schemes 'are best left to National park wardens who can operate them so as to cause the least conflict with the overall aims of park management', and that 'the conservation authorities need not be concerned with a profit motive'. We agree with this in principle, although in the present scheme an average crop of nearly 1000 animals a year of these three species is involved, and would certainly be achieved more efficiently and profitably by engaging private enterprise to undertake a short-period operation, lasting 2—3 months each year. Although the main objective of the scheme proposed is management for conservation, we do not believe that the administration should shy at making a profit in this field. Funds will be needed to monitor the effects of the cropping scheme on habitats and populations.

It is for the Administration to decide, after taking all relevant factors into account, what proportion of the profits should be spent on conservation management and research. However, we strongly urge that imputations of a profit motive (to be expected from 'preservationists') should be neutralized by investing the proceeds in research and management, including fire control and elephant barriers.

12.2. The forest reserves

The importance of the forests in North Bunyoro cannot be too highly stressed. From an economic point of view they contribute a substantial revenue to the Uganda Government (by means of royalties paid by the saw-millers) equivalent to over half the total forest revenue in Uganda. They provide employment directly through the Forest Department and indirectly through the saw-millers, which is not equalled by any other industry in Bunyoro. The Budongo Forest is an important catchment area for Lake Albert, indirectly affecting the large fishing industry on that lake, and there are other valid reasons which have already been discussed, for conserving these forests.

Only a very rough estimate of the value of the present standing timber in these forests can be given. 'There is about 65 million cubic feet of exploitable timber in Budongo valued at over £7 million at present forest fees. This value is being increased annually through silvicultural treatment, but unless elephants are excluded or, at least, their numbers reduced, the capital value and the increment of the forest is badly threatened' (extract from Forest Department paper quoted *in litt.* by A. W. M. Watt, 11 June 1969). When one considers that the refining methods introduced should increase the volume of timber by nearly five times, then it is clear that Budongo is a tremendous asset.

It would appear that the effect of elephants on the forest, particularly in those areas where there is an initial heavy canopy opening through felling and refining, is extremely detrimental to the production of sound timber. The amount of damage has been shown to vary, apparently according to the amount of canopy opening, from 23 per cent in an area subjected to a light canopy opening, to 51 per cent where the canopy opening is heavy. A single plot sampled in a forest (Bugoma) where the elephant movement into the forest is not intense, indicated a total damage incidence of only 12 per cent (Chapter 11). The majority of damage is to the young saplings and poles.

Because some species are more liable to damage than others, there is in process, in the treated areas, a gradual conversion of a stand dominated by species such as *Chrysophyllum albidum, Khaya anthotheca,* and *Cordia millenii*, to one dominated by *Holoptelea grandis and Olea welwitschii.*

The results of the pilot study on *Cynometra alexandri* are also of considerable interest, even though the sample relates only to a very small part of the forest, and a comprehensive study should be undertaken in order to determine whether or not the *Cynometra alexandri* climax is elephant-induced. If this is confirmed then it would transform our ideas of some aspects of the ecology of the Budongo Forest and would have far-reaching effects on the management procedures of the Forest Department.

Although no recent damage sampling has been carried out in either the Rabongo or the Pabidi Forests, it is evident that there has been a progressive deterioration in the quality and state of these forests. Budongo, although at present heavily damaged, would soon recover with protection by exclusion of elephants, and within a few years would show little effect of the elephant damage, although it will have lost up to 15 years increment in certain areas. Pabidi would also benefit from protection although it would take longer to recover than Budongo, but it is doubtful if Rabongo would show much apparent benefit from protection, at least for many years. The soil has become so compacted that establishment of tree species is difficult and it would probably be necessary to undertake some soil disturbance and/or planting in addition to the protection measures, in order to encourage the growth of tree seedlings in preference to grass growth.

It is imperative that protection measures for all the forests are implemented quickly. From the point of view of the Budongo and Pabidi forests this is required because of their economic importance, which will probably increase rapidly in the next thirty years as the world's supply of timber decreases. The Rabongo, however, must be protected in order to preserve what is the only area of high forest in the National Park. To allow the Rabongo Forest to be destroyed would be for the Parks administration to fail to achieve their aim and duty of maintaining ecological diversity. This small area of forest also has considerable tourist potential (as do all the other forest blocks) but it has not yet been exploited in this way.

To consider the protection of the Rabongo Forest first, we recommend that this forest should have a barrier placed around it very soon if it is to survive— preferably an elephant-proof ditch and fence and an effective fire break. On completion of this barrier, which should be located so as to permit expansion of the forest within it, any elephants remaining within the barrier must be shot. At the same time trials should be made of methods to encourage regeneration of trees, including chisel-ploughing to relieve soil compaction and allow tree seedling establishment, preferably combined with tree planting. Further action to encourage expansion of Rabongo would depend on the results of these experiments, which if successful could be extended to other suitable areas within the National Park.

Action within the Forest Reserves must of necessity be more extensive. It might be argued that a forest as large as Budongo has the capacity at least to support a small elephant population and that its impact on the forest could be reduced by altering the management techniques. At present, by opening up large blocks of forest, elephant are encouraged to remain in these young regeneration areas, whereas under natural conditions forest-living elephants probably follow a shifting pattern of use, as randomly located small clearings appear naturally, with consequent patches of young regeneration.

Would it be possible to change from the present system of exploitation to one in which the total area of forest opened up each year remained the same, but was distributed throughout the forest as a series of small areas? The Forest Department give a categorical 'No' in answer. In their opinion the current system is the optimum means of managing the forest. Development other than on the consolidated lines at present used would mean a tremendous increase in road maintenance and building and would be economically unacceptable both to the Forest Department and to the saw-millers. Nor would this necessarily help to solve the problem. Alternatively, it has been shown that once the trees reach approximately ten years of age they are much less at risk of damage; would it therefore be possible to protect the young regeneration areas by means of ditches or fences for the first ten years after canopy opening? This would again be uneconomic, and neither of these hypothetical solutions takes account of the forest edge, which will continue to recede rapidly under the present influences.

We must remember that the primary objective of management is to produce valuable timber as economically as possible. We consider that intensive management of the forest, involving timber stand improvement (salvage felling, treatment, and the creation of large areas of young regeneration) is incompatible with use of the forest by elephant. This is generally agreed in principle for Kenya forests (Logie and Jones 1968) and in Tanzania (Procter 1968), as well as in Uganda. Excluding the 'resident' population, the majority of elephants using the forest probably do so only because conditions outside the forest are unfavourable; they are at a high density; there is seasonal insufficiency and lack of variety of food, and very little shade. Surely, in the long term, this part of the problem can best be solved by tackling it at its root, that is, outside the forest, by improving the relationship between the elephant populations and the habitat, as recommended earlier.

Excluding economic considerations and tackling the problem from an ecological point of view, if the elephants continue to use the forest in any numbers, it will be destroyed as we know it now and converted to scrub vegetation. To permit this is conservationally unsound and it would have considerable repercussions on other animal populations in the forest. For example, if Budongo develops under elephant use into a forest dominated by species such as *Holoptelea grandis* (which is not greatly liked by chimpanzees), there is a danger of seriously reducing the present large chimpanzee population.

The question then arises as to whether we are justified in excluding elephants from the Budongo Forest if they are dependent on it to some extent for food and shelter or for breeding. To what extent are the forest elephants resident and different from the elephants of the surrounding grasslands? It has been demonstrated that the North Bunyoro elephant population as a whole is not critically dependent on the Budongo Forest (Chapter 5). This investigation indicates that fewer than 1000 elephants use the forest seasonally, probably about 800, and about 325 ± 75 are 'residents', possibly hybrids between former truly forest elephants (*L.a. cyclotis*) and the bush elephant (*L.a. africana*). The total population excluding the forest 'residents' is estimated at about 8000–9000. On these figures it appears that less than 10 per cent of the open range (grassland and woodland) populations use the forest seasonally. Furthermore, it appears that these seasonal visitors are mainly from the peripheral high-density areas.

As we have seen, there has been an intensive programme of control shooting in the vicinity of the forest by the Uganda Game Department (in response to requests by the Forest Department) since 1957. This has apparently had the effect of reducing elephant use of the Forest Reserves, including the grassland areas, by up to 50 per cent, but with the progress in forest management and the production of extensive areas of young regeneration, the smaller numbers of elephant appear to have had a much greater effect on the forest than a larger population formerly had.

The Forest Department appear to have assumed that the main problem concerned elephant entering the forest from the National Park. The building of an elephant ditch, or a combination of fencing and ditching, has been under serious consideration despite the high costs of such development (estimated at about £1100 per mile (Woodley 1965). They have been deterred by the costs, by uncertainty about the relation of the elephant population to the forest, and also by the desire to maintain representatives of the natural ecosystems in the forest. In the 1955–64 working plan for Budongo, however, the larger game were excepted from this objective (Philip 1965), which means that at that time the Forest Department had accepted the possibility that elephant might have to be excluded from the forest. If, as the present study indicates, there is a 'resident' population of up to 400 elephants centred on Budongo, the creation of a barrier would not of itself necessarily solve the problem, and in the absence of complementary action, might aggravate it.

Where there are dense populations of elephant it is known that the forest edge is stationary or retreating, although the forest is expanding in the absence of elephant. In the absence of elephant there are therefore strong grounds for supposing that the grassland areas in the Forest Reserves could in time be re-afforested (naturally or by planting), so as to enlarge the forests.

We therefore recommend the elimination and exclusion of elephant from the forests to be carried out in three phases.

First, the intensive cropping of elephants between the National Park boundary and the forests, within the grassland block of the Forest Reserve (Kitigo, Kaniyo, and Pabidi). This would have the objective, not of deterring the elephants from entering the forests, but of eliminating that segment of the surrounding populations which uses the forest. This will probably involve the shooting of several hundred elephants as they enter the Forest Reserves. It will be closely related to the reduction cropping of some 1800 elephants in Blocks 5–10 (Table 12.1), which will probably result in a reduction in the numbers approaching the forest. For this reason no precise figures can be given, but we estimate that it will involve removing perhaps 500 elephants. If the National Parks decide not to reduce their elephant population, the number to be cropped in the Forest Reserve might be as high as 1000. The population in these grasslands should be monitored by aerial counts (at least quarterly) and by the resumption of elephant track counts in the forest. The latter will provide a seasonal index of elephant density by which to judge the effect of these measures.

The second phase, to be carried out during or after Phase 1 (irrespective of whether Phase 3 is implemented) is the construction of an elephant barrier (ditch, fence, or both) along the northern boundary of the Budongo Forest Reserve. Our reason for advocating the construction of a barrier is that political changes outside the Forest Reserves and National Park could result in pressure on the elephant populations, causing a change in their relation to the forest and an increase in elephant use of the forest. Also in the long term, if the forest is to expand, a barrier between National Park and Forest Reserve will be needed. The cost of this barrier might be shared by the National Parks and Forest Department.

The third phase, which should be dependent on the results of a further appraisal of elephant damage in the young regeneration areas, would comprise the elimination of the 'resident' population in Budongo.

In these elephant cropping operations the previous method of employing Game Scouts should be replaced by the method advocated for the reduction cropping in the National Park and surrounding areas. The elimination cropping operations should produce on a conservative estimate a gross return of about £49 000 from Phase 1, and about £30 000 from Phase 3, the net profits to the Forest Department being used towards the construction of approximately 48 kilometres (30 miles) of elephant barrier between the National Park and Forest Reserves.

12.3.   Fire control

The effects of grass fires in enhancing and accelerating the habitat damage caused by elephant have been discussed in Chapter 2. Draconic proposals have now been made involving the extremely distasteful task.of reducing the elephant populations, and we believe that this action alone has a reasonable prospect of reversing current trends of habitat deterioration in North Bunyoro. But clearly to obtain the optimum effect from the reduction cropping it must be accompanied by fire control. By this we mean the prevention or regulation of periodic burns. The present annual burns are too frequent to permit a rapid response of the habitats to a reduction in elephant densities. Despite the fact that 'we have had considerable success with our controlled burning programme over the last two years . . . most of the success has been due to early rains in 1968 and even earlier rains in 1969' (R. J. Wheater, *in litt.* May 1969).

In the case of patches of relict high forest, their decline will continue in the presence of even very limited burning, because the forest tree species are extremely sensitive to fire; where the protective ecotone of bush and successional growth has been destroyed, as in the case of these relict patches, even 'cool' burns attack the forest trees (Plates 2.4, 2.10, Chapter 2; 11.4, Chapter 11). Fire control is therefore essential to complement the reduction cropping and falls into two categories—fire prevention and fire regulation.

With few exceptions fires are caused by man, either deliberately or accidentally. Intentional fires are by far the most serious, because they are usually set well away from roads or tracks and if not contained at an early stage may become very extensive. They are in general associated with poaching, and it follows that the elimination of poaching must be a necessary concomitant of any fire prevention programme. Poaching is rife in the Murchison Falls National Park, but it has not yet received the amount of attention it has in other East African National Parks. Perhaps this is because the type of hunting has not yet endangered the

existence of any particular species, apart from the crocodile (Cott 1968); along
the river anti-poaching measures are now being tightened up. The extremely poor
communications within the Park contribute to this state of affairs.

With the urgent need to prevent fires, the suppression of poaching now assumes great importance. Efficient patrolling and policing of the Park and other
conservation areas are the most important steps in bringing poaching under
control. Two basic methods are in use: first, outposts, involving the dispersal of
rangers in small groups over a wide area, operating from fixed bases; and secondly,
field forces, the concentration of the ranger force into a larger, fully mobile,
centrally based force, able to operate anywhere within the area. The former is
the least effective, and has a number of serious disadvantages. Poachers operating
in large gangs cannot effectively be stopped or arrested by a group of three or
four men; in some cases poachers have actually chased ranger patrols. Operating
on foot from a fixed base limits effective patrolling to within a relatively short
radius of the base, the rangers are out of contact with senior staff, and vice versa.

These, among others, are arguments in favour of a strong, centrally based field
force. To be effective it must be well led and disciplined, and its creation and
operation would initially occupy a Warden full time. It would require its own
independent transport and tentage. We envisage two sections, each with a strength
of 15 men, to operate in the Park, the Karuma Falls Controlled Hunting Areas,
and the Forest Reserves. This would involve cooperation between the various
authorities.

There are however advantages in the system of Ranger Posts. They result in
men being in many areas of the Park who are capable of dealing with the normal run
of poachers who do not come in large gangs. Probably the best arrangement would
be to have a number of Ranger Posts combined with a central Field Force based at
Paraa on which the Rangers could call for assistance.

Accidental fires are even more difficult to prevent, but in general they occur
along the tracks and roads. Travellers in transit through the area, tourists, and
Park, Forest Department, and Game Department staff should be made aware of
the importance of fire, and its undesirability. Burning is a long-established practice
in the vicinity of settlement and habitation, and in these areas it would be more
realistic to concentrate on attempting to limit the spread of fires.

Fires can be contained and controlled by an effective fire-break system, regularly maintained. The more intensive the system, the greater the degree of control
but its extent is determined by financial feasibility. This would be a reasonable
investment for income from the proposed cropping operations. In these long-grass
areas fires are very fierce and while the fire-breaks may halt fires, this is by no
means certain. It is therefore necessary to have sufficient manpower on hand to
extinguish sparks that are wind-blown across fire-breaks. Thus, a mobile fire-
fighting team (on a seasonal basis) is as necessary to an effective fire control
programme as are the fire-breaks themselves.

In the long-grass areas of North Bunyoro the most effective type of fire-break consists of two parallel roads or tracks, between which the vegetation is kept very short by cutting (preferably) or careful burning. In addition to serving as fire-breaks, an extensive track system would greatly facilitate anti-poaching operations, administration, and tourist access. The smaller the fire-broken blocks the more effectively fires can be contained and the easier it is to operate a rotational burning system. The size of the optimal block in terms of finance and practicability can only be learned from experience. Rivers and swamps can be utilized as part of the fire-break system, and blocks on the periphery, along main roads and surrounding areas of particular concern, should be no larger than about 26 square kilometres (10 square miles) in area; internal blocks could be larger.

In the dry season a labour force should be constantly on hand with adequate transport, to move when required to the site of any fires reported. Throughout the dry season a permanent watch from high ground (such as Rabongo and the escarpment) should be kept and this could be augmented by regular aerial patrols. This team would also be responsible for maintaining the fire-breaks.

In the vicinity of the relict forest patches, such as Rabongo, it would be advisable not to attempt to eliminate fire, but carefully to burn back each year under suitable conditions, from the forest edge to a surrounding fire-break, to coincide with the fence and/or ditch proposed earlier. This burning must be under the immediate control of a Park Warden, or other responsible person, and should not be left to junior staff. After the reduction, or elimination of the elephant population in the vicinity has allowed the natural forest-edge ecotone to develop, this process will become easier and the forests should eventually become self-maintaining even in the presence of peripheral fire.

Complete fire prevention could initially be attempted in some areas where there is a high-density of geophytic growth. This experiment should comprise a series of blocks, each of about 400 hectare (1000 acres), adequately protected by well-maintained fire-breaks. It is probable that after reduction of the elephant population and after several years of fire prevention, they would be self-maintaining even if fires did occur, because they would have grown through the young regeneration period when risk from fire is greatest.

Elsewhere in the Park, Forest Reserves, and Karuma Falls Controlled Hunting Area, fire control should initially attempt to regulate burning on a rotation of one year in two. Experiments should be initiated to establish what is the optimum burning regime for this area. At first some blocks will be burnt more frequently than others; some that remain unburnt must be intentionally burnt on a two year rotation. Otherwise very fierce fires may subsequently develop.

These recommendations relate to North Bunyoro, which is the subject of this book, but there is an equal or even more urgent need to improve fire control north of the River Nile in Acholi, especially in the Murchison Falls National Park.

12.4.   Discussion

We regard the current situation as regards conservation in North Bunyoro as extremely unpromising. Without prompt and effective action it can be expected to deteriorate rapidly as the effects of various trends—elephant overpopulation, habitat deterioration, forest management, fire, poaching, and above all the alienation of land by the human population expansion—progressively increase and reinforce one another.

While any one of the measures proposed will have a beneficial effect, only the enthusiastic, early implementation of these measures as an integrated scheme can give any hope of success in the long term for the area as a whole. The demonstration of a viable multi-resource land-use programme would also have the greatest impact on world opinion and be more likely to attract international assistance. In submitting our proposals we have assumed that the separate authorities concerned would work together to bring about a rational integrated solution to their common problems. However, if interdepartmental cooperation proves not to be realizable, the National Parks and Forest Department could undertake separate programmes with a reasonable prospect of success, although it is difficult to see how the other areas could be conserved. In this respect the Forest Department is probably in the most favourable position to proceed alone.

If implementation of the proposals for the areas immediately surrounding the National Park, including the Karuma Controlled Hunting Area, proves not to be feasible, the National Park authorities should consider seriously whether they should not fence and/or ditch the remainder of their boundary, except where it is contiguous with the Forest Reserve (which we have proposed should be fenced and/or ditched by the Forest Department), while at the same time reducing the elephant population to the recommended levels. By taking the initiative in this way, at an additional cost of, say £40 000 (to be financed from the cropping returns) they would lessen the magnitude of the problem facing them when subsistence or group agriculture comes to extend to the Park boundary. This encirclement is inevitable if present trends continue, and if an alternative form of land-use for the surrounding areas cannot be developed.

In this connection we are strongly in favour of the proposals advanced by the Agricultural Development Service (Anon 1967) in a feasibility study for a development programme in terms of cattle ranching and game cropping in areas surrounding the National Park. This would ensure that the Park is not overwhelmed by pressures on the surrounding unused land (Wheater 1968b). It could be flexible and compatible with other forms of agricultural production besides livestock.

Briefly, this scheme allows for the development of about 5200 square kilometres (2000 square miles) adjacent to the Murchison Falls National Park in Acholi and Bunyoro. It envisages legislation to declare the region a Conservation Area with a single statutory Controlling Authority. A central beef breeding ranch of 520 square kilometres (200 square miles) would be developed to supply quality breeding stock to a well organized outranching scheme, and immature stock to fattening areas where game and beef steers would share the available grazing. 'Scientifically planned game cropping' is integral to the scheme and domestic stock would be restricted to 30 per cent of the possible numbers that could be supported as a monoculture, so that competition would be negligible and the interests of the game preserved.

The capital cost is estimated at £1·431 million,[†] although it would be self-financing in the long run, and it would require external finance to the extent of £940 000. On maturity at Year 23 the output per year of domestic stock would gross £649 270, that is £320 per square mile. The yield from game cropping from the outset would be £125 000 gross, or £63 per square mile; this includes cropping within the National Park.

The net annual income from both sources is estimated at £190 per square mile, not very different from our estimate of the probable net income from game cropping alone on a sustained yield basis after the completion of the reduction cropping (£160). This is partly due to the fact that the gross value per head for elephant is set at half our figure, and the basic figures used by Agricultural Services are 'little better than calculated guesses because the information is not yet available from research . . . the data used is very conservative' (Anon 1967). The necessity for initial reduction cropping was not considered and the A.D.S. scheme refers to a larger area, most of the game cropping in fact to be carried out north of the Victoria Nile in Acholi. As applied to North Bunyoro in fact the scheme should produce a more equal net return from livestock and game, totalling about £300 per square mile per year. The gross return from the peripheral areas under cattle ranching alone should be about £1070 per square mile, corresponding to a net income of about £400 per square mile.[†]

The combined ranching–game cropping project has the overriding advantage that it would give local people a financial interest in conserving the area in terms of multiple land-use. It would stabilize the area available to game at the present level, greatly assist in overcoming the poaching problem, and make a very considerable contribution to the control of fire.

Perhaps the greatest drawback is that it is contingent on an effective tsetse clearance programme being planned and implemented. Without this it would not be possible to maintain domestic livestock free from trypanosomiasis. It would involve additional capital expenditure, possibly of the order of £300 000, assuming spraying to average £150 per square mile (Glover 1965, p. 54). According to Nash (1969), however, the cost of spraying *Acacia* savannah in Ankole, Uganda was £276 per square mile. If the alternative method of bush clearance were chosen, it would of course nullify many of the advantages of the scheme from a conservation point of view, and also would be very expensive. In view of the high tick populations we have observed, control of this vector would also be essential.

We understand that this imaginative scheme is not to be implemented, and have put forward our proposals in the light of this decision. However, in view of the more favourable financial estimate that the present study suggests for it, we recommend that its feasibility be re-examined in the light of this new information. It need not in fact alter the present proposals, but supplement them.

In any case we would like to borrow one idea from the A.D.S. scheme, and

, † All values given are at 1967 prices and should be uprated.

suggest that the area of the present elephant range be declared a Conservation Area, with a statutory Authority on which the following organizations would be represented: National Parks, Forest Department, Game Department, the Local Authority, and an internationally recognized ecologist. The area should be enlarged to include Murchison Falls National Park, North elephant range and surrounding areas. At a later date we hope to submit detailed proposals for this northern elephant range. (The elephant ranges are taken as the ecological units or over-all land-use regions, because it is felt that, in each case, they best define the problem area.) At a later date the responsibility of the Conservation Authority could be enlarged to include other forms of land-use, if desirable.

12.5. Summary

We confine our comments to ecological and economic considerations, because although aesthetic and cultural factors are important, we consider that immediate economic considerations are of overriding importance and will determine the survival of this important wildlife area. The National Park and adjacent unoccupied areas are considered separately from the Forest Reserves in formulating management recommendations.

The gross tourist return from National Parks in Uganda was estimated at £1738 per square mile for 1970, compared with a current gross return of £422 per square mile for the Budongo Forest and £383 per square mile from a proposed ranching—game cropping scheme. Current revenue from sport hunting is low. As cultivation comes to occupy more and more land up to the Park boundary the conflict between wildlife and agriculture will intensify; crop destruction will increasingly prejudice local farmers against wildlife and poaching can be expected to increase. The construction of an elephant-proof barrier has been recommended initially along the western boundary of the Park but later to be extended.

The case for conservation cropping of elephant and hippopotamus in the grasslands is summarized and specific proposals made. In the case of elephant the removal of 3500 animals over a four year period is proposed. This should be carried out in two phases, first to reduce the population density at the periphery of the range to that in the central zone, and then to reduce the over-all population over the whole range to an average density of 1·5 per square kilometre. Although a management strategy involving age-specific cropping is desirable, so that the remaining population would approximate to a stable age distribution, it is not feasible. The developed method of random non-selective removal of complete family units is therefore recommended and indeed has some advantages over age-specific management in the short term.

Further reduction cropping of hippopotamus is also recommended, with the objective of achieving an average grazing density of hippopotamus of 7·7 per square kilometre. Detailed quotas for sections of the River Nile and control areas (in which no cropping is to be carried out) are proposed. It is assumed that the meat will be sold for local consumption, as before.

Next, sustained-yield cropping is discussed. There is likely to be a continuing need for this in the management of elephant and hippopotamus populations to conserve habitats. It is a form of land-use that need not conflict with tourism and there are strong arguments for setting up a sustained-yield programme to create a buffer zone around the Park and to demonstrate that National Parks can be of direct economic benefit to local people. The sustained offtake of elephant might involve the removal of up to 5 per cent of the population annually, and in the case of hippopotamus about 6 per cent. Knowledge of buffalo is limited, but a pilot cropping scheme is proposed, based on an offtake of 9 per cent of adult animals.

Over a ten year period the proposed (and we believe essential) programme of reduction and sustained-yield cropping should give a yield of 4700 elephant, 4650 hippopotamus, and 6300 buffalo, worth about £680 000. The net profit should be about £340 000.[†] These cropping programmes should be accompanied by monitoring of populations and habitats and be subject to annual review in the light of further knowledge. It is urged that the proceeds of the cropping should be invested in research and management, including fire control and elephant barriers.

Turning to the forests, the Rabongo Forest must be protected in order to preserve the only area of high forest in the National Park. This can best be achieved by the construction of an elephant-proof ditch and fence and an effective fire-break. At the same time experiments into methods of encouraging the forest regeneration should be conducted.

Action within the Forest Reserves must be more extensive. The present value of exploitable timber in Budongo is £7 million (at 1969 fees) and it is increasing annually through silvicultural treatment. This is seriously threatened by elephant, which are extremely detrimental to the production of sound timber. Several solutions are considered and it is concluded that intensive management of the forest is incompatible with its use by elephant. The North Bunyoro elephants are not critically dependent on the forest, although there are thought to be about 300 residents. The action proposed is to exclude seasonal elephant visitors from the forest and to eliminate the resident population.

As the first phase, in conjunction with the reduction cropping of elephants in the grasslands of the Park and adjacent area, a further 500 may have to be removed within the grassland blocks of the Forest Reserves. The second phase is the construction of an elephant-proof ditch and fence (extending over 30 miles) as a barrier between the residual Park population and the Forest. The third phase, which should be dependent on a further appraisal of elephant damage in the treated areas, would comprise the elimination of the resident population in Budongo. The present method of control by Game Scouts should be replaced by rationally organized cropping to produce an economic yield. Phase 1 should produce a gross return of about £49 000,[†] Phase 3, if implemented, about

† With the recent dramatic increase in the price of ivory (see Appendix F) all values given are very conservative.

£30 000;[†] the net profits to be used towards the construction of the elephant barrier.

Fire control is essential to complement the reduction cropping, and proposals are made for fire prevention and fire regulation. This involves suppressing the activities of poachers, who are the main cause of fires. A Ranger Force organized in a number of Ranger Posts combined with a centrally based, mobile Field Force, is recommended. Both deliberate and accidental fires can be contained by an effective system of fire-breaks and this is discussed in practical terms. Complete fire protection should be attempted in some areas with high densities of geophytes. Elsewhere rotational burning will be necessary and experiments should be initiated to establish the optimum burning regime for this area.

† With the recent dramatic increase in the price of ivory (see Appendix F) all values given are very conservative.

Appendices

Appendix A. Aerial counting

A.1. *Sample counts of large herbivores*

The theoretical advantages of counting samples rather than total area are discussed by Jolly (1969). Stratified random strip sampling from an aircraft has been used in East Africa by Watson (1967), Watson, Graham, and Parker (1969), and Watson, Parker, and Allan (1969), the latter paper being concerned primarily with elephant in the Mkomazi area of Tanzania. Siniff and Skoog (1964) preferred to use stratified random quadrat samples for counting caribou and Watson, Parker, and Graham (unpublished) found distinct advantages of this method over strip sampling, for estimating populations of ungulates in Narok District, Kenya.

We have used aerial random quadrat sampling for elephant, buffalo, hartebeest, Uganda kob, waterbuck, and warthog. Since funds were very limited it was not possible to weight the distribution of sampling between strata as recommended by Cochran (1963). For example, the elephant-density strata were known to be different from those relating to other species (Figs 4.1—4.6). However, the uniform size of the sampling units permitted re-stratification by species in the light of field observations on animal distributions. The advantages of quadrats as opposed to strips are as follows.

1. The observer can stay over a given quadrat for as long as necessary to obtain an accurate count. The disadvantages associated with forward speed (as opposed to circling) and a single direction of travel in strip sampling, are removed.
2. The difficulty of trying to retain a number of differing 'search images' for different species simultaneously is avoided as each quadrat can be searched for one species at a time.
3. The prolonged circling of an aircraft over the quadrat makes any cryptic animals reveal themselves.
4. The difficulty of maintaining the constant strip width required in strip sampling is removed.
5. Altitude can be varied to suit the observer and the species of animal observed.

In the current population estimates, the quadrats were 10 square kilometres (3·9 square miles) in size. The entire area was divided into a grid of 270 such squares, each numbered consecutively. Quadrats were selected randomly (using a table of random numbers) until approximately 25 per cent cover was obtained. In the event of a number being selected two or three times this was recorded and the results of counting that quadrat used as many times as selected in computing the final results. Thus, 61 quadrats were selected, four of them twice and two

three times, making 69 in all. The aircraft used was a Cessna 185 piloted by
I.S.C.P. and observations were made by R. J. Wheater.

Estimates and standard errors were computed for the various species from the
expressions given by Jolly (1969):

$$\hat{Y} = \sum_i N_i \, \bar{y}_i$$

$$\text{and var } (\hat{Y}) = \sum_i \frac{N_i(N_i - n_i)}{n_i} \frac{1}{n_i - 1} \left\{ \sum y_i^2 - \frac{(\sum y_i)^2}{n_i} \right\}$$

where $\hat{Y}$ is the estimated population of animals

N_i is the total number of quadrats in the ith stratum

n_i is the number of quadrats sampled in the stratum

y_i is the number of animals counted in an individual quadrat

$\bar{y}_i$ is the average number of animals per quadrat over the n_i quadrats
sampled

Σ_i denotes summation over the n_i sampled quadrats

var $(\hat{Y})$ is the variance of the estimate

A.2. *Complete counts of elephants*

Three complete area counts were made in November 1966, February 1967,
and August 1967. The aircraft used on the first count was a Cessna 182 and on
the second and third counts a Cessna 185. On all three counts the right-hand door
of the aircraft was removed to facilitate observation. On the first count the aircraft was flown by A. D. Graham with I.S.C. Parker and I. Tippett as observers.
On the second count the aircraft was flown by I.S.C. Parker with R. J. Wheater
and R. Backus as observers, and on the third count the pilot was again
I.S.C. Parker, with R.J. Wheater as observer. In all three counts the pilot
assisted in observation.

The over-all area was divided into a series of 12 blocks, each defined by
obvious boundaries such as streams, roads, escarpments, and cultivation
(Fig. 5.1). For counting, these blocks were subdivided into smaller areas defined
by natural features. Each sub-block was covered by a series of parallel flights,
the distance between which was governed by the altitude at which the aircraft
was flying, the density of elephant, and the vegetation. Block 12 was not covered
in the first two counts, because it was thought that there were few elephants in
this block, and that they were separate from the other communities because the
human settlement along the Karuma-Kiryandongo road (Fig. 5.2) presented a
barrier which elephant would not cross. Information from the Game Department,
Masindi, and the high result from the second count suggested that this assumption
was incorrect, and Block 12 was included in the third count.

In all three series of flights, the aircraft were flown at an indicated air speed of
120 m.p.h., although on occasion when larger herds required more intensive
observation, this was reduced to as low as 65 m.p.h. In open grassland where

elephant densities were moderate or high (such areas comprised about 70 per cent of the areas counted), flight-legs were flown 0·8—1·2 kilometres (0·5—0·75 mile) apart, at an altitude of between 60—90 metres (200—300 feet) above the ground and only elephant that were within 0·4—0·8 kilometre (0·25—0·5 mile) on either side of the aircraft were counted. In the event that herd densities were so high that the pilot was unable both to observe the elephant on his side of the aircraft and fly the machine safely, observation was made from the observer's side only. When this happened the pilot had to duplicate the flight in the opposite direction, before proceeding to the next parallel leg. In counting large herds of more than 50 animals, the aircraft climbed and circled the herd at slow speed, and in addition to being counted it was photographed for later analysis. Photographs were taken on High Speed Ektachrome with a Nikon F camera (35 mm), the frames being examined subsequently under a Zeiss Stereo microscope. It was noted (by comparison with the photographic counts) that herds in excess of about 100 individuals were very difficult to count directly with accuracy.

In very open bush or grassland where elephant densities were low, flights were carried out at an altitude of 200—250 metres (700—800 feet) above the ground and the strip counted on either side of the aircraft was about 2·5 kilometres (1 mile). With this width of strip it is realized that the probability of counting all individuals was sharply reduced, and the results must be regarded as minimum values. Indeed comparison of a 'complete' count with a population estimate based on random sampling suggested that the former might be at least 18 per cent low.

Over *Terminalia-Combretum* woodland, flights were made at 30—60 metres (100—200 feet) above the ground and about 0·4 kilometre (0·25 mile) apart. The presence of elephant in such woodland was discernible, as their tracks show up very clearly in tall grass that is associated with the woodland complex (*Pennisetum purpureum* and *Hyparrhenia* spp.). Moreover, the low passage of the aircraft disturbed the elephants and made them run, so that they became very much more easily seen. When a herd was sighted in this thick cover, the pilot immediately climbed, reduced speed and circled it until a satisfactory count had been achieved.

No counting was possible in the forest, but in all forest patches, except the Budongo Forest, the presence or absence of elephant was determined during low passes over the canopy. In the Budongo Forest no attempt was made to do this—but up to April 1967, the Forest Department were concurrently carrying out track and dropping counts in the forest the results of which were available to us.

The difficulty of seeing elephant in the poor early-morning and late-evening light, mentioned by Buechner *et al.* (1963), was also experienced and efforts were made to avoid counting at these times. We had one unusually good check on counting ability. Aerial reconnaissance was the basis of the cropping system and herds were noted every day from the air prior to shooting. This provided a good check on the accuracy of counting as before a herd was selected it was counted. These counts could be checked later on the ground and counting errors were found to be much less than 5 per cent. However the largest source of error in counting is probably due to missing entire herds, and fatigue becomes a factor in major aerial counts.

For the most part herds were clearly separated (see Figs 5.2—5.4) by at least 0·4—0·8 kilometre (0·25—0·5 mile); but when closer a subjective decision had to be made whether to plot them as two or more groups, as one group, or as two or more separate individuals. In general this meant that if two obvious groups (or individuals) were separated by about 91 metres (100 yards) they were classed as separate. If two groups were as close as 46 metres (50 yards) they were classed as a single herd unless the two individual groups were bunched. Errors in group classification introduced in this way are considered to be slight over-all, but may have been more frequent in areas where elephants were concentrated.

As each elephant herd or individual was counted, its size and location was recorded on a 1:125 000 map. The observer plotted the aircraft's exact course continuously throughout every flight. This, together with the profusion of recognizable land marks, such as rivers, swamps, ridges, and trees; and with the pilots' and observers' great familiarity with the area, enabled the location of herds to be recorded very accurately.

This degree of accuracy reduced the probability of counting the same herd twice in a given block to the extent that it is considered to have been negligible. However, as the counts took three, four, and three days respectively to complete, and at no time were more than four blocks counted in any one day, there remains the possibility that some herds moved from the blocks in which they were initially counted and were recounted in another block during the following day. In this connection it is worth mentioning that, during all three counts, concentrations of elephants were repeatedly re-observed at the place where they were first seen. There were exceptions to this during the second count, when two large groups moved from blocks in which they had already been counted, into neighbouring blocks on the following day. On both occasions these groups were recognizable from their size, and their absence from the original block was confirmed by re-examining it. The duplicated count was then deleted from the over-all results.

Apart from the specific cases mentioned, it is felt that during the periods of all three counts, the population as a whole was fairly static and movement between blocks minimal. No movement during the counts has therefore been taken into account when analysing the results. They are surprisingly consistent, and fall well within the confidence interval of the estimate from the stratified random sample counts (Table 4.1), which supports their validity. However, these 'complete' counts are probably low and estimated densities therefore minimal.

A.3.   *'Complete' counts of hippopotamus*

The River Nile above the Murchison Falls is characterized by numerous rocky, wooded, or swampy islands, complexes of rapids and a strong current. The broader eastern part has a different character with many more islands. Many of the islands and parts of the banks had been partially or completely submerged since the rise in water level in 1961. Although it had fallen from the peak level the river was still above normal in 1967.

In 1964, counts were made from a Piper Colt aircraft and in 1967 a Cessna 185 was used. Both aircraft can seat the pilot and observer side by side. Base maps were prepared to a scale of 1:5000 for the April 1964 count, during which A. D. Graham was the observer. On the basis of this experience, a scale of 1:10 000 was considered adequate for the later counts in 1964 and 1967, on which R.M.L. was the observer. I.S.C.P. piloted the aircraft on all three counts. The rise in water level necessitated substantial re-drawing of the published maps (Uganda Surveys Department, 1:50 000 series Y 732, sheets 30/I, 30/II, 31/I, and 31/III).

Each school or small section of the river was circled at an altitude of 164 metres (500 feet) above river level until it was considered that all the hippo in it had been counted. This involved almost continuous tight turns for several hours each day. Flights were limited to about 2 hours counting in the morning and a similar period in the afternoon. Our strange behaviour attracted vultures from a large area—no doubt it looked as if we had found some very effective thermals—and they increased the hazards and strain of such flying.

The observer carried out all the counting with occasional assistance from the pilot, and the position of hippo schools and individuals was recorded on the maps. The river flows from east to west and the majority of hippo were to be found in slack water in the shelter of islands, promontories, or in backwaters. Fig. 4.7 is an example of the distributions typical of different sections of the river. It is difficult to design a sample counting programme to fit this type of distribution and all counts were 'complete' counts, without confidence limits. However it is certain that there were more hippo in the river than were counted.

In the first two counts thick vegetation on the islands made observation difficult, but by the 1967 count the level of the river had fallen and the banks were clearer of overhanging vegetation. Submerged hippo could be seen lying on the bottom in water up to 5 metres deep, but in some cases hippo retreated into very deep water when flown over. Low numbers were associated with rough water and steep banks.

A.4.   *Earlier aerial counts of elephant in North Bunyoro*

Buechner *et al.* (1963) conducted twelve aerial counts over virtually the same area as those presented in this book. Their results varied between 4141 and 12 389, with a mean of 6958, and the fluctuations were attributed to movements in and out of the area between counts. However, they concluded that the 'fluctuations are not predictable on an annual cycle basis' (p. 47). Their results are so greatly at variance with those of the present study that a comparison of technique is called for.

In their initial count, Buechner *et al.* (1963) observed from an altitude of 244—305 metres (800—1000 feet) above ground and counted elephant in a strip 2·4—3·2 kilometres (1·5—2 miles) from either side of the aircraft. In the present study the visibility of elephant at these distances was tested by sighting a herd in a clearly defined position, counting it at these distances and altitudes, and then flying over the herd at both altitudes and re-counting it while observing from vertically overhead. The herd was discernable at both heights and distances, but it was not possible to count individuals at these distances. Lateral lighting assists in observing elephants to a degree, but even at the altitudes at which these authors made their counts it was not possible to count elephant accurately at the distances given by them, with the naked eye and from a moving aircraft.

Buechner *et al.* (1963) state that all other counts were made from an average altitude of 183 metres (600 feet), varying from 61 metres to 244 metres (200—800 feet). No mention is made of a reduced counting strip width and it is presumed that this remained the same as in the first count. If this was the case, then the undulating nature of the Murchison Falls Park topography is in any case such as to prevent constant vision of a 3·2 kilometre (2 mile) strip.

Another complicating factor is the decreasing spiral system of counting a block used by these authors, which necessitates an initial long peripheral circuit. Other than in the first count, when seven blocks were recognized, they divided the area into three blocks (p. 42). The total area counted was 3885 square kilometres (1500 square miles) and each block was about 1295 square kilometres (500 square miles). Each block would thus have a periphery of about 160 kilometres (100 miles). In the aircraft used for the greater part (an Auster and a Stinson) this would have taken 66 minutes and 58 minutes respectively to fly. In this time our own observations have indicated that an elephant herd normally browsing would often have covered distances of over a mile. The fact that recognition had to be effected on the basis of one fleeting observation made more than an hour previously and that a herd may well have moved a considerable distance in the time and crossed strip boundaries, makes their claim of being able to recognize previously counted herds unconvincing.

However, a point emerging from Buechner *et al.* (1963) was the very localized positions of the large herds, which they used as confirmation of their view that there was little movement. This agrees with our own observations.

The results of all known counts of elephant in North Bunyoro are presented chronologically in Table A.1. The area covered was virtually the same in each case. Analysis of the figures suggests that pilot ability and experience may be of overriding importance in the results obtained. The results obtained by Buechner (8 counts) and Buss (4 counts) as observers give respective averages of 6769 and 7337 elephant per count, a difference of only 568 elephant per count. Both were professional biologists with experience of aerial counting and their results seem to be of the same order. Both covered all seasons. In 1963—4, Buss with another pilot (Savidge) averaged 6726 elephants in the same three blocks. A comparison between pilots gives: Newton, average 5555 for 2 counts; Margach, average

Table A.1
Elephant counts in North Bunyoro, 1957–69

Date		Number	Pilot	Observers
25–31 January	1957	4153	Newton	Buechner
19–21 July	1957	4172	Margach	Buechner and wife
23–5 August	1957	4141	Margach	Buechner and wife
28–30 September	1957	5556	Margach	Buechner and wife
7–9 December	1957	8318	Longhurst	Buechner
4–8 February	1958	6957	Newton	Buechner
30 May–1 June	1958	12 389	Longhurst	Buechner
1–2 August	1958	8732	Longhurst	Buss
24–6 October	1958	6763	Margach	Buss and wife
26–8 February	1959	5461	Margach	Buss and wife
12–14 May	1959	8392	Margach	Buss and Brooks
6–8 August	1959	8463	Treen	Buechner and Brooks
17–18 July	1963	5611	Savidge	Buss and Mrs. Savidge
24–7 October	1963	6126	Savidge	Buss, Mrs. Savidge, and Wing
6–11 March	1964	7454	Savidge	Buss, Mrs. Savidge, and Wing
8–11 May	1964	7815	Savidge	Buss, Maxwell, and Mrs. Savidge
16–20 November	1966	7779	Graham	Parker and Tippett
16–20 February	1967	8713	Parker	Wheater and Backus
11–14 August	1967	7913	Parker	Wheater
26–8 May	1969	9364 ± 2736	Parker	Wheater

5748 for 6 counts; Savidge, average 6726 for 4 counts; and Longhurst 9813 for 3 counts. Both Newton and Margach were inexperienced amateurs in respect of both flying and research, but Longhurst had flown professionally, was a professional biologist, and had an extensive experience of this type of work. Admittedly Longhurst's average of 9813 contains no long dry-season count, but even if the average long dry-season count of Newton and Margach is counted as part of Longhurst's score, his average is still 8741 elephant per count.

A further very important factor which should be considered is the intensity of counting, measured here by the counting rate. In the present study the rate of counting was very much lower than that of Buechner *et al.* (1963) (Table A.2). In terms of elephant per hour it was only 34 per cent, and in square kilometres per hour it was only 23 per cent of the former rate. Direct comparisons with Buss and Savidge's (1966) counting rates are not possible, but again the data suggest that the counting intensity was much less than in the present study. The difference in numbers counted is not directly proportional to counting intensity (square kilometres per hour) as appeared to be the case with hippopotamus over the range of counting intensities (kilometres per hour) compared. But the time interval between the series of counts was greater and there were probably large changes in the number of elephant present in the area. Also hippopotamus in the water can only be counted in the immediate vicinity of the aircraft, whereas in

Table A.2

Comparison of counting rates during three series of elephant counts

	Total flying time (h)	Total area (km²)	Total elephants counted	Rate (km²/h)	(Elephants/h)
Buechner *et al.* (1963)	*ca* 76	46 600	83 497	613	1099
Buss and Savidge (1966)	66·73	83 231	51 048	1247	765
Present study	65	9324	24 405	143	375

open country elephant can often be counted from a distance of 2 kilometres or more.

It is not possible to separate the operator effect (pilot and/or observer experience and ability) from the time effect, and the apparent fluctuations in numbers observed are likely to be a combined manifestation of changing numbers, together with the operator effect. There were enormous fluctuations in numbers observed in the earliest series. It is possible that this was largely a time effect, though we incline to the view that the operator effect was more influential.

For reasons discussed in this book, we conclude that there is now little seasonal change in elephant numbers present in the counting area. In 1957—9 the peripheral movement may have been greater than at present, though we question whether it was sufficiently large to account for the great fluctuations recorded. Thus the influence of the date of counting (the time effect in any one year) is probably negligible now, but may have been important in the earlier series. If so, then with only a few counts in the year, the average figure could be quite high or low purely by chance—the chance that the counting dates coincide with the peaks or troughs in elephant numbers.

Buss and Savidge (1966) remark that 'during the 1 year period of our study an average of approximately 6750 elephants were in the S. Murchison area, *or about 1000 fewer than the number reported for this same area between 1958 and 1959* [Buechner *et al.* 1963, p. 47]. (We believe the 1958—9 counts are most representative of the numbers of elephants in the area during the earlier period of study)' (their italics). However, Buechner *et al.* (1963) state that their first three counts 'suggested accuracy greater than could have been achieved'. They say that although these counts were lower than subsequent ones, 'our impression is that care exercised in the first three counts was equal to that of later counts and that we had enumerated not less than 90 per cent of the elephants present'. The evidence of these two sets of counts is not sufficient to support the conclusion that there were 1000 fewer in 1963—4 than in 1958—9.

These points strongly suggest that the variability in the totals achieved by Buechner *et al.* (1963) and Buss and Savidge (1966) may be the result of inadequate method and application. They also suggest that comparisons between the totals for the three series of counts are not meaningful. However, with the contraction of the elephant range and consequent seasonal stability in elephant numbers, a relatively small number of counts per year should be meaningful now.

Appendix B.   Details of information recorded and material collected from cropped elephants

B.1. *Body measurements*

Measurements were made with a steel tape, to the nearest centimetre.

1. Over-all body length (OL): measured from tip of trunk, along curves of body to tip of tail.
2. Crown-rump length (CRL): from a point, level with the anterior angle of the eyes, to the base of the tail, along the curves of the body.
3. Occiput-base of tail (OBT): from the bony ridge, which can be felt through the skin, along the curve of the body.
4. Tail length (TL): excluding tail bristles, which can add more than 50 centimetres.
5. Back length, ear to base of tail (BL): from the posterior border of ear at junction with the head, to the base of the tail, measured in a straight line. The stretched tape touches the convexity of the dorsal ridge, and the measurement was read at right angles to the tape. This measurement is equivalent to the back length as measured on aerial photographs for analysing the age structure of elephant populations (Laws 1969b). It approximates to the shoulder height (Measurement 6).
6. Shoulder height (SH)[†]: the fore leg is manipulated until it locks straight and the measurement taken from the edge of the sole of the foot to the crest of the scapula. This is a straight line measurement and the reading of height is taken by sighting on the two scapulae (upper and lower as the animal lies on its side) moving one's eye until the two dorsal edges come into line with each other and with a point on the tape.
7. Shoulder height, curved (SHC): taken along the curvature of the body (for comparison with the records of other workers) from scapula to sole of foot.
8. Half girth behind fore-legs (G/2): from crest of spine to sternum.
9. Diameter of each foot (FD): longest measurement across sole.
10. Circumference of each foot (FC): around outside of foot, including nails, at the level of the sole.
11. Tusk measurements:
    (a) circumference at base (after removal and cleaning;
    (b) circumference at lip (after removal and cleaning);

---

† The anatomy of the elephant is such that the limb joints are locked to form rigid columns when the animal is standing. The fore part of the body is suspended from the scapulae which are the highest part of a standing elephant. The straight shoulder height is therefore a very good dimension for describing linear growth and, because the variance is low, it can be used to estimate the ages of living elephants in the field.

    (c) lip to tip (before removal);

    (d) total length, along convex curvature (after removal and cleaning).

12. Mandible length: longest dimension, measured with calipers from the rostrum at the symphysis, the most anterior point of the jaw, to the bulge on the posterior margin.

Measurements numbers 6 and 11 were recorded for all animals, but the others were only recorded for a proportion of the total number.

B.2.   *Organ weights*

1. Live weight: obtained for a small subsample by weighing the carcase entire (if less than 1000 kg) or in pieces, taking care to collect and weigh blood and other fluids.
2. Dissected hind-leg: for estimating live weight (Laws *et al.* 1967). Smith and Ledger (1965) have found that this relation can be used to predict live weight for several other African mammals. We consider that for elephant it gives better data on live weight than do actual weighings in pieces, owing to the variability that could be introduced under field conditions by differential fluid loss and evaporation.
3. Heart.
4. Lungs and attached trachaea.
5. Spleen.
6. Brain: a small number of records since removal is time consuming.
7. Stomach fill: obtained by weighing the ligatured stomach full and empty.
8. Intestine fill: obtained by measuring large intestine full and empty. In large animals this was a lengthy process as the gut had to be ligatured and weighed in sections.
9. Kidneys: weighed with and without perirenal fat. (In order to standardize the procedure the fat between two lines at the level of each end of the kidney and transverse to its long axis was collected. The elephant kidney is multi-lobular and the fat is most conveniently detached by removing it together with the connective tissue capsule of the kidney.)
10. Temporal glands: weighed separately.
11. Adrenal glands: connective tissue capsule removed; weighed separately.
12. Thyroid gland.
13. Mammary glands: combined weight.
14. Ovaries: weighed separately.
15. Uterus and vagina.
16. Conceptus weight: obtained by weighing uterus and vagina with and without conceptus.
17. Embryo or foetus.
18. Testes: combined weight, less Wolffian ducts and ductuli efferentes.
19. Seminal vesicles:[†] weighed empty after seminal fluid expressed.

[†] These organs (and the sperm smear, B.3.3. below) are best obtained after removal of the hind-leg when the obturator foramen of the pelvis affords entry to the tract.

20. Seminal vesicle fluid: weighed in deep pan balance.
21. Prostate gland.[†]
22. Bulbo-urethral gland.
23. Tusk weights, separately.

B.3.   *Other records*
  1. Toe nail count.
  2. If female, sexual condition:
    (a) lactating or not, as indicated by attempt to express milk from the breast;
    (b) anoestrus, cycling, or pregnant, from examination of ovaries and uterus, and presence or absence of corpora lutea and/or embryo or foetus;
    (c) foetus if present was sexed, measured and weighed; the umbilical cord length was recorded;
    (d) placental scar counts made on fresh, non-pregnant uteri in the field (Laws 1967a).
  3. If male, sperm smear taken from wolffian duct near ampulla (Short, Mann, and Hay 1967, Fig. 1) and examined under high power microscope. Motility of sperm tested by addition of seminal vesicle fluid.
  4. Mandibles examined for anomalies—supernumerary teeth (Laws 1966) jaw abscesses (Laws and Parker 1968).
  5. Presence of sticks in the temporal gland.
  6. Obvious abnormalities.
  7. Parasites.
  8. Aortae, dissected out and examined for arteriosclerosis (McCullagh and Lewis 1967).
  9. Rectal temperature.

B.4.   *Material collected*

  A comprehensive range of specimens was collected. In practice it was most efficient and economical for trained African assistants to collect all material as a routine. All of them were able to dissect out the larger organs for weighing, but several men specialized in the collecting of one or more difficult organs (e.g. adrenal, seminal vesicle, prostate, bulbo-urethral, thyroid, brain). Only limited collections were made of some specimens (1–6, 7, 9, and 10 below).
  1. Sample of whole blood, refrigerated.
  2. Blood serum sample, refrigerated.
  3. Blood smears.
  4. Milk, from a small number of females, refrigerated (McCullagh 1969c).
  5. Urine direct from incised bladder; preserved with Toluene (McCullagh 1969a).
  6. Eye lens: fixed in 10% formalin, subsequently oven-dried and weighed (Laws 1967b).

  † These organs (and the sperm smear, B.3.3. below) are best obtained after removal of the hind-leg when the obturator foramen of the pelvis affords entry to the tract.

7. Whole eyes (McCullagh and Gresham 1969).
8. Stomach content samples: *ca* 250–500 grams.
9. Depot fat, refrigerated (Duncan and Garton 1968).
10. Aortae: fixed in 10% formalin.
11. Material for histological examination: temporal glands, adrenal, thyroid, mammary gland, corpus luteum slices, uterus, testis section, seminal vesicle, prostate, bulbo-urethral, foetal gonad (all these collected as small pieces and fixed in Bouin's fluid); both ovaries, embryo or small foetus (fixed in 5% formol-saline) (Perry 1974).

    Post mortem time to collection was short—rarely more than 1·5–2 hours, and often much less. Blood and milk samples were usually collected within 15–20 minutes of death.

    The subsequent preparation of selected subsamples for histological examination was by standard methods, staining with haematoxylin and eosin. A subsample of dated corpora lutea was stained for lipids by Oil Red O.

    Fixed ovaries were subsequently weighed, sliced on a commercial meat slicer (slices *ca* 3 millimetres thick), and examined for corpora lutea, corpora albicantia, and follicles.
12. Lower jaw: cleaned for age determination (Laws 1966). Mandibles from early samples were also photographed to provide a permanent record of the dentition. Ages were determined in the course of the field operations (by R.M.L. or I.S.C.P.).
13. Both tusks: these were available for examination for a limited period—effectively the duration of the field operation—because they were sold to pay for the cropping operations.

    All records were entered on *pro forma* field data sheets and a duplicate copy was made. One set of all records is held by Wildlife Services Ltd. and one set by R.M.L.

Appendix C. Method of estimating the mean age at sexual maturity and its confidence interval

The method used to estimate the mean age of sexual maturity was as follows: let $x_1, x_2, x_3 \ldots, x_k$ be the ages in years of the elephants such that all elephants of age x_1 or less are almost certainly immature and all those of age x_k or more are almost certainly mature. If r_i of the n_i elephants of age x_i are found to be sexually mature then $p_i = r_i/n_i$ is an estimate of the proportion of elephants reaching sexual maturity by age x_i. Further $(p_{i+1} - p_i)$ is an estimate of the proportion of elephants reaching maturity between the ages x_i and x_{i+1}. Since $p_1 = 0$ and $p_k = 1$, the mean m of the distribution of the age when sexual maturity is attained would be estimated by

$$m = \sum_{i+1}^{k-1} \left\{ (p_{i+1} - p_i) \frac{(x_i + x_{i+1})}{2} \right\} . \tag{1}$$

Because of sampling error some values of $(p_{i+1} - p_i)$ might turn out to be negative, but the estimation equation (1) would still apply.

If elephants of every age from x_1 to x_k are observed, then $x_{i+1} - x_i = 1$ (= d, say). The variance V of the estimate m is then given by

$$V(m) = d^2 \sum_{i=2}^{k-1} \frac{P_i(1-P_i)}{n_i}, \qquad (2)$$

where P_i is the expected proportion of elephants reaching maturity at age x_i. It is reasonable to obtain P_i values by drawing a smooth curve on a graph of p_i versus x_i.

This method is used frequently for the analysis of quantal response data in biological assay and is known as the Spearman-Kärber method (Finney 1964).

It happens in our data that elephants of some ages between x_1 and x_k are not represented, i.e. $x_{i+1} - x_i = 1$ usually, but not always. This does not affect the estimation equation (1) for m, but the estimate of the variance has to be revised.

If $x_{i+1} - x_i = d_i$ (i.e. $x_2 = x_1 + d_1$

$$x_3 = x_2 + d_2 = x_1 + d_1 + d_2$$

$$x_4 = x_3 + d_3 = x_1 + d_1 + d_2 + d_3 \text{ and so on})$$

then

$$V(m) = \sum_{i=2}^{k-1} \left\{ \frac{P_i(1-P_i)}{n_i} \frac{(d_i + d_{i-1})^2}{2} \right\}. \qquad (3)$$

Note that in this equation if each $d_i = d$, then (3) simplifies to (2).

It is known that results such as (2) and (3) would tend to give an underestimation of the variance of m about the true but unknown mean μ. The extent of the error depends on the spacings between the x_i values (i.e. on d_i). Thus, if the age is given in months rather than years, the error would be smaller. In our data, the n_i values are small, and are spread over quite a wide range of x_i values—under these conditions the extent of error in the estimation of variance is usually negligible.

We have given special attention to the B.C.F.R. female elephant data. Here $x_1 = 9$ and $x_k = 34$—quite a wide range. The n_i values are small and the p_i values show large fluctuations. Naturally, one is suspicious of estimates produced from such a set of data. If, however, these data are grouped into age classes, a reasonably smooth picture emerges. The estimates from the grouped and ungrouped data are remarkably close (Table 9.1).

The formula used to provide *crude approximate* 95 per cent confidence intervals is the mean plus or minus two standard errors of the mean. This receives support from the fact that the standard errors for the ages of the pubertal groups of males and females (Chapter 9) are very similar to those estimated for sexual maturity by the method described above.

We are indebted to Mr. K. Lakhani, Biometrics Section, The Nature Conservancy, London, for suggesting this method and for carrying out the computations for us.

Appendix D. Elephant shot on control by the Game and Forest Departments, and by Licensed Hunters, in Bunyoro, 1925—68 (source: Game Department Annual Reports)

Year	Control	Licence	Year	Control	Licence
1925	141	–	1947	190	76
1926	132	64	1948	107	110
1927	107	82	1949	266	84
1928	146	111	1950	230	88
1929	268	101	1951	217	105
1930	272	48	1952	106	75
1931	293	28	1953	200	86
1932	326	35	1954	119	83
1933	221	12	1955	231	97
1934	204	53	1956	239	154
1935	357	66	1957	236	134
1936	444	52	1958	474	114
1937	530	104	1959	528	142
1938	349	94	1960	386	177
1939	284	69	1961	617	104
1940	No data	–	1962	No data	–
1941	No data	–	1963	1067	54
1942	No data	–	1964	907	84
1943	No data	–	1965	759	96
1944	No data	–	1966	731	97
1945	No data	–	1967	655	–
1946	181	40	1968	464	–

Appendix E. Plot sampling for forest damage

Four areas were selected in Budongo and Bugoma forests for sampling for elephant damage. The sampling technique was simple, consisting of laying down parallel lines at 420 metres (440 yards) intervals; along these lines square plots of 252 square metres (121 square yards) were laid out adjacent to each other. A list of desirable species was drawn up and in each plot all the desirable species present of sapling size and over were recorded. Desirable species of smaller size than saplings were not considered to be established. The area covered by the sample was 2—2·5 per cent of the total area of the compartment.

Four qualities were enumerated in each case, namely, (a) size class, (b) type of damage, (c) chance of survival, and (d) age of damage. These were further subdivided as follows:

(a) *Size class*

All measurements were made at breast height.

Sapling: over 180 centimetres (6 feet) in height to 13 centimetres (5 inches)
girth
Pole: 15 centimetres (6 inches) girth to 28 centimetres (11 inches) girth
1 :   30 centimetres (1 foot) girth to 58 centimetres (1 foot 11 inches) girth
2 :   61 centimetres (2 feet) girth to 89 centimetres (2 feet 11 inches) girth
3 :   91 centimetres (3 feet) girth to 119 centimetres (3 feet 11 inches) girth
4 : 122 centimetres (4 feet) girth to 150 centimetres (4 feet 11 inches) girth
5 : over 152 centimetres (5 feet) girth

(b) *Type of damage*
  (a) leader broken, no new one grown
  (b) leader broken, new one grown
  (c) bark removed
  (d) branch pulled off
  (e) tree trampled or uprooted

(c) *Survival*
  (*i*) excellent chance—damage only slight
  (*ii*) good chance provided no more damage occurs
  (*iii*) chances of survival fair but timber will be defective
  (*iv*) chances slight, timber will be useless
  (*v*) no chance

(d) *Age*
  R: recent (under 6 months)
  O: over 6 months
The results are presented in Tables 11.2—11.5

Appendix F. Estimate of gross value of the products from an average animal of each species—elephant, hippopotamus, buffalo[†]
Elephant
Average live weight 3800 lb (Laws 1966).

		£
Meat	1000 lb @ shs 1/- per lb	50
Hide	120 square feet @ shs 5/- per square foot	30
Ivory	20 lb @ shs 18/- per lb	18
Total		£ 98

Hippopotamus
Average live weight 2150 lb (Laws 1964c)

[†] Currency is East African pounds and shillings.

Meat	Carcase @ shs 300/- per animal	15[1]
	700 lb @ shs 1/- per lb	(35)[2]
Hide	28 square feet @ shs 5/- per square foot	7
Ivory	4 lb @ shs 10/- per lb	2
Total		£ 24 (£44)[2]

Buffalo

Average adult, live weight *ca* 1000 lb (Grimsdell 1969)

		£
Meat	300 lb @ 1/- per lb	15
Hide	no current sales, estimated	2
Total		£ 17

Notes. 1. In the early cropping operations (1965) the carcase was sold to local buyers for £20, but the price was reduced to £15 (presumably for political reasons) on a ruling from the Ministry of Information and Tourism.

2. If the carcase is sold as boned meat on a unit weight basis it is worth more than double.

3. These estimates of value only apply if adequate effort is put into processing and marketing. Thus, the Agricultural Development Service estimates (Anon 1967) are: elephant £50 Hippopotamus £30·5, buffalo £16·5. In the case of elephant this is roughly half the figure presented here.

Provisional estimate of suggested royalties (Ugandan £; in 1968 1 U£ = 1 £ sterling)

Species	Unit value £	Unit cost £	Unit profit £	Royalty £
Elephant	98	50	15	33
Hippopotamus (1)	24	12	4	8
(2)	44	22	8	14
Buffalo	17	8·5	2·5	6

Note. The values given above are based on 1969 prices and are now considerable underestimates. For example, the value of elephant ivory increased to shs 100/- per lb in 1973 thus increasing the average value for elephant nearly twofold (from £98 to £180) and considerably strengthening our arguments for management.

On this basis the combined royalties for Years 1–4 would be £167 100 (or £189 600 if the higher value applied to hippopotamus). Subsequent annual royalties should average £11 600 (or £12 500 if the higher value applied to hippopotamus). On this basis the net 10 year income would be £236 700 (alternatively £264 500).

It is suggested that this should be divided between the National Parks and other authorities in the ratio that the area of the Park (810 square miles) bears to that part of the range outside the Park (243 square miles); that is roughly 3:1.

Addendum

The draft of this book was completed in 1970 and some new information has
come to hand since then. Three pieces of information are particularly relevant.

Elephant densities

The density of elephants in the Luangwa Valley, Zambia is now known to be
4·77 per square kilometre, not 0·07—0·30 per square kilometre as reported on
p. 133 (Caughley, personal communication). This is due to much more efficient
aerial counting technique and is the highest density yet reported for any elephant population.

Large herds

We have recent confirmation of the hypothesis, advanced on pp. 100—1 and
163, explaining the large herds as a gross manifestation of 'bunching' behaviour.
Douglas-Hamilton (personal communication) reports that, with the recent excessive poaching of elephants for ivory inside and in the vicinity of Lake Manyara
National Park, Tanzania, a number of the matriarchs now well known through his
admirable behaviour study were killed; the leaderless herds remaining have shown
a tendency to coalesce to form larger herds.

Effect of control shooting on population size

Recent research by one of us (I.S.C.P.), on the Customs and Excise returns of
ivory exports from Uganda, indicates that Game Department data on elephant
shot in Uganda between 1925 and 1974 are totally unreliable. From the volume
of ivory exported it would appear that the number of elephant shot in Uganda
may be anywhere between two and ten times the number given. For example,
in 1973 the East African Customs and Excise records indicate that Uganda
exported about 12 tons of ivory to Hong Kong. The Hong Kong Customs and
Excise returns indicate that 112 tons of ivory were imported from Uganda. The
discrepancies, which have varied in magnitude from year to year, extend a long
way back in time.

These data do not however change our conclusions but indicate that they are
conservative. Thus, many more elephant were shot in Uganda than are recorded
in Appendix D; the reduction in the North Bunyoro population due to hunting
and control shooting (pp. 233, 246) must have been greater than our calculations
have indicated, and the initial 1946 population would have been much higher than
the 22 000 suggested (p. 245).

Bibliography

Alexander, F. (1952). Some functions of the large intestine of the horse. *Q.Jl exp. Physiol.* **37**, 205–14.

— (1963). Digestion in the horse. *Progress in nutrition and allied sciences* (ed. D. P. Cuthbertson), pp. 259–68. Oliver and Boyd, Edinburgh

Anon. (1925–30, 1932, 1934–9, 1947, 1949, 1950, 1954, 1955). *Uganda Game Department, Annual Reports.* Government Printer, Entebbe, Uganda.

Anon. (1965). *Report on Uganda census of agriculture,* vol. 1. Government Printer, Entebbe, Uganda.

Anon. (1966). *Report on Uganda census of agriculture,* vol. 3. Government Printer, Entebbe, Uganda.

Anon. (1967). *Report on a project to develop the Murchison Falls area of Uganda.* Uganda Development Corporation; Uganda Livestock Industries Ltd., Kampala, Uganda. (Typescript)

Anon. (1970). How to destroy the Murchison Falls. *Oryx* **10**, 207.

Anon. (1970). Nuffield Unit of Tropical Animal Ecology. Progress Report for the Quarter ending June 30th 1970. (Typescript)

Arvill, R. (1967). *Man and environment.* Penguin Books, Harmondsworth.

Asdell, S. A. (1965). *Patterns of mammalian reproduction* (2nd edn). Constable, London.

Atlas of Uganda (1962). Department Lands and Surveys, Uganda.

Attwell, R. I. G. (1970). Some effects of Lake Kariba on the ecology of a flood plain of the mid-Zambezi Valley of Rhodesia. *Biol. Conserv.* **2**, 189.

Bainbridge, W. R. (1967). The reaping of the game harvest in Zambia. *Zambia,* January 1967, 39–46.

Baker, S. W. (1866). *The Albert Nyanza, great basin of the Nile.* Macmillan, London.

— (1874). *Ismailia.* Macmillan, London.

Baker, J. R. (1938). Evolution of breeding seasons. In *Evolution: essays on aspects of evolutionary biology* (ed. G. R. de Beer) presented to Professor E. S. Goodrich.. Clarendon Press, Oxford.

Bandy, P. J. (1965). *A study of comparative growth in four races of black tailed deer.* Ph.D. thesis, University of British Columbia.

Bax, P. N., and Sheldrick, D. L. W. (1963). Some preliminary observations on the food of elephants in the Tsavo Royal National Park (East) of Kenya. *E. Afr. Wildlife J.* **1**, 40–53.

Bell, R. H. V. (1969). *The use of the herb layer by grazing ungulates in the Serengeti National Park, Tanzania.* Ph.D. thesis, University of Manchester.

— (1970). The use of the herb layer by grazing ungulates in the Serengeti. In *Animal populations in relation to their food resources* (ed. A. Watson), pp. 111–14. Blackwell, Oxford.

Benedict, F. G. (1936). *Physiology of the elephant.* Carnegie Inst. Wash. Publ. 474.

Bere, R. M. (1961). An outline of the status of the major mammal species (and the crocodile) in the Uganda National Parks in 1960. In *Report and accounts of the Trustees of the Uganda National Parks, year ended 30 June 1960.*

Bertalanffy, L. von (1938). A quantitative theory of organic growth. *Hum. Biol.* **10**, 181–213.

Beverton, R. J. H. and Holt, S. J. (1957). On the dynamics of exploited fish populations. *Fishery Invest., Lond.* Ser. 2, **19**.

Bindernagel, J. A. (1968). *Game cropping in Uganda.* Uganda Game Department.

Bishop, W. W. (1964). The later Tertiary and Pleistocene in Eastern Equatorial Africa. In *African ecology and human evolution* (ed. C. Howell and F. Bourlière), pp. 246–75. Methuen, London.

Bolwig, N. (1965). Observations on the early behaviour of a young African elephant. *Int. Zoo Yb.* **5**, 149.

Boyd, J. M. (1965). *Travels in the Middle East and East Africa.* Nature Conservancy, London. Nuffield Fellowship Rep. (Duplicated)

Brasnett, N. V. (1944). The growing of *Chlorophora excelsa* in Uganda. *E. Afr. agric. J.* **10**, 83–9.

Bredon, R. M. (1964). The influence of animal management and nutrition on the infertility of cattle. *Agric. vet. chem. agric. Eng.* **5**, 69–73.

– Horrell, C. R. (1961). The chemical and nutritive value of some common grasses in Uganda. I. General pattern of behaviour in grasses. *Trop. Agric., Trin.* **38**, 297–304.

–– (1962). The chemical composition and nutritive value of some common grasses in Uganda. II. The comparison of chemical composition and nutritive values of grasses throughout the year, with special reference to later stages of growth. *Trop. Agric., Trin.* **39**, 13.

Brooks, A. C. and Buss, I. O. (1962). Past and present status of the elephant in Uganda. *J. Wildl. Mgmt* **26**, 38–50.

Brown, D. W. J. (1968). Game control in Kenya. In Proceedings of the Symposium on wildlife and land use. *E. Afr. agric. For. J.* **33**, 209–12.

Bryden, M. M. (1972). Growth and development of marine mammals. In *Functional anatomy of marine mammals* (ed. R. J. Harrison) vol. 1, pp. 1–79. Academic Press, New York.

Buechner, H. K. (1961). Territorial behaviour in Uganda kob. *Science* **133**, 698–9.

– (1963). Territoriality as a behavioural adaptation to environment in Uganda kob. *Proceedings of the XVI International Congress of Zoology*, vol. 3, pp. 59–63.

– Buss, I. O., Longhurst, W. H., and Brooks, A. C. (1963). Numbers and migrations of elephants in Murchison Falls National Park, Uganda. *J. Wildl. Mgmt* **27**, 36–53.

– Dawkins, H. C. (1961). Vegetation changes induced by elephants and fire in Murchison Falls National Park, Uganda. *Ecology* **42**, 752–66.

– Golley, F. B. (1967). Preliminary estimation of energy flow in Uganda kob (*Adenota kob thomasi* Neumann). In *Secondary productivity of terrestrial ecosystems* (ed. K. Petrusewicz), p. 243–54. Polska Akademia Nauk, Instytut Ekologii, Warsaw.

– Schloeth, R. (1965). Ceremonial mating behaviour in Uganda kob (*Adenota kob thomasi* Neumann). *Z. Tierpsychol.* **22**, 209–25.

Burton, R. F. (1860). *The lake regions of Central Africa.* Longmans, London.

Buss, I. O. (1961). Some observations on food habits and behaviour of the African elephant. *J. Wildl. Mgmt* **25**, 131–48.

– Johnson, O. W. (1967). Relationships of Leydig cells characteristics and intra-testicular testosterone levels to sexual activity in the African elephant. *Anat. Rec.* **157**, 191–6.

– Savidge, J. M. (1966). Change in population number and reproductive rate of elephants in Uganda. *J. Wildl. Mgmt* **30**, 791–809.

— Smith, N. S. (1966). Observations on reproduction and breeding behaviour of the African elephant. *J. Wildl. Mgmt* **30**, 375—88.

Carrick, R. and Ingham, S. E. (1962). Studies on the southern elephant seal, *Mirounga leonina* (L.). IV. Breeding and development. *C.S.I.R.O.Wildl. Res.* **7**, 161—97.

Casati, G. (1891). *Ten years in Equatoria* (Trans. J. R. Clay). Frederick Warne, London.

Caughley, G. (1966). Mortality patterns in mammals. *Ecology* **47**, 906—18.

Churchill, W. S. (1908). *My African journey*. Hodder & Stoughton, London.

Clark, K. (1968). The reconciliation of wildlife conservation with forestry. *E. Afr. agric. For. J.* **33**, 213—16.

Cochran, W. G. (1963). *Sampling techniques* (2nd edn). Wiley, New York.

Coe, M. (1972). Defaecation by African elephants (*Loxodonta africana* (Blumenbach)). *E. Afr. Wildlife J.* **10**, 165—74.

Cole, L. C. (1954). The population consequences of life history phenomena. *Q. Rev. Biol.* **29**, 103—37.

Cott, H. B. (1968). Nile crocodile faces extinction in Uganda. *Oryx* **9**, 330—2.

Croze, H. (1972). A modified photogrammetric technique for assessing age-structures of elephant populations and its use in Kidepo National Park. *E. Afr. Wildlife J.* **10**, 91—115.

Dale, I. R. (1954). Forest spread and climatic change in Uganda during the Christian era. *Emp. For. Rev.* **33**, 23.

Darling, F. F. (1960). *Wildlife in an African territory*. Oxford University Press, London.

— (1970). *Wilderness and plenty.* B.B.C., London.

Dassman, R. F. (1963). *The last horizon*. Macmillan, New York.

— (1964). *African game ranching*. Pergamon Press, London.

— (1968). *A different kind of country*. Macmillan, New York.

Daubenmire, R. (1968). Ecology of fire in grasslands. *Adv ecol. Res.* **5**, 209—66.

Davis, D. E. and Golley, F. B. (1963). *Principles in mammalogy*. Rheinhold, New York.

Dawkins, H. C. (1949). Timber planting in the Terminalia woodland of northern Uganda. *Emp. For. Rev.* **28**, 226—47.

Dorst, J. and Dandelot, P. (1970). *A field guide to the larger mammals of Africa*. Collins, London.

Dougall, H. W. and Bogdan, A. V. (1958). The chemical composition of the grasses of Kenya. I. *E.Afr. agric. J.* **24**, 17—21.

—— (1960). The chemical composition of the grasses in Kenya. II. *E. Afr. agric. For. J.* **25**, 241—4.

— Drysdale, V. M., and Glover, P. E. (1964). The chemical composition of Kenya browse and pasture. *E. Afr. Wildlife J.* **2**, 86—121.

— Sheldrick, D. L. W. (1964). The chemical composition of a day's diet of an elephant. *E. Afr. Wildlife. J.* **2**, 51—9.

Douglas-Hamilton, I. (1972). *On the ecology and behaviour of the African elephant*. Ph.D. thesis, University of Oxford.

Dunbar, A. R. (1959). European travellers in Bunyoro Kitara 1862—1877. *Uganda J.* **23**, 101—17.

Duncan, W. R. H. and Garton, G. A. (1968). The fatty acid composition and intramolecular structure of triglycerides from adipose tissue of the hippopotamus and the African elephant. *Comp. Biochem. Physiol.* **25**, 319—25.

East African Statistical Department (1960). African population of the Uganda

Protectorate. Geographical and tribal studies. *East African Population Census, 1948,* p. 59. Nairobi.

Eggeling, W. J. (1935). Uganda Forest Department Correspondence Files 143/2/33, Entebbe, Uganda (quoted by Buechner and Dawkins (1961)).

— (1947a). *Working plan for the Budongo and Siba Forests,* first revision—period 1945–1954. Government Printer, Entebbe.

— (1947b). Observations on the ecology of the Budongo Rain Forest, Uganda. *J. Ecol.* **34,** 20–87.

— (1964). A nature reserve management plan for the Island of Rhum, Inner Hebrides. *J. appl. Ecol.* **1,** 405–19.

Fagan, B. M. and Lofgren, L. (1966). Archaeological sites on the Nile–Chobi confluence. *Uganda J.* **30,** 201–6.

Falconer, T. (1797). *The voyage of Hanno* (Translated and accompanied with the Greek text). T. Cadell, Junior, and Davies, London.

Field, C. R. (1966). Nuffield Unit of Tropical Animal Ecology. Progress Report for the Quarter ending September 1966. p. 4. unpublished.

— (1968a). A comparative study of the food habits of some wild ungulates in the Queen Elizabeth National Park, Uganda, preliminary report. *Symp. zool. Soc. Lond.* **21,** 135–51.

— (1968b). *The food habits of some wild ungulates in Uganda.* Ph.D. thesis, Cambridge University.

— (1971). Elephant ecology in the Queen Elizabeth National Park, Uganda. *E. Afr. Wildlife J.* **9,** 99–123.

— Laws, R. M. (1970). Animal populations in the Queen Elizabeth National Park, Uganda. *J. appl. Ecol.* **7,** 273–94.

Finney, D. J. (1964). *Statistical method in biological assay.* Charles Griffin, London.

Food and Agriculture Organization (1968). Report to the Government of Zambia on wildlife and land-use survey of the Luangwa Valley. United Nations Development Programme no. TA 2591. F.A.O., Rome.

Ford, E. (1933). An account of the herring investigations conducted at Plymouth during the years from 1924–1933. *J. mar. biol. Ass. U.K.* **19,** 305–84.

Fosberg, F. R. (1961). The island ecosystem. *Man's place in the island ecosystem.* 10th Pacific Science Congress, Honolulu.

Foster, J. B. and Coe, M. J. (1968). The biomass of game animals in Nairobi National Park, 1960–66. *J. Zool., Lond.* **155,** 413–25.

Fowler, C. W. and Smith, T. (1973). Characterizing stable populations: An application to the African elephant population. *J. Wildl. Mgmt* **37,** 513–23.

Garstin, Sir W. (1904). *Report upon the basin of the Upper Nile with proposals for the improvement of that river.* Cairo, National Printing Dept.

Glover, J. (1963). The elephant problem at Tsavo. *E. Afr. Wildlife J.* **1,** 30–9.

Glover, P. E. (1965). *A review of the recent knowledge on the relationship between the tsetse fly and its vertebrate hosts.* Presented at First International Congress on Parasitology, 1964. (Mimeo)

— (1968). The role of fire and other influences on the savannah habitat, with suggestions for further research. *E. Afr. Wildlife J.* **6,** 131–7.

Grimsdell, J. G. R. (1969). *Ecology of the buffalo,* Syncerus caffer, *in Western Uganda.* Ph.D. thesis, Cambridge University.

Gwynne, M. D. and Bell, R. H. V. (1969). Selection of vegetation components by grazing ungulates in the Serengeti National Park. *Nature, Lond.* **220,** 390–3.

Hafez, E. S. E. (1953). Conception rate and periodicity in the buffalo. *Emp. J. exp. Agric.* **21**, 15–21.

Hanks, J. (1969a). Growth in weight of the female African elephant in Zambia. *E. Afr. Wildlife J.* **7**, 7–10.

– (1969b). Seasonal breeding of the African elephant in Zambia. *E. Afr. Wildlife J.* **7**, 167.

– (1972). Growth of the African elephant (*Loxodonta africana*). *E. Afr. Wildlife J.* **10**, 251–72.

Harrop, J. F. (1962). Soils. In *Atlas of Uganda*, p. 22–3. Lands and Surveys Department, Uganda.

D'Hoore, J. (1959). Soil map of Africa south of the Sahara. *Proceedings of the 3rd International African Soils Conference, Dalaba.*

Huggett, A. St. G. and Widdas, W. R. (1951). The relationship between mammalian foetal weight and conception age. *J. Physiol., Lond.* **114**, 306.

Huxley, J. S. (1961). *The conservation of wildlife and natural habitats in Central and East Africa.* UNESCO, Paris; Columbia University Press, New York.

Huxley, Sir J. (1962). Eastern Africa: the ecological base. *Endeavour,* **21**, 98–107.

Johnson, O. W. and Buss, I. O. (1965). Molariform teeth of male African elephants in relation to age, body dimensions, and growth. *J. Mammal.* **46**, 373–84.

–– (1967). The testis of the African elephant (*Loxodonta africana*) I. Histological features. *J. Reprod. Fert.* **13**, 11–21.

–– (1967). The testis of the African elephant (*Loxodonta africana*) II. Development puberty and weight. *J. Reprod. Fert.* **13**, 23–30.

Jolly, G. M. (1969). Sampling methods for aerial censuses of wildlife populations. Workshop on the use of light aircraft in wildlife management in East Africa. *E. Afr. agric. For. J.* **34**, 46–9.

Jordan, P. A., Botkin, D. B., and Wolfe, M. L. (1971). Biomass dynamics in a moose population. *Ecology* **52**, 147–52.

Juko, C. D. and Bredon, R. M. (1961). The chemical composition of leaves and whole plant as an indicator of the range of available nutrients for selective grazing by cattle. *Trop. Agric., Trin.* **38**, 179–87.

Katete, F. X. (1968). The mistake at Murchison Falls. *Africa na* **3**, 8, 18–21.

Krumrey, W. A. and Buss, I. O. (1968). Age estimation, growth and relationships between body dimensions of the female African elephant. *J. Mammal.* **49**, 22–31.

Lamprey, H. F. (1964). Estimation of large mammal densities, biomass and energy exchange in the Tarangire Game Reserve and the Masai steppe in Tanganyika. *E. Afr. Wildlife J.* **2**, 1–46.

– Glover, P. E., Turner, M. I. M., and Bell, R. H. V. (1967). Invasion of the Serengeti National Park by elephants. *E. Afr. Wildlife J.* **5**, 151–66.

Langdale-Brown, I., Osmaston, H. A., and Wilson, J. G. (1964). *The vegetation of Uganda and its bearing on land-use.* Government Printer, Entebbe, Uganda.

Laws, R. M. (1953). The elephant seal (*Mirounga leonina* Linn.) I. Growth and age. *Sci. Rep. Falkland Is. Dep. Surv.,* no. 8, 1–62.

– (1956). The elephant seal (*Mirounga leonina* Linn.). II. General, social and reproductive behaviour. *Sci. Rep. Falkland. Is. Dep. Surv.,* no. 13, 1–88.

– (1960). The southern elephant seal (*Mirounga leonina* Linn.) at South Georgia. *Nork Hvalsfangsttid.* **49**, 466–76, 520–42.

– (1964). The Nuffield Unit of Tropical Animal Ecology. Progress Report–June 1962 to May 1963. In *Report of the Uganda National Parks for the year ended June 1963,* pp. 23–30.

— (1966). Age criteria for the African elephant (*Loxodonta a. africana*). *E. Afr. Wildlife J.* **4**, 1—37.

— (1967a). Occurrence of placental scars in the uterus of the African elephant (*Loxodonta africana*). *J. Reprod. Fert.* **14**, 445—9.

— (1967b). Eye lens weight and age in African elephants. *E. Afr. Wildlife J.* **5**, 46—52.

— (1968a). Interactions between elephant and hippopotamus populations and their environments. *E. Afr. agric. For. J.* **33**, 140—7.

— (1968b). Dentition and ageing of the hippopotamus. *E. Afr. Wildlife J.* **6**, 19—52.

— (1969a). Aspects of reproduction in the African elephant, *Loxodonta africana. J. Reprod. Fert.* Suppl. **6**, 193—217.

-- (1969b). The Tsavo Research Project. *J. Reprod. Fert.* Suppl. **6**, 495—531.

— (1970a). Biology of African elephants. *Science Prog.*, Oxford **58**. 251—62.

— (1970b). Elephants as agents of habitat and landscape change in East Africa. *Oikos* **21**, 1—15.

— Field, C. R. (1965). The Nuffield Unit of Tropical Animal Ecology. Second Annual Report—June 1963—June 1964. In *Report and accounts of the Trustees of the Uganda National Parks, 1963/64*, pp. 28—41.

— Parker, I. S. C. (1968). Recent studies on elephant populations in East Africa. *Symp. zool. Soc. Lond.* **21**, 319—59.

—— Archer, A. L. (1967). Estimating live weights of elephants from hind leg weights. *E. Afr. Wildlife J.* **5**, 106—11.

—— Johnstone, R. C. B. (1970). Elephants and habitats in North Bunyoro, Uganda. *E. Afr. Wildlife J.* **8**, 163—80.

Leggat, G. J. (1965). The reconciliation of forestry and game preservation in Western Uganda. *E. Afr. agric. For. J.* **30**, 355—69.

Lenkeit, W. (1933). Time required for food to pass through the digestive tract of domestic animals. *Ergebn. Physiol.* **35**, 573.

Leuthold, W. (1966). Variations in territorial behaviour of Uganda kob *Adenota kob thomasi* (Neumann 1896). *Behaviour* **27**, 214—57.

Logie, J. P. W. and Jones, G. A. (1968). Land use planning for forestry in Kenya. *E. Afr. agric. For. J.* **33**, 59—62.

Lugard, F. D. (1893). *The rise of our East African empire.* Blackwood, Edinburgh.

Maberry, M. B. (1963). Breeding Indian elephants, *Elephas maximus* at Portland Zoo. *Int. Zoo. Yb.* **4**, 80—3.

McCullagh, K. G. (1969a). The growth and nutrition of the African elephant. I. Seasonal variations in the rate of growth and the urinary excretion of hydroxyproline. *E. Afr. Wildlife J.* **7**, 85—90.

— (1969b). The growth and nutrition of the African elephant. II. The chemical nature of the diet. *E. Afr. Wildlife J.* **7**, 91—8.

— (1970). *Arteriosclerosis in the African elephant.* Ph.D. thesis, Cambridge University.

— Gresham, G. A. (1969). Eye lesions in the African elephant (*Loxodonta africana*). *Res. vet. Sci.* **10**, 587—9.

— Lewis, M. G. (1967). Spontaneous arteriosclerosis in the African elephant. Its relation to disease in man. *Lancet* ii, 492—5.

— Lincoln, H. G., and Southgate, D. A. T. (1969). Fatty acid composition of milk fat of the African elephant. *Nature, Lond.* **222**, 493—4.

Mackworth-Praed, C. W. and Grant, C. H. B. (1952). *Birds of eastern and north eastern Africa*, Ser. 1, vol. 1. Longmans Green, London.

——(1955). *Birds of eastern and north eastern Africa*, Ser. 1, vol. 2.

Longmans Green, London.

Marshall, B. and Bredon, R. M. (1963). The chemical composition and nutritive value of elephant grass (*Pennisetum purpureum*). *Trop. Agric. Trin.* **40**, 63–6.

Milne, G. (1935). Some suggested units for classification and mapping particularly for East African soils. *Soil Res.* **4**, 183–98.

— (1936). *A provisional soil map of East Africa.* Crown Agents, London.

Mitchell, F. (1968). The economic value of wildlife viewing as a form of land use. *E. Afr. agric. For. J.* **33**, 98–103.

Moreau, R. E. (1933). Pleistocene climatic changes and the distribution of life in East Africa. *J. Ecol.* **21**, 415–35.

— (1938). Climatic classification from the standpoint of East African biology. *J. Ecol.* **26**, 467–96.

— (1966). *The bird faunas of Africa and its Islands.* Academic Press, London and New York.

Morrison, C. G. T., Hoyle, A. C., and Hope-Simpson, J. F. (1948). Tropical soil vegetation catenas and mosaics. A study of the south-western part of the Anglo Egyptian Sudan. *J. Ecol.* **36**, 1–84.

Myers, N. (197.). Tsavo National Park, Kenya, and its elephants: An interim appraisal. *Biol. Conserv.* **5**, 123–32.

Nash, T. A. M. (1969). *Africa's bane, the tsetse fly.* Collins, London.

Nishiwaki, M., Ohsumi, S. K., and Hibiya, T. (1958). Age study of sperm whale based on reading of tooth laminations. *Sci. Rep. Whales Res. Inst., Tokyo*, no. 13, 135–53.

Njiri, F. A. (1971). The wildlife merger. *Africana* **4** (8), 10, 42.

Odum, E. P. and Odum, H. T. (1959). *Fundamentals of ecology* (2nd edn). Saunders, London.

Osmaston, H. A. (1956). Determination of age/growth and similar relationships in tropical forestry. *Emp. For. Rev.* **33**, 193–7.

— (1959). *Working plan for the Kibale and Itwara Forests.* Uganda Forest Dept.

Owen, R. C. R. (1905). Northwestern Uganda. Sketch map of part of Unyoro. *Geogrl. J.* **25**, 296, 352.

Parker, I. S. C. (1964). The Galana Game Management Scheme. *Bull. epizoot. Dis. Afr.* **12**, 21–31.

— Watson, R. M. (1969). *Crocodile (Crocodylus niloticus Laurenti) distribution and status in the major waters of western and central Uganda in 1969.* Wildlife Services Ltd. Report to Uganda Fisheries Dept. and Trustees of Uganda National Parks. (Manuscript)

Patton, D. R. (1968). *Luangwa Valley game populations.* Dept. of Game and Fisheries, Zambia. (Manuscript)

Penman, H. L. (1950). Evaporation over the British Isles. *Q. Jl R. met. Soc.* **76**, 372–83.

Perry, J. S. (1952). The growth and reproduction of elephants in Uganda. *Uganda J.* **16**, 51–66.

— (1953). The reproduction of the African elephant, *Loxodonta africana. Phil. Trans. R. Soc.* B **237**, 93–149.

Perry, J. S. (1974). Implantation, foetal membranes and early placentation of the African elephant, *Loxodonta africana. Phil. Trans. R. Soc.* B **269**, 109–35.

Petrides, G. A. and Swank, R. G. (1966). Estimating the productivity and energy relations of an African elephant population. *Proceedings of the*

IX International Grasslands Congress, Săo Paulo, Brazil, January 1965.
p. 831–42.

Philip, M. S. (1965). *Working Plan for the Budongo Central Forest Reserve (including Budongo, Siba, and Kitigo Forests)*, third revision. Government Printer, Entebbe, Uganda.

Phillipson, A. T. (1963) The nutritional physiology of the adult ruminant. *Animal health, production, and pasture* (ed. A. N. Worden, K. C. Sellers, and D. E. Tribe), pp. 221–60, Longmans, London.

Pienaar, U. de V., Wyk, P. van, and Fairall, N. (1966). An aerial census of elephant and buffalo in the Kruger National Park, and the implications thereof on intended management schemes. *Koedoe* 9, 40–107.

Pitman, C. R. S. (1931). *A game warden among his charges*. Nisbet, London.

Pratt, D. J., Greenway, P. J., and Gwynne, M. D. (1966). A classification of East African rangeland, with an appendix on terminology. *J. appl. Ecol.* 3, 369–82.

Procter, J. (1968). Forestry and wildlife land use planning in Tanganyika. *E. Afr. agric. For. J.* 33, 63–8.

Ramsay, R. M. and Rose Innes, R. (1963). Some quantitative observations on the effects of fire on the Guinea savanna vegetation of northern Ghana over a period of eleven years. *Sols Afr.* 8 (1), 41–86.

Ransom, A. B. (1965). Kidney and marrow fat as indicators of white-tailed deer condition. *J. Wildl. Mgmt* 29, 397–8.

Reinwald, H. and Hemingway, P. (1968). Some economic considerations in game cropping for export. *E. Afr. agric. For. J.* 33, 104–9.

Reynolds, V. (1965). *Budongo: a forest and its chimpanzees*. Methuen, London.

Richards, P. W. (1964). *The tropical rain forest: an ecological study*. Cambridge University Press.

Ricker, W. E. (1948). *Methods of estimating vital statistics of fish populations*. Indiana University Publications, Science Series, no. 15.

— (1958). *Handbook of computation for biological statistics of fish populations*. Fishery Research Board Canada, Bulletin 119.

Riney, T. (1955). Evaluating condition of free-ranging red deer (*Cervus elephas*), with special reference to New Zealand. *N. Z. J. Sci. Tech.* B 36, 429–63.

Sadleir, R. M. F. S. (1969). *The ecology of reproduction in wild and domestic mammals*. Methuen, London.

Sansom, H. W. (1952). *The trend of rainfall in East Africa*. E. Afr. Met. Dept., Tech. Mem. no. 1.

— (1954). *The climate of East Africa*. E. Afr. Met. Dept. Mem. 3, no. 2.

Scheffer, V. B. and Wilke, F. (1953). Relative growth in the northern fur seal. *Growth* 17, 129–45.

Schweinfurth, G., Gatzel, G. F., Felkin, R. W., and Hartlaub, G. (1888). *Emin Pasha in Central Africa*. George Philip, London.

Sergeant, D. E. (1962). *The biology of the pilot or pothead whale, Globicephala melaena (Traill) in Newfoundland waters*. Fisheries Research Board, Canada, Bull. 132, pp. 1–84.

Sharman, G. B. (1955). Studies on marsupial reproduction II. The oestrous cycle of *Setonix brachyurus*. *Aust. J. Zool.* 3, 44–55.

Sheldrick, D. (1972). Tsavo: the hard lessons of history. *Africana* 4 (10), 14–16, 26–8.

Shield, J. W. (1965). A breeding season difference in two populations of the Australian macropod marsupial *Setonix brachyurus*. *J. Mammal.* 45, 616–25.

Short, R. V. (1969). Notes on the teeth and ovaries of an African elephant (*Loxodonta africana*) of known age. *J. Zool., Lond.* **158**, 421—5.
— Mann, T., and Hay, M. F. (1967). Male reproductive organs of the African elephant, *Loxodonta africana. J. Reprod. Fert.* **13**, 517—36.
Sikes, S. K. (1966a). The African elephant (*Loxodonta africana*): a field method for the estimation of age. *J. Zool., Lond.* **150**, 279—95.
— (1966b). The elephant problem in Africa: random slaughter or selective husbandry? *Afr. Wildlife* **20**, 225—37.
— (1968a). The African elephant, *Loxodonta africana*, a field method for the estimation of age. *J. Zool., Lond.* **154**, 235—48.
— (1968b). Observations on the ecology of arterial disease in the African elephant (*Loxodonta africana*) in Kenya and Uganda. Comparative nutrition of wild animals (ed. M. A. Crawford). *Symp. zool. Soc., Lond.* no. 21, 251—73.
— (1971). *The natural history of the African elephant.* Weidenfeld and Nicholson, London.
Simon, N. (1962). *Between the sunlight and the thunder: the wildlife of Kenya.* Collins, London.
Siniff, D. B. and Skoog, R. O. (1964). Aerial censusing of caribou using stratified random sampling. *J. Wildl. Mgmt* **28**, 391—401.
Smith, N. S. and Ledger, H. P. (1965). A method of predicting live weight from dissected leg weight. *J. Wildl. Mgmt* **29**, 504—11.
Southwood, T. R. E. (1966). *Ecological methods with particular reference to the study of insect populations.* Methuen, London.
Spence, D. H. N. and Angus, A. (1971). African grassland management—burning and grazing in Murchison Falls National Park. In *The scientific management of plant and animal communities for conservation* (ed. E. Duffey). Blackwell, Oxford.
Spinage, C. A. (1970). Population dynamics of the Uganda defassa waterbuck (*Kobus defassa Ugandae* Neumann) in the Queen Elizabeth Park, Uganda. *J. anim. Ecol.* **39**, 51—78.
Stuart-Smith, A. M. (1966). *Report on a visit to the Rabongo Forest, Murchison Falls National Park.* Forest Department, Entebbe. (Typescript)
Swynnerton, C. F. M. (1924). *Report on the control of elephants in Uganda.* Government Printer, Entebbe, Uganda.
Tackle, D. (1968). Multiple use planning, grazing fee assessment, forage allocation, and stocking control. U. S. Forest Service methods. *E. Afr. agric. For. J.* **33**, 51—8.
Tanner, J. M. (1962). *Growth at adolescence.* Blackwell, Oxford.
Tassell, R. (1967). The effects of diet on reproduction in pigs, sheep and cattle. V. Plane of nutrition in cattle. *Br. vet. J.* **123**, 459—63.
Taylor, C. R. and Lyman, C. P. (1967). A comparative study of the environmental physiology of an East African antelope, the eland, and the Hereford steer. *Physiol. Zool.* **40**, 280—95.
— Spinage, C. A., and Lyman, C. P. (1969). Water relations of the waterbuck, an East African antelope. *Am. J. Physiol.* **217**, 630—4.
Tener, J. S. (1964). *Game management in Uganda.* Uganda Game Dept. (Mimeo).
Thomas, A. S. (1940). Grasses as indicator plants in Uganda. *E. Afr. agric. J.* **6**, 19—22 and 77—80.
— (1942). Note on the distribution of Chlorophora excelsa. *Emp. For. J.* **21**, 42—3.
Thomas, H. B. and Scott, R. (1935). *Uganda.* Oxford University Press, London.

366   Bibliography

Tyler, S. J. (1969). *The behaviour and social organization of the New Forest ponies.* Ph.D. thesis, Cambridge University.
Usuelli, F. (1933). Time spent by food in rumen of cattle. *Profilassi* **6**, 7 (cited by Phillipson (1963)).
Vandeleur, C. F. S. (1897). Two years' travel in Uganda, Unyoro, and on the upper Nile. *Geogrl. J.* **9**, 369–93, 472.
Walford, L. A. (1946). A new graphic method of describing the growth of animals. *Biol. Bull.* **90**, 141–7.
Watson, R. M. (1967). *The population ecology of the wildebeeste (Connochaetes taurinus albojubatus Thomas) in the Serengeti.* Ph.D. thesis, Cambridge University.
— (1968). *Report on aerial photographic studies of vegetation carried out in the Tsavo area of Kenya.* (Typescript)
— Bell, R. H. V., and Parker, I. S. C. (1972). Men and elephant. *Africana* **4** (11), 20–1.
— Graham, A. D., and Parker, I. S. C. (1969). A census of the large mammals of Loliondo Controlled Area, northern Tanzania. *E. Afr. Wildlife J.* **7**, 93–59.
— Parker, I. S. C., and Allan, T. (1969). A census of elephant and other large mammals in the Mkomazi region of northern Tanzania and southern Kenya. *E. Afr. Wildlife J.* **7**, 11–26.
Wheater, R. J. (1968a). The second five year development plan. Murchison Falls National Park. Uganda National Parks. (Unpublished manuscript)
— (1968b). Land use proposals for Murchison Falls National Park and surrounding area. *E. Afr. agric. For. J.* **33**, 19–22.
Willock, C. (1964). *The enormous zoo. A profile of the Uganda National Parks.* Collins, London.
Wing, L. D. and Buss, I. O. (1970). *Elephants and forests.* Wildlife Monographs, no. 19, pp. 92.
Wood, A. J., Nordan H. C., and Cowan, I. McT. (1962). Periodicity of growth in ungulates as shown by the genus *Odocoileus. Can. J. Zool.* **40**, 593–603.
— Cowan, I. McT. (1968). Post-natal growth. In *A practical guide to the study of large herbivores* (ed. F. B. Golley and H. K. Buechner), pp. 106–13. Blackwell, Oxford.
Woodley, F. W. (1965). Game defence barriers. *E. Afr. Wildlife J.* **3**, 89–94.
Worthington, E. B. (1958). *Science in the development of Africa.* C.C.T.A., London.
Wynne-Edwards, V. C. (1962). *Animal dispersion in relation to social behaviour.* Oliver and Boyd, Edinburgh and London.

Author Index

General Index